S0-AGP-334

A TREASURY OF AMERICAN INDIAN HERBS

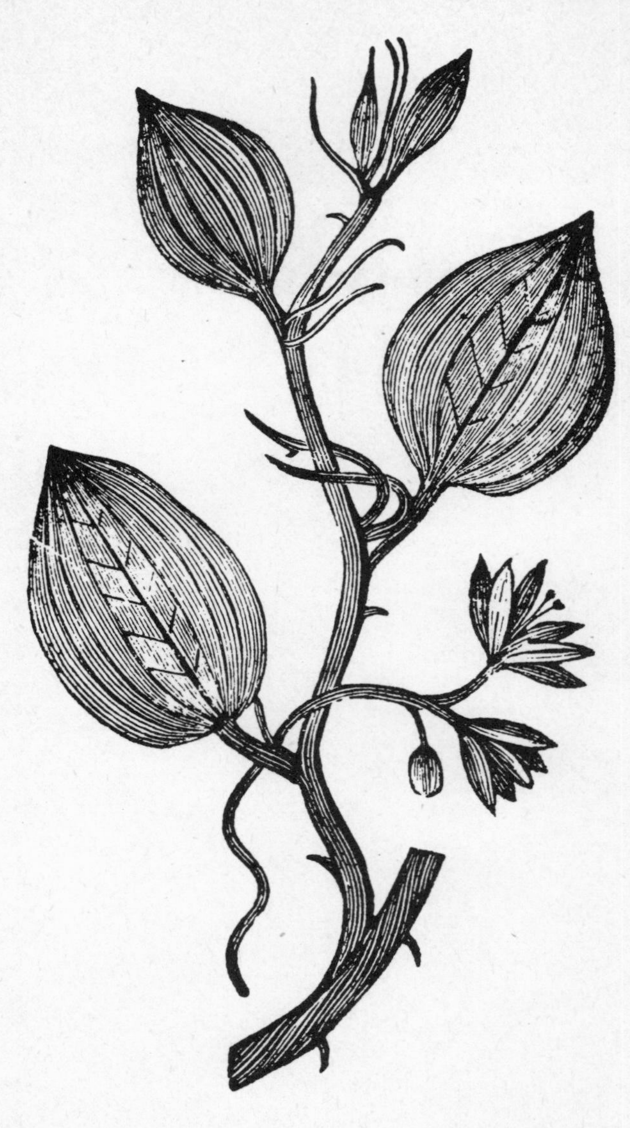

A TREASURY OF AMERICAN INDIAN HERBS

Their Lore and Their Use for Food, Drugs, and Medicine

Virginia Scully

BONANZA BOOKS • NEW YORK

Acknowledgments

It is difficult to make proper acknowledgments, for so many people opened to me the doors of their knowledge. It is impossible to list them all.

Foremost is Colonel William C. Rogers, owner of the ranch in Wyoming who, with me, discovered the myriad of mountain herbs and speculated as to their uses. A short time previously there had been a catalytic encounter with Bertha Dutton, Director of the Museum of Navaho Ceremonial Art at Santa Fe, who plunged me into acute awareness of the Indian scene and the Indian people. From the merging of these two elements sprang the seed for this herbal.

Libraries gave of their immense store of learning: public libraries and private collections and those libraries containing specialized knowledge, such as the Heye Foundation in New York, the American Indian section of the Newberry Library in Chicago, and there, also the John Crerar Library where its director, Mrs. Violet Lynch, by graceful gesture, cheered me when, at its inception, the job seemed of overwhelming proportions. There was the excellent collection at the Denver Botanic Gardens, and in Denver, too, some fascinating and useful (old) books at the library of the Denver County Medical Society.

There were, of course, the various appropriate organizations: the Bureau of Ethnology of the Smithsonian Institution, the Bureau of Indian Affairs, the Department of Agriculture's Plant Industry Station at Beltsville, Maryland, and others. Dr. Louis O. Williams

---

Library of Congress Catalog Card Number: 75-108063

This edition is published by Bonanza Books
a division of Crown Publishers, Inc.
by arrangement with Crown Publishers, Inc.
a b c d e f g h
Manufactured in the United States of America

of the Botany Department of Chicago's Field Museum of Natural History, read early pages of the manuscript and was approving and encouraging.

There were contacts with the various Indian schools and special thanks go to Lawrence W. Capps and librarian Gertrude Giesen of the Intermountain Indian School at Bingham, Utah. Phil Bear Shield of the Shoshone Reservation at Fort Washakie not only was most helpful but also suppled an introduction to Tommy Left Hand at Taos.

John Champe, who since his retirement from the faculty of the University of Nebraska makes frequent trips to Washington, D.C., as expert witness on Indian land grants, told me much that was not in the books and, with a lifelong background of Indian knowledge, read the completed manuscript. His wife, Flavia, dancer and teacher of the dance, gave of her expertise on the techniques and symbolism of Indian dances. Fred A. Rosenstock of Denver, publisher and seller of Indian and rare Western books, was a most helpful guide in his area.

For my knowledge of pioneer adaptations of Indian herbal usages, I am indebted especially to Kate B. Carter of the Daughters of Pioneers in Salt Lake City, whose meticulous filing of all possible data on the Mormon past was placed with utmost cooperation at my disposal. Mention must be made, too, of the late Kate Arnold who, coming West as a young girl after the Civil War, became housekeeper of the famous Sheridan Inn. I spent a week with her, and, since her mind and recollections (some of them publishable) were vividly clear, I learned such items as that Buffalo Bill Cody, who owned the Inn at the turn of the century, would eat his morning gruel only if cooked by an Indian woman and that he frequently supped with "his" Indians on succulent fatted dog.

But there were scores of others whose recollections were woven into the fabric of this book, the anonymous men and women who recalled how dogwood bark (aspirin) saved Father's life or how Grandma's erysipelas was cured by poultices of hot buffalo dung. To all these people, whose names I never knew, my gratitude and thanks.

Contents

CAUTION:

The author cautions readers that the greatest care should be exercised in the identification and use of herbs, many of which can be extremely dangerous if used indiscriminately.

A Treasury of American Indian Herbs is limited to the Indians of the Rocky Mountain region and this dedication is offered to them in their struggle to maintain their racial identity and moral integrity.

As a people, they are choosing not the muddy and often polluted "mainstream" that threatens to suck into its sluggish current the very foundations of our national heritage, but instead are striving to maintain the centuries-old standards of their tribal life along the small clear brooks that, uncontaminated by man, flow from their mountain heights.

With appreciation and humility, I salute them.

Introduction

On a late-summer day several years ago, I stood in a mountain meadow in central Wyoming. This was to be my home and I was still dazed by the glory of it. At the 7,000-foot level, the ranch clung to the bounteous breast of Albany Peak, and its forests and streams, its sunlit glades and surrounding mountains merged into one of the few remaining unspoiled natural areas in our country today.

Bounded by the dark dignity of lodgepole pine, I was absorbed that afternoon into a world of color. There were flowers everywhere, of every size and hue. Three thousand feet below, at the foot of the precipitous trail we had climbed, spread the golden plain and, distantly across the plain, the winding green line of willows and cottonwoods that bordered the Platte River and obscured the view of old Fort Laramie.

Once, it had not been old. Once, it had been the vital fort on the Oregon Trail. Once, on leaving it, every man and woman in the tremendous procession of pioneers had felt a tightening of the throat and the resolution as farewells were said to the small garrison of this last haven of protection. Whips were cracked and the wagons turned westward into the ominous unknown.

They had crossed the plain below us, these weary men and women, crossed to the great mountain that towered above our ranch, Laramie Peak, reaching more than 10,000 feet toward the sky. In a sweeping semicircle, they had passed this landmark and left the Platte and hurled themselves across the barrens to the Sweetwater that led them to the South Pass. Beyond that lay the Parting of the Ways. Some took the right-hand track that led to Oregon, and some, the arid left-hand track that ended in California. Many finally reached their goals.

Those hundreds upon hundreds of dust-shrouded covered wagons had passed this way, welding the links of empire, and from our mountain home we could hear the hoofbeats of history.

But some had not reached the western sea. Over those decades of the great migration, countless thousands had died along the way. There always was sickness. What did you do for an infected foot or an arrow wound or for a man dying of malnutrition and exposure? During the long months on the trail, your meager supply of medicines had long since been exhausted. What did you do when your baby was strangling with croup?

What did you do? You asked the wagonmaster. That seasoned mountain man or *voyageur* knew what to do, just as he knew what herbs to find for soup if you had run out of supplies. He knew because he had learned from the Indians—those earliest Americans who had found their life-giving herbs in the barks and berries of the shrubs beside me, in the barks and roots of the trees behind me, in the flowers that on a sunny summer afternoon spread a vivid carpet beneath my sandaled feet.

At that moment, this book was born.

As a modest first step, I bought two books, Pesman's *Meet the Natives,* and Craighead and Davis' *Field Guide to Rocky Mountain Wildflowers.* Armed with these, I took to our field and was guided. On the warm Saturday afternoons of late summer and early-arriving fall, I identified scores of plants and my eyes were opened to the hitherto unnoticed wealth that sprang from the soil of our rocky and wooded acres with their rivulets and sunlit glades. Raspberries were there and mountain strawberries, kinnikinnick and wild garlic, onions in profusion and, along the streams, great beds of wild asparagus to be moved next autumn to our vegetable garden. There were countless more.

Still totally ignorant of the uses of these myriad herbs, I took to the books of neighboring libraries. From that reading, two facts emerged. I had hardly begun. There was so much to be discovered that had been noted only in fragments, if at all. To put together these bits and pieces, to amplify and interpret them, to record these findings and share them with others—that was a challenge and a joy. I went to work.

I traveled to New York and Chicago and Washington and Denver, and to Salt Lake City where the inimitable Kate Carter of the Daughters of Pioneers almost submerged me with punctiliously documented data acquired and classified in a life dedicated to preserving the past. I delved in public libraries and private libraries and, later, in medical libraries, and in museums where sympathetic scientists were disconcerted to discover that I did not know an *Erigeron peregrinus* from an *Aquilegia coerulea*.

But I did know the daisy from the columbine. I made a decision and so laid the cornerstone of this book: Botanical names would be used only when needed for clarification.

If a botanist happened to encounter it, his informed mind would instantly slap the tag *Achillea millefolium* onto a proudly erect plant, strongly scented and decorative with its flat white flower clusters. But for every scientist there would be scores of others like me who, having identified the yarrow, wanted only to learn its manifold virtues. In this book, yarrow is yarrow.

Yarrow had been highly valued—it still is—by the Indians who showed its uses to the settlers. Did the descendants of those settlers as well as the Indians still use it today? I realized that I had to talk to those descendants of the incoming whites who lived much as had their forebears, in the "old-fashioned" way. How to do it? Two props proved invaluable, a knitting bag and a bus ticket.

In almost every western town, one may find a decrepit building, usually needing paint, with a dejected sign denoting it as a hotel. One might hurry past it, mentally designating it as a "joint." Sometimes that is so. But if the building is in the old but respectable part of town, if the curtains are clean and there are some serviceable chairs on the porch, then the knitter will have found her "location."

Such a hostelry is always run by a member of the ranching community. His wife is usually the cook. It is frequented by ranch hands and ranch families in town to buy supplies. But in the small rooms upstairs, with their faded furnishings and paucity of closets (and of plumbing), are the "regulars," widows who have spent their lives on ranches only to find it physically and financially impossible to keep them going after their husbands' deaths.

If a middle-aged woman, modestly garbed in sweater and skirt, were to check into one of these spartan cubicles and in the late afternoon, when the smell of cooking is beginning to permeate the premises, were to be found in the "front room," comfortably knitting and rocking in one of the wornout chairs, in no time she would find herself surrounded by the widows and by an aged widower or two who edged in along the fringe. If the knitter led the talk where she wanted it, she soon would learn a great deal about herbs and their cooking and their uses as medicine, and of how Grandma learned all this from the Indians. The discussion would continue through dinner, all of us at one long table on which the permanent exhibits of condiments and toothpicks had been surrounded by bowls and platters of "hearty" dishes.

With luck, one might be invited next day to walk through the fields and nibble the young lamb's tongue or to watch an "old-timer" dig and line a roasting pit as the Indians had taught him. (The roast emerged superbly succulent.)

The second open sesame produced a stream of information that sometimes burst into a veritable geyser. On eastern bus trips, the sensible traveler is reticent to the point of silence. But west of the Missouri, we talk. Indeed, indeed, we talk.

There are certain tacitly understood mores. Strangers are always suspect. Undesirables are scrutinized and discarded. Unmannerly long-hairs and the ostentatiously unwashed are consigned to the nethermost rear. But the rest understand one another. In these sparsely settled regions, people come from similar backgrounds. They worry about the drought. They brag about the calving. They are proud of their youngster's showing at the 4-H Club. They consult as to what dress should be bought for daughter's graduation and where it should be bought and how much it should cost. At the mention of cost, a hush falls. Then someone says, "Maybe you could make it yourself. When my granddaughter married . . ."

They were wary of me at first. I carried a briefcase. I wore a beret (the only sensible headgear in high winds and desert dust). I had been caught saying "tomahto" instead of "tomaato" and had erred grievously in stating that I was going to the station. In the West, you go to the "deepot." But when the woman next to me coughed, I said, "Did you ever take onion juice and honey as the Indians did?"

We were off. I put my beret in my tote bag.

Word gets around. By the end of the first year, strangers would come to me with a recollection of how Great-aunt used flax for rheumatism or sage tea for the stomach ache. I knew I had established contact when a businessman who commuted to Denver by bus invited me to share his doughnuts one morning. Soon he pointed out the bridge under which, while the snow was still on the ground, the first watercress appeared. The reason for his hospitality now emerged. "Is it true," he asked, "that Indian women ate watercress during labor?" I assured him that it was, and is, a widespread custom. "I must tell Lily," he said.

So, as has been true for aeons, the past by word of mouth passes to the present, that herbal knowledge held still by descendants of the pioneers but, more important, cherished, amplified, and handed down to succeeding generations by their teachers, the Indians.

It was more difficult to establish an informal relationship with the latter. The herbs and knowledge of their uses were theirs, and are so viewed still. They hold this knowledge close to their tribal breast. The medicine men would not talk at all and though I did manage to extract fragments of information from the older women, it was not much. Only by living with them until confidence has been established is it possible to learn their secrets. They have endured such racial maltreatment and patronage and insolence that their mistrust and fear of a white skin are endemic. Why not? Very long ago, they shared their knowledge with the newcomers. The newcomers' thanks was to cut off their food supply.

After that, knowledge no longer was freely given. The herbs are theirs and also the knowledge of how to use them. It is understandable that the medicine men with whom I talked told nothing. Why should they give away their trade secrets? But it was the old women who revealed the depth of their suspicion toward a white woman. They did not show this in speech. They did not have to. It blazed from hard black eyes and in hands that, when intrusive questions were asked, were flung forward in dramatic repudiation.

Sometimes the young girls, especially of the small high-school and college groups, did talk, and they were helpful. But in every case, these intelligent youngsters made me promise not to reveal their identity. Why?

Because they are young enough to be afraid that they will be laughed at for keeping the old ways, yet not old enough to see them or themselves in their evolutionary environment and so be filled with pride.

That is the outward and visible reflex. But basically it is because they are torn by inner conflict. Their dress and postures are "modern." Their minds are being oriented toward today. One girl is going to be a doctor, three are in nurses' training. One is studying to teach, one to become a lawyer. ("We must defend ourselves," says the law student.) Their channeled minds tell them to repudiate the customs of the past. But their hearts are governed by instincts that date back unbroken into the darkness before there was history.

The white man is separated from that obscure past by the sedative wall of centuries of civilization. The red man has no such barrier. The Rocky Mountain Indian did not quite reach the point that we call civilized. Given only a fraction more of time, he would have done so. He was balancing on the verge when the white man destroyed all the culture he had built.

He found himself fettered to the white man's whims. For generations he showed his resentment only in lies and horse stealing and sloth and the sullenness or silence that comes from a hopeless and broken will. He went where he was sent, he lived in the squalor assigned to him. But he brewed his herbs for medicine and in his heart he still worshiped the old gods. With no barricade of imposed "civilization" between him and those seemingly submerged stirrings, he felt in his deepest being praise and prayer to the sun and the rain, the wind and the *maíz* and the beasts that he had worshiped for aeons as symbols of the Earth Mother and of the Creator. "The Creator made the world. Come and see it," prays the Pima today as he has prayed through the enormous spread of time.

The Indian lived in a state of worship. Every aspect of nature was evocative of praise or prayer. His strong and effective tribal organization was of high and strictly enforced morality. In practical matters, he handed down to his sons the acquired knowledge from the past—how to kill a beast or an enemy, how to treat the clawing of a mountain lion, how to break a fever—and this knowledge was exchanged or shared with other tribes. But not with outsiders. He had learned from the white man.

When the scientists and social investigators finally came on the scene, he was wholly pragmatic. "If I give you this information, what will you give me?" He dickered, poker-faced, over superficialities while all the time he nursed within him those esoteric attitudes and secrets that are his inheritance from the dimmest past.

That past may be more distant than we have hitherto thought. Twenty, thirty, forty million years ago, the clock continuously pushed back by the findings of that radioactive isotope known as Carbon 14, small, sporadic migrations crossed from Asia to North America over the Bering Strait land bridge. The whole migratory movement probably covered up to twenty-five thousand years.

By then the hemisphere was dotted with little nomadic clusters, the tribal nuclei kept apart and isolated by the great distances that separated them, their amazingly pure bloodstreams thus kept undiluted. And so they remained. "If," wrote William Brandon, "the American Indians can claim direct descent [from the first arrivals on the hemisphere] and some undoubtedly can, then they are by far the oldest known race." As small proof of the above, let me present the charming Maya baby I once held on the doorstep of her thatch home deep in the rain forests of the Petén in northern Guatemala. At the base of her spine, there was a blue mark like a bruise. This was the Mongolian spot. In the centuries upon centuries since their ancestors crossed the Bering Strait, these Indians have kept intact their Asiatic inheritance, their racial identity.

When, as the Zuñi say, in the "fogs of creation, in the mists potent with growth," the first men set foot on the Western Hemisphere, they found a green land prepared for them. Man, *Homo sapiens,* had emerged from the mists of creation in the Tertiary period of the Cenozoic era. In the era that preceded it, the Mesozoic, the whole world had been remade.

The Great Ice Age had reshaped the land masses and climates, giving them much the lineaments of today. The angiosperms had appeared and triumphantly covered the once gray world with color. Flowering plants and deciduous trees vied with the ancient conifers and cycads for roots in the now soft soil. They flourished and spread over all the land. When the Indians came, they found—nothing so limited as Eden—but the whole earth spread before them as a garden of herbs.

They used the herbs for food. They found in them their sources and secrets of healing. They experimented, and never stopped experimenting. They were the world's first scientists.

This book offers, humbly and gratefully, some of the cumulative herbal knowledge of the world's oldest race, knowledge that was acquired in unbroken quest over twenty or forty thousand years.

Part One
Food and Drink

To appreciate the herbs whose uses are contained in the following pages, we need to see them with the depth of vision of Indian eyes. We must see in the small western sunflower its seeds, high in nutritive value, to be ground into meal for bread and gruel and a coffee-like drink. We must see its roots, to be decocted into a soothing wash for rheumatism, and its stem, to be infused into an anti-malarial potion.

We must see the whole plant. So we must see it also on a hillside at dawn, facing the east as the Indian faces the east in prayerful greeting to the rising sun: all nature in harmony—the dawning day, the stillness, the dew-freshened flowers, and man—all one. Man, a part of nature. Nature, a part of man.

The acrid smell of alkali desert soil after a rain, the mighty voice of storm sweeping across great empty spaces, the awesome lightning, the silent snows, the first small flower of spring—all is beauty. All is life. The Indian identifies himself with that beauty and integrates his life into it.

They did not talk to me of this, the elders, the old women, the young girls. This is their inner sanctuary, to be protected from alien eyes. But it is there to be read —in art, in attitudes, in behavior patterns. Besides, how could the Indian make the white man understand? John Collier, the former Commissioner of Indian Affairs, has written: "The White man lives for momentary gratification, the Indian for his Being within." That is a gap bridgeable by only a few.

Increasingly, in the cities, the white man's day begins with a Bloody Mary and ends in sexultation. The Indian's day begins exaltingly before the rising sun.

It ends as it began. In 1954 in Santa Fe, New Mexico, there was an unheralded meeting, the first of many. Those attending were college men, Indian intellectuals who came together, not as a tribe, for they were of various tribes, but, as they put it, as a "nation." Leader Herbert Blatchford immediately put first things first.

"In our early childhood," he told his companions, "we, as American Indians, have been taught the distinction between the living and the lifeless. We have been taught to value the spirit of man as a significant factor in human environment. We are a deeply and uniquely religious people."

The others agreed in unanimity. To them, the living life is the whole life of body, mind, and spirit. To them, the "mainstream" of modernity is a mechanized corpse, lifeless, without a soul.

In early childhood they were taught of the gods and of their relationship with the gods. They were taught of beauty and of things of the spirit. Their parents were their teachers and the elders of the tribe, as these had been taught when they were young in a kinship relationship that had endured for millennia before the white man came.

Now Washington was saying that this tribal system, these close-knit families with their love and loyalty one toward another, must be broken up. Young Indians must leave their tribal life and enter the "mainstream." "The social-cultural integration of Indians is a primary goal of formal education," James Officer, Assistant Commissioner of Indian Affairs, told a university conference. The words merely mirrored a more effete age than that of 1882 when an Indian Bureau report on the schooling of "savages" stated that the children were to learn to speak English and to be "taught the manners and ways of the Whites; in a word, Americanized."

In the decades since that dictum, the gap between the Indian and the white man has widened as Indian youth encountered the white man's world. His participation in his country's wars, followed by further education, usually in college, endowed him with adult eyes. He looked and evaluated. At the end of nearly a century of the Americanization policy, the Indians have held their kinship world intact. The difference is that not only is the gap broadening between the cultures but now the Indians are becoming articulate in white man's terms. Even the tribal elders, for the first time, are speaking out.

As was right and proper in their social family, the young people had consulted with their elders before leaving the reservation for college. The elders (who actually had been behind their thinking) told them they would help them to go, that they must learn all they could of the white man's ways—and then return.

So the youngsters went to college. They worked hard and they stoically stood the jibes that were the fate of reservation Indians. They learned, too, much about the white man's America. But they were not Americanized in the white man's meaning of the word. They took their life with them. As one University of Oklahoma Indian student said, "My tribe is within me. It gives me strength."

When college was done, some went to the cities for a while. Most returned to the tribe, returned with modern know-how of real estate and marketing and modern agriculture, of medicine and law and nursing. But in things of the spirit, of their racial inheritance, they still turned to their elders for the advice that has been theirs for uncountable centuries. Thus, tribal life has been strengthened; now the relationship is reciprocal, young and old seeking knowledge from the other.

Stan Steiner, to whom in his *The New Indians* we are indebted for this current picture, talked about it with young Navaho Herbert Blatchford. "It is time," the latter told him, "to face the fact that the Indians are skeptical of Anglo-American culture."

So the current picture is of increased strength as

the Indian leader of tomorrow returns with increased awareness and modern skills, without having compromised a single one of his beliefs as a red man. To use the imagery of other ancient dwellers in tents, he has lengthened his cords. But he has also strengthened his stakes.

His sense of beauty still finds visible expression as it always has and always will, so long as the Indian gives personal priority to things of the spirit. It is a life of poetry, always integrated in nature. Take the "Song of the Wild Rose," a Dakota poem recorded in the Bureau of Ethnology's thirty-third annual report to the Smithsonian Institution. Explaining that by "mother" is meant Mother Earth, "a living conscious, holy being," the translation reads:

When a maiden is ready to wed
Pin wild roses all over her dress,
And a rose in the hair of her head;
Put new moccasins onto her feet.
Then the heart of the mother will give
Her the songs of her own heart to sing.
And she'll sing all the moons she may live.
Ti-li-li-li, ta-la-la-loo, ta-la-la-loo.

Of his dancing, the Indian says that he now has three kinds: one dance for the gods, one dance for himself, and one dance for the tourists. He delights in his symbolic dancing. The sound of drums raises atavistic stirrings. With a cottonwood leaf, he can make a sweet, flutelike song like that of some other worldlybird. He delights in all earth's gifts. He is *not*—let the point be emphasized—sensual or sybaritic. He is part of the earth. He does not want to inherit it. He just wants to live on it as part of it. He exults in the "mere living." He likes all the good things of earth, including a good dinner Indian style.

The western Indians were gourmets, experts in

matters of good food. Their steaks were charcoal broiled, the succulence of their roasts assured by their thick leaf covers. Their stews and soups were seasoned with herbs, ranging from onion to oregano. All this has been carefully attested in the journals of the early explorers who, however educated and sophisticated, lavished praise on the Indian woman's intuition for fine cooking.

It was the consensus that their vegetable casseroles were the first on American soil. Probably before Europe developed the dish, the Indians were using, not bags or oiled paper, but a cleansed animal bladder into which went the fish or meat bits, the vegetables and seasonings, so that they would blend and retain the flavor in the cooking.

When the Indian traveled, he did not have to depend on the tasteless jerky while hunting or on the warpath. Fastened before him was Indian-type hardtack to be eaten with his pemmican, a cake made of ground meat and dried berries.

The Indians used berries and fruits generously, drying quantities for winter. Their teas were delicious and, when on the trail, they did not drink questionable water but boiled it, tossing in a bunch of herbs they had brought with them to make a tea. Their honey-sweetened fruit drinks (always non-alcoholic) were delicate and cooling. For all this, they gave thanks to their gods of sun and rain and gentle spring air.

Here are some of the "fruits" of the western Indian land.

Absinthe

This sage, growing from the plains to the timberline, was used for flavoring.

Aconite

See Monkshead.

Alfalfa

Growing along streams and in wet meadows, up to about 9,000 feet, alfalfa can be distinguished from other clovers by the coiled pods. It was much used by the Indians who doubtless were familiar with it as far back as the time of Virgil (who wrote of its virtues). Spanish friars found alfalfa planted in Mexico and took the seeds with them to plant when they built their California missions. Soon, alfalfa was growing all over the land. Little by little, it spread eastward.

Alumroot

Reaching from the foothills to the timberline, this is a delicate little plant, often hiding in rock crevices. Its small green flowers are in short spikes. Another variety, the small-leafed, also common on the rocky slopes of the foothills, has smaller leaves and longer spikes; its flowers are yellow.

The Indians especially cherished alumroot as an eyewash and as a poultice for the sores of man and horse. But centuries before, in England, alumroot had found favor for another purpose: secret writing. Instructions written in 1663 direct: "Take fine allum, beat it small and put a reasonable quantity of it into water, then write with said water. The work cannot be read but by steeping your paper in fair running water."

American Dittany

See Basil.

Amole

See Yucca.

Anemone

The anemone is also called the windflower "because they say the flowers never open but when the wind

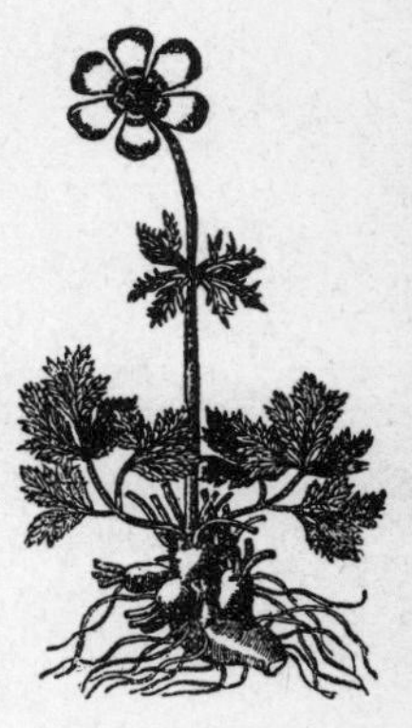
ANEMONE

bloweth. Pliny is my author; if it be not so, blame him." So wrote Nicholas Culpeper in 1653. The Indians, seeing it nod and bow before the spring breezes, called the anemone "the flower of the wind." There are numerous varieties in the Rocky Mountain area, all short lived. The Indians considered them strong medicine, as, in other terms, did Nicholas Culpeper.

Angelica

This tall stout plant of the parsnip family grows widely on the plains and high into the mountains. Its uses were medicinal and are so listed in the "Maladies and Medicines" section of this book.

Anise

Strongly scented, stemless, with yellow flowers and long leaf stalks, anise prefers to grow on the dry hillsides of subalpine heights. Indians used it for flavoring as had man in other areas from very ancient times. Egypt valued it and Pliny made a note concerning the herb. In Europe anise has been cultivated and, for hundreds of years, has been used in the making of liqueurs and cordials and the flavoring of cakes and tarts.

Apple, Indian or Prairie

See Breadroot.

Apple, Squaw

The squaw apple can be found only in the dry soil of the western slope of the foothills and montane. A "free blooming" shrub, its blossoms resemble those of the familiar apple tree. But not its fruits. The absurd little apples can be eaten and the Indians did so. But don't! Their taste is obnoxious.

Arrowgrass

This is not a true grass. Its thickish leaves are

round on one side, flat on the other, and above the leaves protrudes a stem closely covered with a raceme of overlapping pale green flowers. Most arrowgrass grows in the Mediterranean region but the two species in the Rocky Mountain area are widespread. The Indians parched and ground the seed for meal. Learning from them, the pioneers also roasted the seeds and used them as a coffee substitute.

Arrowhead

This is the famous wapato, called swamp potato by the pioneers. The beautiful upright plant, with leaves that are shaped like an arrowhead and with clusters of white blooms, is found up to about 7,500 feet in or near water. At the ends of the long rootstocks are the tubers, valuable for their starch. Indians taught white men how to loosen these by poking with sticks—or their toes. Released from the parent plant, the tubers rose to the surface. The Indians ate them raw, though the taste is a bit bitter. Boiled or roasted, they have the consistency of a potato and the taste of a water chestnut. Lewis and Clark, wintering near the mouth of the Columbia River, traded with the local Indians for quantities of the highly nutritious wapato.

In his 1882 *Dictionary of Popular Names of the Plants which Furnish the Natural and Acquired Wants of Man in all Matters of Domestic and General Economy,* the Englishman John Smith listed wapato as a "North American article of food of the native population."

JERUSALEM ARTICHOKE

Artichoke, Jerusalem

How it got its name, nobody seems to know. It looks like a rather warty version of the familiar artichoke but how Jerusalem got into the picture is likely to remain one of the minor mysteries.

This *Helianthus tuberosus* once inhabited only the West but it had spread all the way to the East Coast long before the coming of the white men, one of the secrets of its success being its apparent immunity from most pests. Growing in fairly moist soil in open places up to about 7,000 feet, it is a perennial stemming from underground tubers and sometimes reaching the height of 15 feet.

Not to be confused with the globe or French artichoke which is an edible thistle, the Jerusalem artichoke is a member of the sunflower family and the Indians used the seeds in the same fashion. Its tubers were particularly valuable since they contained a considerable percentage of inulin, a carbohydrate. The Indians ate these tubers raw or cooked as a vegetable, and they stored a supply against winter shortages. The raw tuber taste has been described as "sweetish, their substance watery." Champlain seems to have been the first newcomer to comment on the Indians' artichoke. He made a note of it in his 1605 journal and, because it was a tuber, called it a *pomme de terre*.

Ash, Mountain

This beautiful shrub, with its white flower clusters and vivid red berries, is found in the foothills and montane. It is most common on the sunlit western slope, often forming dense thickets in the canyons and along the streams. Of the dozen or so species, only three are found in the Rocky Mountain country, up to about 9,000 feet.

The berries of the mountain ash are low in fat and protein but very high in carbohydrate content with a notable amount of tannin. The Indians ate the berries, fresh or dried, the latter often ground to meal. The settlers used them for jams and jellies.

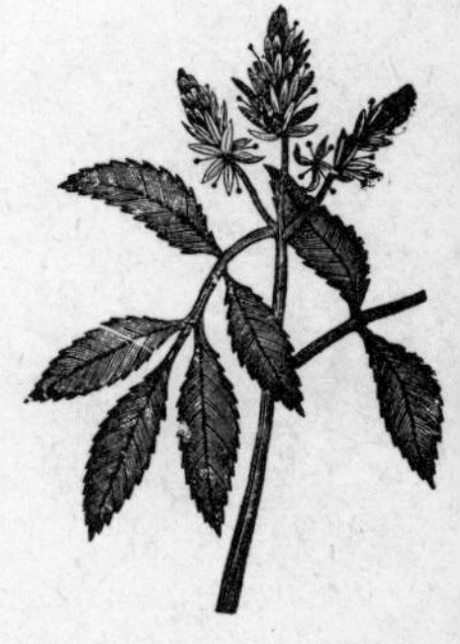

MOUNTAIN ASH

The seeds have wings and protuberances that keep them on top of the forest's leaf carpet. Thus, they are touched by the first spring sunlight. This early flowering was welcomed by the Indians, but their four-legged neighbors already had been sustained for months by the bounteous-giving mountain ash. Bears ate the berries in autumn, birds ate them in winter and in the long lean months of cold and snow, moose delicately nibbled the tender twigs, even as they do today.

With such gifts to beasts and humans, small wonder that in Norse mythology, Yggdrasill, which binds together the earth and heaven and hell, is a gigantic ash tree, the Tree of Life whence first sprang Man.

Asparagus

Asparagus is an Old World plant of the lily family. It is not indigenous to the United States. It is not listed in the books as a Rocky Mountain plant. But the fact remains that in some damp shady spot you will find the erect green shoots of wild asparagus.

Someone brought the seeds to the new land—or else it was the wind. But once over here and on its own, the sturdy asparagus did the rest. Since it adapts to almost any soil, it lost no time in escaping the confines of cultivation and setting forth to cover the earth, at least from the Atlantic to the Pacific or vice versa. Rich in mineral salts, containing vitamins A and B, delightful to eat either hot or cold, wild asparagus became a welcome addition to the Indian diet. Settlers used the hard thick stems as a potherb. Elk favor the young shoots.

Asters

As the days grow shorter in late summer, flowers grow taller; they have had more time to grow and set their seeds. One such is the aster, and the slopes of the foothills, the montane, and the subalpine turn vivid with their sprinkled color. In all, there are some 250 species of asters of which perhaps 35 are found in the Rocky Mountain region. They usually grow in wooded areas, always where there is moist soil. Frémont, climbing the great peak that was to bear his name, found asters growing on the high slopes.

ASTERS

The Indians boiled and ate the leaves of numerous species but big game animals are more catholic in their tastes. They enjoy flowers, leaves, and stems.

Avens, Long-plumed

This member of the rose family is sometimes called prairie smoke or old man's whiskers, both named because of the eye-catching feather-like styles that wave the seeds into the wind for distribution. The flowers are russet pink on a leaning stem, the sepals and bracts being usually pink, though occasionally green or lavender. Its fernlike leaves are the first green things to emerge as the snow begins to melt. Seeing them, the Indians rejoiced. They dug the roots and cooked and ate them but they particularly savored them boiled into a beverage that tastes rather like sassafras tea.

B

Balsamroot

This conspicuous plant of the sunflower family has golden yellow flowers and large leaves that are white below. It is found in the foothills from South Dakota to Colorado, on dry sunny slopes up to 8,000 feet. Of about a dozen species in North America, some half dozen occur in the Rockies.

Indians ate the young tender sprouts and the large roots, either raw or cooked; these are resinous, woody, and taste like balsam. They also winnowed and cracked the seeds.

Elk and deer graze on the young shoots. Bighorn sheep find leaves and flower heads their preferred spring food. Horses are especially fond of the flowering heads.

Baneberry

See Chinaberry.

Basil (American Dittany)

Basil is unknown on the plains but the small herb —used by the settlers like chervil—is fairly common on the high dry areas of the foothills and montane. The Indians cherished it as an aromatic flavoring.

BALSAM

Beans

A wide variety of beans were cultivated by the Indians. These, in turn, spread wild again over extensive areas. There were always beans growing wild or to be had for the trading. Of these, the red bean and the peyote were common in the lower reaches of the foothills. Old-timers who developed the wild bean for their use followed the accepted adage, according to the Sheridan (Wyoming) Press (February 28, 1889), that "oats may take a horse out, but beans will bring him back home again."

Bearberry

So called in the East. In the West it is the important kinnikinnick, which see.

Beard-tongue

For all kinds, *see* Pentstemon.

Beargrass

This member of the lily family is found on mountain slopes, in open high forest, and in alpine fields where its small white flower racemes look at a distance like one very great flower. These huge clusters of white are all the more spectacular in contrast to their background of lodgepole pine and alpine and Engelmann spruce. A northern herb, beargrass reaches south into Wyoming. Indians dried and bleached it for clothing and fine baskets as, in the Northwest, they still do.

Elk and Rocky Mountain goat enjoy the leaves, which remain all winter, and they avidly seek the flowers, flowering stalks, and seed pods. Other game animals also eat the tender plants, as, regrettably, do the spruce mice which sometimes kill them. Beargrass leaves are so slippery that even professional woodsmen, steeping on them, have found their feet pulled out from under them.

Bear's Breeches

So called because of their wide, clasping leafstalk. *See* Cow Parsnip.

Bedstraw

There are some three hundred species of bedstraw scattered over the earth, eleven in the Rocky Mountains. These grow in damp soil, chiefly in open woods and hillsides, but also in meadows from the low plains to about 9,000 feet. It is a slender, upright plant, rough, hairy, with whorled leaves and numerous small white flowers. Indians made purple dye from the roots and used the dried plant for bed ticking.

Beechwheat

See Buckwheat.

Beeplant, Rocky Mountain

Reddish-lavender flower clusters, long stamens protruding, found in waste places and sandy areas to about 7,000 feet—such are the characteristics of the four species of beeplant found in the Rocky Mountain region. Indians boiled and ate the leaves and flowers. But the odor is so disagreeable that the family name is Capparidaceae which comes from the genus name for goat, *Capra,* which it is supposed to resemble in smell. Incoming white men were more explicit. They called it stinkweed.

Berries

Berries are listed under their specific names. True berries are defined as any juicy fruit with seeds in the endocarp or mesocarp. Typical examples include blueberry, currant, gooseberry, grape, tomato. Atypical but botanically listed are melons, bananas, oranges, and so on. By definition, blackberry, cinquefoil, dewberry, loganberry, ninebark, raspberry, strawberry are not berries.

Berries, whether or not botanically "true," figured largely in the Indians' diet and medicine and as articles of trade. Thus, Frémont, in Bear River valley, notes in his journal for August 23, 1843, how, on stopping at a Shoshone village, "we obtained from them a considerable quantity of berries, among which service berries were the most abundant."

The Indian woman always thanked the bear formally for guiding her to edible berries, hidden rose haws, and wild honey.

Bilberry

See Blueberry.

Bistort

From the valley floor to the timber line, bistort bends to the summer breeze, its swaying clusters of tiny white or pink plumy flowers looking at a distance like bits of floating cotton.

Bistort is a valuable member of the buckwheat family. Indians used it in soup and stews and ate the rootstocks. Raw, these are starchy and "puckery." Boiling improves them, but they are at their best when roasted on coals. This gives them a nutlike flavor.

Some 35 species are found in the Rockies, but there are some 150 species spread over the world and for many generations bistort has been used as a "famine food" in times of emergency by Chinese and Japanese, Russians and western Europeans, and by Indians from the Eskimos to those of northern Mexico.

In our Rocky Mountain area, black bear and grizzly eat the roots, as do rodents. Deer and elk savor the foliage.

Bitterroot

This precious and beautiful herb is found on rocky dry soil, on stony ridges, and on foothills and mountain tops up to about 8,000 feet. In the Rockies, there are six species.

From white to pink to rose, bitterroot is the only flower so colored that appears leafless. It is and it isn't. A small multitude of leaves burst into the sunlight almost before the snows have melted. They are withered and gone before the flowering.

The starchy but highly nutritious roots of the bitterroot were so important an Indian food that a grain sack full of cleaned roots was a fair exchange for a horse. The Indians located the roots early in the spring by the sudden appearance of little bunches of leaves. This was the moment at which the roots were tender and at their most nutritious, since the stored starch had not yet been utilized by the developing flower.

Dug with a pointed stick, the roots looked like a forked radish. Their outer covering, usually soaked loose, was easily peeled and the fleshy white core was ready to be boiled, baked, or powdered into meal. Boiled, it is jelly-like and tastes like rice but with a bitter aftertaste which is not noticeable if it is used in soup or stew. Large quantities of roots were set aside for trade or stored for winter.

The Shoshones introduced their *gunga* to the mountain men, who liked it. But the first white man to record collecting it (and the man who gave it its English name) was Captain Meriwether Lewis who did so in 1806, calling the spot where he found it in western Montana, Bitterroot Valley. In tribute, this most useful member of the portulaca family was named for the noted explorer, *Lewisia rediviva.* Soon, in the same area, there was a Bitterroot River and, of course, the picturesque Bitterroot Range. It was inevitable that the bitterroot should become the state flower of Montana.

Bittersweet

This vinelike and decorative plant, with its purple flowers and red fruit, is a member of the Solanaceae family which includes deadly nightshade, and like it, bittersweet contains a poisonous alkaloid, solanine. This is mostly concentrated in the unripe berries and decreases

BITTERSWEET

to a nontoxic state in the ripened fruit. Cooking is said to destroy solanine.

The Indians learned from experience that partaking of the unripe berries could cause paralysis and death to man or beast. They tended to avoid the risk. But the settlers used the berries for pies and preserves. Ring-necked pheasants fancy the lush ripe berries during the winter months.

Blazing Star

See Gayfeather.

Bluebell, Mountain

This lovely herb, also called harebell, with its violet-blue bell-shaped flowers, is found in almost any location in the Rocky Mountain region from 5,000 to 12,000 feet. It lives in grassy meadows among the conifers, and its flowers, usually clustered on branching rootstock, hang down from slender perennial stems. Because of this modest demeanor, the bluebell, in ancient English days, was the symbol for delicacy and humility.

Animals make the most use of the bluebell. Deer and bear and domestic sheep feed on the entire plant. Rockchuck use it through the summer. Pika (rock rabbit) cut and dry the stems and hide them in rock crevices for winter use. Elk bands not only graze the bluebells, but bed down among their leafy stems and pendant flowers. Young elk are born under a cover of tall bluebells.

Blueberry

We all know it—the low erect shrub with its alternate leaves and small lonely little pink or white flowers. We recognize the bluish fruit that turns almost black on maturity. In our foothills area, we know where to find it—in lodgepole forests and other locations where the soil is acid. Of the 60 to 70 species of blueberry, 15 are found in the Rockies from 6,000 to 9,000 feet. The Indians knew them all. When the berries were ripe, the

Indian women lined their baskets with sweet fresh fern to keep fresh the precious fruit.

Blueberries, however, are not a gift only for humans. They are eaten by rodents and grouse, by coyotes and martens, and by deer and elk which consume the leaves of the tender young growth. But, particularly, they are eaten by the bears.

From June through September, blueberries are the staple food of the grizzly and black bears. The fruit ripens first, of course, in the valleys. The bears are there. Then, higher and higher, the berry crop is ready and the bears move up the mountains with it, wanting nothing else to eat for considerable periods of time except the succulent juicy blueberries. In a poor season, it is said that the bears will travel ten to fifteen miles a day to a berry patch.

Borage

See Miner's Candle, Gromwell.

Breadroot

This important Indian fruit was also known as Indian or prairie apple or Indian turnip. French Canadians call it *pomme blanche* or *pomme de prairie.*

A member of the pea family, its flowers are blue-purple, so pale as to be almost white. Since they are the only indication of the whereabouts of the roots, these must be dug while the stems are young and strong, not later than early July. When the summer is further advanced, the dried broken stems tumble about at the whim of the wind so that they have become known by their familiar appellation of tumbleweed.

The Indians, having gathered the roots before the tops died down, boiled them or roasted them whole, in which case they tasted like yams. Some they ground into meal on a metate and made into cakes that they baked over coals. Above all, they peeled the roots, cut them into thin strips, dried and kept them in a cool place, or they braided together bunches of the roots and hung them on the tent poles for winter use.

Lewis and Clark carried west with them blossoms of breadroot made into cakes. Frémont noted in his diary for July 23, 1842: "During the day I had remarked among the hills, the *Psorales esculenta,* the bread root of the Indians. The Sioux used the root very extensively and I have frequently met with it among them cut into thin slices and dried."

Buckwheat

Originally called beechwheat, the buckwheat family includes bistort, dock, and sorrel. Botanically, it is not a true cereal but, from the gastronomical point of view, it "belongs," since its seeds yield the flour from which emerge the breads, pancakes, and puddings.

The wild buckwheat stalk is tall, stout, and branched. Its leaves are long and narrow. Its small blossoms are greenish-yellow and their triangular seeds are winged. It is common in the foothills and montane and, higher, in the subalpine; the flowers are a rich pure white that later turns to rose. The antelope buckwheat of the heights is similar, with similar umbrella-like flower clusters. Both are woolly.

Wild buckwheat grows in open, dry soil; at lower elevations, it is common in sagebrush. It is particularly valuable because it grows on soil so poor that it will not support true cereals and because it is almost free of insect pests. Of about 150 native North American species, 50 or so are found in the Rocky Mountain area.

The Indians ground the seeds for meal to be used in bread and they also made porridge as is still done by them and by white folk in some "backwoods" parts of our country today. The Indians savored particularly the honey from the buckwheat flowers.

Buffaloberry

Known also as bullberry or chaparral berry, the

buffaloberry is a treelike shrub common in the foothills and montane. Still higher, there is the Canada Buffaloberry and in the Wyoming mountain country there is a variant locally called the silver berry. The Canada variety is happiest on the north slope but others prefer the sunnier western slope.

The scarlet (female) berries are bitter but edible. In 1882, it was recorded officially that they "form a considerable portion of the food of the Utah Indians," a limited statement since they provided food for all Indians within their range and for those with whom they traded.

Trappers and mountain men made full use of the berries and it was they who taught the settlers how to concoct a beverage known to them as "soopolallie." Pioneer wives made the berries into excellent jelly.

Mrs. L. Dunning of Otter Creek and Sheridan, Wyoming, recalls that at the turn of the century the Cheyenne Indians brought bullberries from the "head of the draw" to her parents' ranch. Because of the thorns on the bushes, the berries were hard to pick so the Indians waited until frost, then beat them off onto a blanket. The buffaloberries cooked like apple jelly and were "particularly good with roast." Later, when she was mistress of her own ranch home, Mrs. Dunning substituted for nonexistent tomatoes the bright red bullberries in making her catsup.

Bulbs and Roots

These were dug by the Indians after the plant had ripened its seed. Bulbs then could be kept safely until used. If dug too green, they would spoil.

Bulrush

The bulrush is found in mud or shallow water from sea level to about 8,000 feet. Of some two hundred species, twenty live in the Rocky Mountain area. With their dark green round stems and their clusters of erect brown bristly flower spikes, they are familiar to everyone, and, over the region as over the rest of the world, they are used in times of shortage as "famine food." But the Indians considered as a delicacy the crisp young shoots and stem bases as a sweet spring salad, and they ate the rootstocks raw or ground into meal for bread.

The bulrush is also generous to animals. Its seeds are consumed by waterfowl. It gives nesting cover to redwing blackbirds and others including Canada geese, and it is not only a staple food of muskrats but is used by them in building their homes.

Bunchberry

The charming bunchberry, a member of the dogwood family, appears to have a single white flower but actually the stem supports four large white bracts beneath a surrounding cluster of tiny whitish-purple flowers. These in time yield to bright red berries enjoyed by Indians, white-tailed deer, and other forest denizens.

Buttercup

From the plains to the heights, the buttercup gladdens the eye with its caught sunlight—all the more reassuring since it is one of the earliest growing things to appear. It can be found reaching for the sun from edges of snowdrifts, sometimes pushing through several inches of snow and ice. According to one botanist, "The heat given off during the respiration of the growing plant, is sufficient to melt a hole an inch or so in diameter." There are about forty species in the Rockies from the low valleys to the alpine where the mountain buttercup relieves the bleakness with fields of yellow flowers.

The Indians boiled and ate the roots, parched the seeds, and made meal for bread. The juice was used for a yellow dye. There appears to have been no communication between the Indians and the incoming settlers on the subject of buttercups since the latter seem to have confined their uses to the making of pickles from young buttercup flowers steeped in vinegar.

C

Cabbage

Growing in gypsum and related soils up to some 7,000 feet, wild cabbage is actually a mustard—tall, sturdy, with delicate yellow-fringed flower clusters and drooping stalked pods. But its large bunch of broad leaves looks like a cabbage, is the texture of cabbage, and is eaten as cabbage though the Indians learned by experience and experiment that the cooking water had to be changed several times to avoid emetic results.

Cactus

Of the 120 genera and 1,200 species of cactus, all native to the West, only seven species are to be found in the Rocky Mountain area. These prefer hot and dry locales but altitude does not deter them. In the foothills we find the pincushion, common ball cactus of the mountains with rose-colored blooms in June; the wide cactus, rather like the prickly pear, this being limited to the sunny western slope; the king's crown, a ribbed cactus called by other local names, piled in mounds with vivid scarlet flowers (it prefers the western slope). The devil's claw flaunts exquisite purple flowers and the tiny ball cactus has green blooms.

Above all, there is the opuntia, the familiar prickly pear. It may stray to a sunny spot on a mountainside or cling to a seemingly bare rock or settle in a meadow surrounded by lodgepole pine. In dry areas, it is virtually omnipresent. This has made it literally a lifesaver for the bitter juice in its stems quenches the thirst of travelers in a barren and dry land.

The Indians ate it raw or cooked. They made it into sweets. They chewed it like gum. They dried the pulp and made it into cakes and stored them. Some

Indians made a rite of the producing of cactus juice, the pot being presided over by the mother or mother-in-law.

Cactus has been recognized as a useful plant for centuries. Theophrastus, in 288 B.C., gave the name to a spiny plant and this was adapted by Linnaeus who listed the cacti as the family Cactaceae.

Camas

The Indian quamash or camas, "Queen of the Bulbs," most significant of the western plants, actually played a part in the history of the Indians, so vital was its role in their life pattern. With breadroot and cous, camas constituted their basic starch food.

Camas are found as high as the subalpine. They grow along streams or in moist meadows, so closely covering vast areas that in springtime the effect is that of lakelets of brilliant blue. These flowers, grouped on spiny racemes, are spectacular. Stems are unbranched, leaves resemble long grass, and plants rise an inch or two from ovate bulbs that look like onions. Only one of the six species, all of North America, is found in the Rockies.

Another member of the family also resides in the area. This is the toxic death camas. Very similar in form, it can be a threat to the uninitiated. Through untold hundreds of years, the Indians had learned how to differentiate between one of the greatest bringers of life and the bringer of death. They marked them in the flowering season and remembered where they grew, the quamash with its big blue flowers, the death camas with blossoms yellow and small.

Starchy and nutritious, the bulbs can be eaten at any season, but they are best in the autumn. Boiled, they have a potato-like flavor but are less mealy and are a bit gummy, sometimes even slimy. They can also be eaten raw or baked, roasted, dried and pounded to meal. The Indians did all these, and still do.

They waited until after the seeds were ripe, then dug up the bulbs. The favored procedure began with the digging of a deep hole that was lined with fire-heated stones. The bulbs were placed inside and baked.

In many tribes, the camas feast was a tribal festival. Men brought in hard wood and green branches as their ancestors had for countless generations. Old women and grandchildren did the digging with their fire-hardened crooked sticks. Skin bags were beside them to receive the bulbs.

After a day's burning, the oven was raked and ready, a bed of hot ashes being left that was about twenty feet in diameter. On this were placed the washed bulbs, then a layer of ashes, some coals, more ashes, camas, branches, then layers of dry grass to cover the whole. Following ancient ritual, the care of the camas pit was divided among four women to tend the coals and ashes until the cooking was completed in twenty-four to twenty-six hours.

Now the feast was ready. It was an important social event. Large openwork flat baskets were waiting and with forked sticks the bulbs were laid on them to cool. When they were lukewarm, the black outer coating was easily stripped off and the bulbs pressed between the women's hands until they looked like thick brown cookies. Their odor was tantalizing, rather like vanilla and spice.

They tasted like a cross between brown and maple sugar so that, being very rich and sweet, the taste ultimately became cloying. By ancient practice, the Indians then ate salt meat after which they returned to their camas feast. This process was repeated until their year-long camas appetite had been satisfied. A few were eaten as dessert, then the bulk of the bulbs were hung in sacks to dry and to be brought out on some special occasion. This ritual is still practiced in a few communities, as is the making of molasses by boiling the bulbs in water until it almost evaporates. Indian children are still discovering, as did a hundred generations of other children, that if they eat too much of the sweet, the effect is purgative.

Lewis and Clark made the same discovery. They used camas extensively but complained that too many of them caused acute dysentery.

A chief vegetable item in the diet of the western Indians, camas became equally important to trappers, explorers, mountain men, and pioneers. Westbound settlers learned about the bulb from the Indians and some concocted a camas pie which is still served in some prairie communities, notably in Nebraska.

The Nez Percé Indians brought camas into history, dramatically and tragically. For thousands of years, they had centered their life in the springtime on the gathering of the camas and their ritual celebration. Then, suddenly, the white men shut them out from their camas fields. Under Chief Joseph, they left their confinement on the Clearwater River in Idaho to which they had been moved and went south to their old camas hunting ground for their annual supply of the bulbs.

This breaking of the reservation bounds started the Chief Joseph War, which proved to be the greatest and most brilliant military feat of the American Indian in fighting for his home and his way of life. Under their great leader, they almost won sanctuary to the north. But the "Americans" were too many and too strong. Never again did the Nez Percé journey southward as free men to dig and store their camas. In the spring the deer and elk and moose still graze on the bright blue fields.

The Indians' word for this priceless lily became the base for the scientific name, *Camassia quamash* with which it was endowed by John Torrey, a nineteenth-century botanist with the Pacific Railway Survey.

Carrot, Wild

See Cicely, Sweet.

Cattail

The broad-leafed cattail is common on the plains and foothills up to about 7,000 feet, two of the four American species being found in the Rocky Mountain region.

The Indians ate the ends of the new stems in the spring and savored the tender shoots, enjoyed during the flowering but before the pollen developed. Raw or boiled, with the flavor of cucumber, these were held to be a great delicacy.

The lower part of the stem and the roots are highly nutritious, containing nearly pure starch. Without knowing why, the Indians considered cattail a valuable and pleasant food. The rootstock was dug up easily with a pointed stick and eaten raw or roasted in hot coals. Many of these were stored for winter and the core of the larger roots was ground to meal which, in food value, was equal to rice or corn.

The Indians taught the settlers about the uses of this common cattail, including its fun as a sweet savored by the newcomers and by Indian children to this day. Cattail sap is candy to the Nevada Indian children and the Paiute young still roll it into balls and eat it, complete with whatever insects may be entangled in its gummy stickiness.

There were other uses. Cattail leaves were woven into mats and the female flowers proved to be excellent tinder, their "fuzz" exploding into flame. Modern hunters also have discovered the convenience of cattail fuzz and "Smokey Bear" is definitely nervous over their experiments.

Indians knew, of course, of the insulating quality of cattail down, and mountain men and pioneers stuffed it into their boots to prevent frostbite. Early settlers stuffed it into their quilts.

Wild things make full use of cattails. Muskrats and geese eat even the rootstocks. Elk enjoy the early spring shoots. Waterfowl nest in the tall green growth, which offers cover to other winged creatures as well. Since ring-necked pheasants always choose to roost among the cattails, the extent and spread of cattail growth is used as a measure of how many pheasants will winter in the area.

Chan

See Chía.

Cherries

Of the hundred or so species of wild cherry, only three or four can be found in the area of the Rockies. These grow along the creeks or in the moist soil on hills and mountain slopes up to about 8,000 feet, although the chokecherry climbs a thousand feet higher. This highly valuable western chokecherry is a tall shrub or small tree up to 25 feet which in May bears long racemes covered with innumerable small white flowers. These sweetly scented clusters, drooping against fine-toothed leaves and spotty brown bark, give place to single-stemmed fruit. The small (3⁄8″ in diameter) puckery-mouth black cherries were of priceless worth to the Indians and later to mountain men, explorers, and pioneers.

Indians ate the cherries fresh. They made a decoction of young shoots and bark, taken as a vegetable. Most important, they dried them, placing them in flat baskets and turning them daily until ready for use. The dried berries were made into biscuits or cakes for winter use and added as a flavoring to the pemmican. They made tea from the cherry stems and bark, and jelly and syrup from the fruit. They gave a bit of dried cherry biscuit to babies with the stomach ache. And they taught the white men these things.

The Astorians used the cherries when weak from semi-starvation. Lewis and Clark and their men used them. Mountain man Hugh Glass kept himself going by eating chokecherries after being mauled by a grizzly.

John C. Frémont recorded in his journal after leaving the Platte River and reaching the Sweetwater, "On the banks were willow and cherry trees. The cherries were not yet ripe but in the thickets were numerous fresh tracks of grizzly bear which are very fond of the fruit." When his coffee was expended, "a kind af tea was made from the roots of the wild-cherry tree."

Chewing Gum

Because it was a dry world with unending dust, frequent water shortages, and burning sun, the Indians chewed any available herb that would moisten their mouths. These appear to have been most satisfactory:

Clematis: The early settlers learned from the Indians to chew it also as a remedy for colds and sore throat.

Dandelion: Most popular because, with its touch of latex, it lasted longer. It was also most available since some form of dandelion was to be found in almost any location.

Gumwood: Indians chewed the leaves.

Hawkweed: Indians learned to coagulate the milklike juice into a chewing gum.

Hollyhock: Stems proved to be excellent mouth moisteners.

Lettuce: The blue-flowered wild lettuce (chicory) supplied gum from the roots.

Licorice: This was chewed raw, in moderation.

Milkweed: The Shoshones, in particular, had learned the knack of collecting milkweed milk, pressing and molding it in the hand until it was firm enough to chew.

Pussytoes: These prevalent catspaws or everlastings were most useful.

Rabbitbrush: This is an ugly plant with knots and lumps and other such protuberances on its limbs. These, however, contained enough moisture to provide a welcome chewing gum.

Salsify: The juice was collected, coagulated, and chewed. Its value was double. It not only provided moisture but also was held by the Indians to be a remedy for indigestion.

Spruce Gum: Like several other conifer gums, that of the spruce was much used, and was preferred by the mountain men who perfected its use with the nicety of a dilettante. The gum had to be chewed about three days before it was considered by the experts to be at its best.

If it was too soft, it stuck to the teeth. If too hard, it disintegrated into powder.

Chía

Chía is a sage—low, scrubby, and with a stimulating odor, especially on a hot noon or when a shower has laid the dust. The Indians roasted the seed, ground it to meal, and made a gruel that was one of the peace offerings to the first visitors to California. Whether the sailors liked it or not is not recorded.

Chía, also called chan, was highly prized. There was a very healthful drink made from the seeds, and it is said that one tablespoon of the seeds was sufficient to sustain life for twenty-four hours for an Indian on a forced march. By 1891, it was so valued in California that it cost from six to eight dollars a pound. The Indians gathered their own and so could afford to be lavish. They surrounded their blankets or beds of branches with a circle of green chía. This is claimed to be infallible in keeping away the bedbugs and is still used for that purpose.

"Chico"

See Saltbush.

Chicory

This is a tall, sturdy perennial found along the roadsides or in waste places up to about 6,000 feet, higher if growing in protected wet meadows. Its pallid blue radial flowers rather resemble the dandelion pattern and the Indians used it as they did the dandelion.

Chinaberry

Also called baneberry, this member of the buttercup family is found up to 9,000 feet and boasts a large basal leaf and small white blossoms clustering from thickly laden racemes. The fruit is unique in the area. Its shiny oval berries, occasionally red but generally white, resemble, to those so minded, china. The plant has no known herbal value and is included here because it shows how the Indians warned latecomers against what was not good for them. The charming berries appear to have a bad effect on the heart, and the rootstock produces violent purgative and emetic effects.

Chinese Lanterns

These crinkled-leaved plants, sprawling upward a foot or more, are also called ground cherries. The half dozen species in the Rocky Mountains grow in dry soil up to some 7,000 feet and no one would pay any attention to them were it not for their bladder. This calyx elevates them from anonymity into a spot of unique admiration from all beholders.

After the unregretted passing of the dingy flowering season, the calyx expands into a small parchment-like balloon, and a dozen vivid vermilion balloons, waving on their stems like so many Chinese lanterns, bring joy to the eye. To the Indians, there was practical satisfaction as well. They opened the gay pods and extracted the yellow berry within. These they ate raw or dried for seasoning.

Cicely, Sweet

Cicely, with its small purple or white blossoms, grows high, preferring the upper foothills and montane up to 10,000 feet. It is a member of the carrot family and settlers frequently referred to it as wild carrot.

Herbalist Gerard wrote in 1636 that "Sweete Chervill is also called Sweete Cicely" and that it was used much among the Dutch people "in a kinde of Lobolly or hotchpot" which they "do eat, called Warmus." The leaves "are exceeding good, wholesome and pleasant among other sallad herbs, giving the taste of Anise seed unto the rest. The seeds eaten as a sallad whiles they are yet green, with oile, vineger and pepper, exceed all other sallads by many degrees and wholsomenesse for the cold and feeble stomacke.

SWEET CICELY

"The roots are likewise most excellent in a sallad, if they be boiled and afterwards dressed as the cunning Cooke knoweth how better than myself; notwithstanding I used to eat them with oile and vineger, being first boiled, which is very good for old people that are dull and without courage; it rejoiceth and comforteth the heart, and increaseth their lust and strength."

The Indians went the famous herbalist one better. They, too, used the leaves and the roots. But more. Though there seems to be no record that they had associated the aphrodisiac qualities of the herb with human beings, they had discovered that feeding sweet cicely to their horses put them in good shape for foaling.

Cinquefoil

The leafy cinquefoil blossoms with yellow blooms like buttercups but its true virtue resides in the lengthy creeping runners on which the plant rests. In the Rockies, there are some thirty species, one or more of which can be found almost anywhere you look, in moist soil or saline, shadowed or in open glades, in lowland valleys or at 8,000 feet. Other cinquefoils are scattered about the globe. Thus, Gerard in 1597 pointed out to his fellow London urbanites that cinquefoil "lodged upon brick and stone walls, especially upon the bricke wall in Liver Lane."

CINQUEFOIL

But its uses in those days were not always beneficial in Merrie Old England. Coles, in his *Art of Simpling*, written in 1656, recorded, "The 'ointment' witches use is made of the fat of children dug up from their graves and mixed with the juice of smallage, Wolfsbane and cinquefoil and fine wheat flour."

While all this was going on in the country that claimed to recognize only France as a near equal in cultural flowering, the North American Indians of the West were happily eating the berries, making dyes, and savoring the long, thin, highly nutritious roots of the cinquefoil which, when boiled or roasted, tastes somewhat like sweet-potato-cum-parsnip.

Clematis

The seeds of the clematis are carried by the wind over rivers and deserts, mountains and plains. Spread over the earth are more than a hundred species. Only three or four are found in the Rocky Mountain area, where in the thickets and woods it grows profusely up to about 8,500 feet.

It was used profusely by the Indians for purposes ranging from hair to horse medicine. Its fibers were made into rope. Its delicate seed-carrying styles, waving like silken plumes, fragile as feathers, were used for tinder. "Old maid's bonnet," the pioneers called clematis, as outdoor men still do, or heather flower because of the sheen of the dark blue flowers, pendulant from sturdy stems.

Clover

The ancient symbol of domestic virtue and good luck for women, there are more than three hundred species of clover in the North Temperate Zone. These include the high-altitude alpine clover and the white, said to be the original shamrock. The coarser red clover predominates in the foothills and, like other species, is important summer food for Canada geese, grouse, and their kinfolk. For deer, elk, and bears, it is choice forage.

With high protein content, clover is very nutritious —as the Indians discovered several aeons ago. They ate—and eat—it raw or cooked and looked forward to a late-spring treat of boiled clover buds.

Corn Smut

Though most of the uses of this predecessor of commercial penicillin are listed in the "medicines" section, this fungus was used also as food by the Pawnees and Omahas, who gathered the spores as soon as they appeared. These were white, fine, and said to be delicious.

Cottongrass

See Sedge.

Cottonwood

Valued and invaluable to the Indians, the cottonwood follows the valleys and bounds the western streams. Modern white Americans, struggling to maintain the neatest lawn in the neighborhood, prefer the male cottonwood since the females are veritable litterbugs, strewing their breeze-blown cotton all over the place.

But the Indians cherish the young pods, among the first green thing to be welcomed after the dreary diet of the winter months.

The double-headed ceremonial drums of the Pueblo Indians are still fashioned of cottonwood, burned and scraped into shape. In one Arizona area, the cottonwood root, thick but light in weight, is still used to carve the small sacred images known as Katchina dolls.

Cous

Cogswellia cous or Wyeth biscuitroot, whatever called, cous were preeminently important to the Indian economy. The thirty-odd species in the Rocky Mountain region are found from Montana to Colorado in the arid plains and foothills. Flowers are yellow, stems often deep lavender, roots fleshy and thick, generally three in number about golf-ball size and placed one above another.

These roots were one of the three basic sources of starch in Indian diet and were much sought. One of the first food roots to emerge in spring, they smell and taste like parsley. The Indians gathered them in great quantities and ate them raw or ground into meal to be formed into flat cakes.

These cakes were made large enough to be strapped to the saddle and remained edible for long periods and over long distances. This vital quality caused cous to be in constant demand and the Indians used them as an important economic commodity. Lewis and Clark recorded several times in their journal of trading generously in buttons and beads for cous roots and cakes. (They spelled the word *cows,* which caused understandable consternation back East since the Rocky Mountains and Columbia Basin were supposed to be without cattle.)

In cous, the chain of discovery is vividly clear. Lewis and Clark learned from the Indians and Lewis recorded the information for the scientists in Washington. The Indians, in turn, had learned from the bears. Where the grizzly sniffed and pawed beneath the melting snow at winter's end and with his long sharp claws unearthed his succulent morsel, there the Indians followed and dug nearby and found the cherished roots.

Cow Parsnip

Along the streams on high mountainsides grows the tall plant whose wide, interlocking leafstalk caused it to be known by the first white arrivals as bear's breeches. Before the flowers appeared, the Indians ate the young tender leaves and stalks of the cow parsnip as greens, either raw or cooked. The cooked roots resemble rutabaga.

Cowslip

The water-craving cowslip, with its white flowers like buttercups and its shiny dark green leaves, is found at altitudes from 7,000 to 10,000 feet. There are only two species of this marsh marigold in the United States and only one in the Rocky Mountain region. But the Indians found that one and used it, bitter though it is, as a potherb.

COWSLIP

Cranesbill

See Geranium, Wild.

Creosote Bush (Greasewood)

An 1882 dictionary states that the creosote bush has a "strong odor disagreeable to travelers and animals," that it is "unfit for firewood," and that its "only apparent use is to fix desert sands."

So it does, but, growing up to and above 6,000 feet,

this erect aromatic shrub with its white bark and yellow flowers has many other uses. The writer should have consulted with the Indians before he made his pronouncement.

As the Indians pointed out, where the creosote bush grows, the settler does not homestead; the creosote bush tells him that the soil is alkaline and unfit for planting.

Its chief contributions to culture is the gummy substance it exudes, the resinous achievement of a tiny scale insect which punches the young twigs, lays its eggs in the hole, and, during the exercise, exudes the gum. The Indians found this lac invaluable in affixing arrowheads to their shafts, patching cracked pottery and, above all, in applying the lac to their woven grass baskets to make them watertight.

The Spaniards developed from the lac a concoction for sick cattle and for saddle galls on their horses. But they, too, did not like the salty stimulating aroma. They termed the creosote bush *hediondilla,* "the little bad smeller."

Mormon housewives of Utah, hard pressed at first to feed their families, gathered the tender young twigs of the creosote bush, cut and boiled them, a recipe that endured. Today the potherb is served with butter or cream sauce.

I never found evidence that the Indians ate boiled greasewood twigs. But it is certain that they did. They tried and proved every growing thing.

Cucumber

The familiar *marah* of the Mexican Indians, the wild mock cucumber is a tall climbing annual with greenish-white flowers and round seed pods, prickly but delicate as tissue paper. When ripened, these pods pop open, spilling their big brown seeds into the wind. The Indians roasted these and found them particularly efficacious in kidney trouble.

They, of course, ate the leaves and fruit as spring greens even as the settlers learned to do, if they did not already know. John Evelyn, gathering material in 1679 for his *Discourse of Sallets,* reported the cucumber leaves to be "the most approved salllet alone or in composition . . . to sharpen the appetite and cool the liver."

Back in the days of Shakespeare, it is said that a distilllation of bruised cucumber "cleanseth the skin," and "cureth the reddest face that is; it is excellent also for sunburning and freckles." The Indians did not need it for freckles, but they used a cucumber decoction to cool the skin that had been overexposed to the weather.

Currants

Currants everywhere contributed to life and the joy thereof. There was the squaw currant of the high mountains, drought resistant, pinkish of blossom, with fuzzy tasteless berries. There was the buffalo currant of the plains and piedmont, with its sweet-smelling yellow flowers and good-tasting black berries. There was a black currant found in the damp woods of the foothills and the greenish-flowered American black currant and the golden currant with its odor delightfully spicy under a summer sun. Altogether, there are about twenty-five species in the Rocky Mountain region.

The Indians used all varieties, preferring the black currants to dry for their pemmican and for winter use. They ate the berries raw or cooked and as currant soup. They used them as seasoning for their stews.

Pioneer women were happy when currants came into view on their western pilgrimage, and in a few years currant jelly brightened the crude dining tables from the mountains to the Pacific. Lewis and Clark already had recorded the "vast variety of wild berries," especially the black currants "which were delicious and more pleasing to the palate than those grown in their own Virginia home gardens."

The western birds and rodents, the deer and elk

and glutinous black bears could attest to this. They had been feasting on similar currants for a few million years.

D

Daisies

Daisies sprinkle the plains and hills and even the overshadowing mountains like so many shining, multicolored dewdrops. There are the townsendia and whiplast of the high zones, the low and cut-leaved and foothills of the lowlands and piedmont, the oxeye, decorative and introduced into the West. Above all there is the magnificent purple Easter. Pink daisies and white and rose purple. Like the Italians and the Spaniards, the Indians ate the young roots.

DAISIES

Dandelion

The herb with leaves like lion's teeth, the *dent-de-leon,* is found all over the world. A half dozen species flourish in the moist areas of the Rockies. All over the world, too, the formula is the same: young leaves for salad, roots for potherbs, flowers for wine. In Europe and later in North America, roasted roots were used as a coffee substitute, tasting rather like chicory.

The Indians did not make wine but otherwise had

savored the young leaves and roots for untold generations, and they chewed the rubbery stems like gum.

So deeply entrenched and widespread was the Indian use of the dandelion that John Josselyn almost certainly was in error when in his *New England Rarities,* published in 1663, he claimed that the dandelion was unknown until the arrival of the Pilgrim fathers. This is not to say that these worthies did not inadvertently bring a few seeds hidden behind their shoe buckles or caught in their hosen, for dandelions had been in Europe a very long time. But had he traveled westward, we may safely surmise that he would have partaken of his dandelion greens in some Rocky Mountain meadow.

DANDELIONS

As it was, he could have enjoyed them back across the sea; in 1679, John Evelyn noted that the greens were "wholesome and little inferior to Endive. . . . The French country people eat the roots." Highlighting the indestructability of the lowly dandelion, he added that it was with this "homely sallat the Good-wife Hecate entertained Theseus."

Datura

See Jimson Weed.

Deadly Nightshade

See Nightshade.

Dock

The three most common varieties, all used constantly by the Indians, are curlydock, yellow dock, and burdock. The dock called curly derives its name from the wavy margins of its smooth dark green leaves. Growing from one to three feet tall from its yellow fleshy root, it bears insipid green flowers and striking brownish-red fruit rather like coffee beans. Find it in moist ditches along the roadside or in waste places up to about 6,000 feet. The burdock will be found in similar locations and will dominate the docks since it grows tall, from two to six feet.

DOCK

Burdock's name reveals all: it is almost literally covered with burs that split apart when ripe.

Indians used the dock freely, as medicine, as hair treatment, as tobacco substitute. They used it as a potherb, usually with sorrel or lettuce. It was one of their most dependable greens, the leaves and stems eaten raw or boiled, often cooked with dandelion leaves, pleasant to the taste though a bit sour because of the oxalic acid content. But the Indians' invaluable discovery was that boiling any of the docks with meat makes it cook more rapidly than otherwise.

The Indians cherished their docks but not so Charles F. Millspaugh, M.D., who in 1892 listed them among his medicinal plants but commented that dock is an "herb so rank that man, the jackass and the caterpillar are the only animals that will eat it."

Dogbane

See Hemp.

Dogwood

Dogwood's delightful bunches of small white or blue fruit were eaten by many Indian tribes. Its wood is tough and was used to make their bows and baskets. It offered crotches that were almost perfectly Y-shaped, to go into the making of cooking racks, kettle hangers, slingshots. It contains cinchona which the Indians used in decoction for fever. Useful to man, dogwood is equally useful to animals. Containing enough protein, carbohydrates, and fat to sustain life, dogwood is obtainable to animals through at least the early part of a mountain winter.

It is a tall shrub, sometimes reaching fifteen feet. The bark is reddish and new growth is vividly red. It grows in bogs and damp valleys and the three Rocky Mountain species climb as high as 7,500 feet.

But it is the flower that makes the dogwood beloved, the little white flowers that sprinkle the sunlit hillsides with spring snow. It is the flower that fashioned the Legend of the Dogwood.

DOGWOOD

It is said that, because it is so tough, dogwood was used to make the Cross. And it is said that after that, the dogwood tree never again grew tall enough for such a purpose. But that purpose was never to be forgotten. It was to be remembered forever in the flower, shaped like a cross, petals spattered in the red of blood and, in the heart, the Crown of Thorns.

The Elder and the Elderberry

The elder (*Sambucus pubens*) is a tall shrub, growing up to ten feet, with clusters of diminutive white flowers and, in autumn, bright red or roan brown berries. Its near kin, the elderberry (*Sambucus coerules*), more closely resembles a tree and its berries are blue. These, along with five or six other species in the Rockies, will be found in moist soil in woods and open glades and along the streams from the plains to the high mountains up to 10,000 feet. We describe these two species together since in many instances, there is no distinction made in the records of the "manifold properties of the Elder Tree."

In the *Materia Medica,* the list is impressively long of the uses of the elderberry from early times; many of these uses, which the Indian had discovered for himself, are listed under "Medicine."

The Indians used the leaves and flowers of the elder in the usual ways, as salad, as a berry drink, and for seasoning. They were particularly fond of fried flower heads. But there were multiple other uses.

The white wood was used for pegs and skewers. The large shoots were whittled into arrow shafts. Some tribes called the elder "The Tree of Music" because in spring, when the tender pith could be removed easily, they made their flutes. These were dried with their leaves still on. The white newcomers learned this technique from the Indians and today the men who know their outdoor lore can hollow the pliant stem and make a whistle that will lure the bugling elk to his undoing.

The white men and women also knew a thing or two about the elder. They knew that the blue elderberries were best for making jelly. They knew how to use them in ketchup and chutney. They beat the small flowers into their pancake batter and fritters. They made flavoring and tea and excellent wine. They used the buds to make a superlative pickle. The leaves they made into a decoction to be sprinkled over their choice plants to keep them from being eaten by caterpillars.

There still are women out where the elders grow who use the flowers in buttermilk to clear their complexions. But John Timbs, recording medical herbs in 1876, commented that in England wine distilled from the elder flowers was rivaling buttermilk as a cosmetic in the rural districts. So much was the elder in demand that herbalist Gerard in 1597 instructed his city readers that it could be found "in untoiled places, plentifully in the lane at Kilburne Abbey by London."

But the roots of the elder go far deeper than sixteenth-century England, deep down into the folklore that preceded or marched beside history. In Germany, superstition decreed that the hat must be doffed before an elder tree. In medieval times, it was claimed that Judas hanged himself on an elder tree; hence, to be crowned with elder was to disgrace the wearer. Simultaneously, in the English Midlands, it was claimed that the Cross had been made of elder and therefore it was a sacred symbol not to be burned.

Superstition persisted. Coles, in his *Art of Simpling* (1656), noted that the "common people need to gather elder leaves on the last day of April and affix them to their doors and windows in order to prevent witches from entering their houses."

But there were no witches in the Rocky Mountain West. The Indians drank their elderberry tea and bowed in worship to the setting sun.

Endive

See Chicory and Lettuce. "In the United States, endive is known as chicory."

Ephedra

No plant could be more awkward or unattractive than ephedra, also known as joint fir or Mormon tea. It grows high up on dry, bare mountainsides. It is "leafless," with a stripped and naked look in spite of the jaundiced-yellow-green flowers that protrude from its joints.

It is wholly adapted to its arid environment and, within the dimensions of its environment, no plant could have been more useful to the Indians.

Ephedra was roasted and ground into the Indian "bitter bread." It was, and with the Navaho still is, made into a beverage from the pre-roasted stems. It was a valued chewing gum and Mary Austin, student of the Indians, states that "because of the activating properties of the mucous membrane, desert tribes of California on making long journeys," where there is insufficient water, still "chew ephedra stems and they prescribe tea made of it as a precaution against thirst."

Everlasting

Found in the foothills and mountains almost to the timberline, the single species of everlasting in the Rocky Mountain region was used as chewing gum. But of its varied uses, the majority were most potently medicinal.

Fairybells

In the damp black soil of mountain glades up to some 8,000 feet, the modest fairybells display pale yellow to white bell-shaped flowers which become the smooth-skinned globose berries that are brightly yellow-orange.

Temptingly luscious, these are sweet and savored by the Indians, especially the Blackfeet, who still eat them raw.

FENNEL

Fennel

Along the Laramie River and other upland streams grows the fennel with its innumerable small seeds that are used as flavoring all over the world. Besides this use, the Indians ate the stems like celery, and the seeds, leaves, and roots in the usual way. It is doubtful if they had learned, as in England, that these were used to make "people lean who are too fat." Boiled in barley water, the seed and leaves in decoction increased the milk of nursing mothers and there were other medicinal uses.

Ferns, Horsetails, Joint Firs, and Bracken

This category covers too wide a range to be listed in detail here, but its uses were all about the same as these: The Indians boiled the roots as starchy food and medicine. In springtime, the settlers ate the tops like asparagus or soaked them in water with wood ashes and, after twenty-four hours, cooked them as potherbs.

Fireweed

Fireweed is most useful for the reason its name implies. It is the first plant to enter burned-over land and bring it to life again—beautifully, for it is one of the loveliest plants in the Rocky Mountains. Its flowers are strong colored, pink or purple or magenta. Its seed pods are long and decorative. It often grows in large spreads, especially in disturbed areas where its softly colored mantle hides fire's devastation.

The Indians, needless to say, experimented with it and found that the young shoots and leaves were edible if boiled as a potherb. Its roots, dug in early spring, were best boiled. When the Canadian *voyageurs* arrived on the scene, they preferred not to hurry matters and waited to use them as potherbs until the tender leaves were more fully grown.

Flax

The flax family are herbs. Nineteenth-century textbooks, particularly that on botany by Doctor Asa Gray of Harvard, used flax as the pattern plant to introduce students to "vegetable structure."

In lower elevations the flax flowers are yellow but the wild flaxes of the plateau blossom with spectacular blooms—sky blue, saucer shaped, too large for the slender stalks which sway and bow under their weight. After the flowers, along about August, come the watched-for seed pods.

Blue flax *(Linum lewisi)* is an early riser completely "unscrewed" by 5:20 A.M. and retiring to sleep about two in the afternoon. Its habitat is the dry region of plains and hills up to about 8,000 feet. Of some one hundred species, five are found in the Rockies. Frémont, in his 1842 expedition, found the blue flax in the Bear River valley, and it was identified in 1862 at the foot of Long's Peak.

The ancients of Egypt and Asia used the flax seeds for food, and in equally ancient times so must have the Indians, as they still do, cooking the savory, highly nutritious seed to mush or using it as seasoning. But, as with all plants, the Indians used every part of the blue flax to its fullest potential.

Residue from the crushed seeds became oil cake or meal. Fibers were made into fishing lines, cordage, ropes. Most of all, the blue flax provided a score of highly valuable medical uses (see "Maladies and Medicines").

Four O'clocks

You can set your clock by the four o'clock. It opens in the late afternoon and blooms until morning and is as regular in its habits as the sun. There is a whole family of these delightful herbs, decorating the high plains and mountains. Of these, the most conspicuous are the showy with rose or purple funnel-shaped blooms and the fringe cup with its pink-purple flowers and its preference for dry soil. The Paiutes call the plant *hewovey* and the Shoshones, *penosamobe*. They used the dry root as did the settlers, who called it "the impetigo plant."

Fritillary

The fritillary, with its deep purple bell flowers marked with yellow-green spots, is difficult to find, because of its rarity and because it hides among the hillside bushes. It was searched for and found and valued by the Indians for its pure starch corm, which they ate raw (excellent) or cooked when it then tasted like rice. The green seed pods, either raw or cooked, were a delicate spring treat.

G

Garlic

The way to tell garlic from wild onion is to note the position of the umbel. If the flower cluster stands up straight, it is an onion; if the swaying stem bends so that the flowers bow downward, it is garlic, the *Allium cernuum,* the "nodding onion."

Indians consumed quantities of garlic, raw, cooked, and as medicine. The wild garlic has a very strong taste, but the Indian woman in using it as seasoning proved herself a veritable gourmet. Never too little, never too much garlic flavored the meat or went into the stewpot, a fact attested by generations of explorers, mountain men, and westbound travelers.

In the Rocky Mountain area, the dwarf pink garlic, with its delicate pink flowers and sickle-shaped leaves, abounded from the high mountains to the plains, as it abounded elsewhere. It will be recalled that wild garlic saved Marquette and his party from starvation as they followed a large body of water southward from the Green Bay. When they had reached the foot of the great lake, the explorer priest named that night's camping spot for the lifesaving herb, giving it its Indian name, *Cigaga-Wunj,* "Place of the Wild Garlic"—Chicago.

Like strong-minded people, garlic always evokes strong opinions *pro* and *con.* Aristophanes wrote that athletes chewed garlic to put them on their mettle before entering the stadium. According to Virgil, the harvest reapers should be fed garlic to maintain their strength. Naturalist Pliny recommended it for medical use, this coinciding with Indian usage. San Martín and O'Higgins ordered garlic put into the nostrils of horses and mules that collapsed from lack of oxygen in their famous crossing of the Andes, and their men sniffed or chewed garlic to counter mountain sickness, thus proving the worth of the ancient Spanish proverb, *Ajo puro y vino crudo, passar el puerto seguro*—"Pure garlic and wine to cross the high mountain pass safely."

The effete John Evelyn scorned the high-tasting herb. "We absolutely forbid its entrance into our salleting," he wrote in 1699; and " 'Tis not for Ladies' Palats nor those who court them." But those were the ladies and gentlemen. Did these gentlemen sometimes grow restive and envy the more uninhibited goings-on behind the closed curtains and down the dark alleys of the town? In the words of the old Spanish saying, did they *suspiran por los ajos y cebollas de Egypto?* Beneath their satins and pretty manners, did they "sigh for the garlic and onions of Egypt?"

Gayfeather

Gayfeather is also named blazing star and both appellations are but fumbling attempts to describe the indescribable. The flowers, rose to purple, are so intense a concentration of color that such adjectives as "bright" or "brilliant" fail to make the picture.

Widespread in the foothills east of the Continental Divide, gayfeather was much sought by the Indians in the fall because of the corm from which it grew. Unlike the bulb of a plant which is fleshed and layered like an onion, the corm is solid, a reserve food high in nutritional value.

Gentian

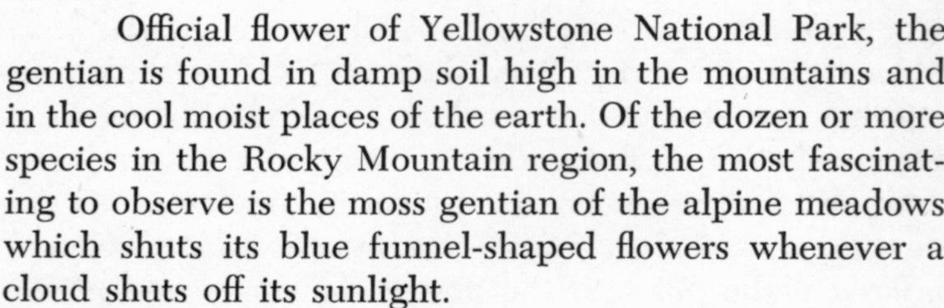

Official flower of Yellowstone National Park, the gentian is found in damp soil high in the mountains and in the cool moist places of the earth. Of the dozen or more species in the Rocky Mountain region, the most fascinating to observe is the moss gentian of the alpine meadows which shuts its blue funnel-shaped flowers whenever a cloud shuts off its sunlight.

GENTIAN

Indians ate the fleshy roots. Elk enjoy the tender new growth in the spring. But its chief value was and is in its medicinal properties.

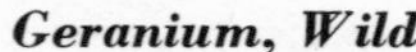

Geranium, Wild

The pods of this pinkish-purple flowered desert mallow have given the wild geranium two other names. Because of the visual effect that the pods produce, the plant has come to be called cranesbill or storksbill.

The wild geranium grows high, up to 9,000 feet, and tall, from one to two feet, with its flowers bunched above its deep-thrust woody root. Highly nutritious, it provides food for man and beast, the Indians enjoying the young plants as greens. Bear, deer, and elk use it as forage. The moose, as usual, is more finicky, fastidiously selecting the most delicate flowers and upper leaves which it prefers to all other greens.

Goldenrod

Symbol of good fortune, goldenrod is familiar to all, at the end of summer being almost omnipresent. It grows in flat lands and in the mountains up to about 8,000 feet. It is catholic in its choice of habitat, thriving in sunlit woods or stony highways or in waste places. There are about a hundred species in North America, some ten or twelve in the Rockies. Aside from its uses in their pharmacopoeia, the Indians sprinkled the powdered leaves on horses' sores, and from the flowers made a yellow dye.

Gooseberry

This sturdy shrub thrives best in the well-drained areas of the foothills. Its berries are colored the lively red-brown of wine and are edible though puckery. The Indians ate them raw or mashed them into their pemmican. A dish highly favored by them was sweet young corn cooked with gooseberries.

Grains de Boeuf (Hippophas)

Indians enjoyed both prevalent species, the red (Nuttall's *Shepherdia argentia)* and the yellow-berried. When introduced to them, the *voyageurs* and mountain men favored them so highly that they even traveled to a location near the source of the Platte River where they had found a veritable concentration of their *grains de boeuf*.

Grape

The Oregon or holly. grape has an underground system for perpetuating itself. It is a low shrub, seldom a foot high, but its stem stretches long under the soil and from this unseen pipeline new plants arise at intervals. The leaves are holly-like with pricking spines. The dark-blue-to-purple berries develop from clusters of vivid yellow flowers. Though there is a slight distinction between the holly grape *(Berberis repeus)* and *M. aquifolium,* which is the state flower of Oregon, it is so minimal that scientists seldom differentiate between them. In the Rocky Mountain area and westward, it is called the Oregon grape. Very nearly evergreen, it is a common ground cover in the foothills.

Indians ate the berries and added them as flavoring to their meat and made them into soup. They ate the crisp young leaves as did the later comers who called them "miners' lettuce." They found, as had the Indians, that the sweetened juice was particularly refreshing, tasting, not unreasonably, like their familiar grape juice. From the flowers and woody roots came the strong yellow dye used by the Indians for basketwork and clothing.

MEADOW GRASS

Grasses

Earth gave to the Indians wild wheat and rye and oats. There was bunch grass invaluable for grazing which Frémont first noted on Bear River near the Great Salt Lake. There were low-growing grasses in the dry country and the high grasses of the river valleys. And there was the admonition to every tenderfoot going west, "Never eat grass. You will die in agony."

Greasewood

See Creosote Bush.

"Greens"

The Indians are known to have used fifty-nine different herbs as greens, either cooked like spinach or eaten as salad. We have certified to date fifty-seven of these, as noted in the text. These greens were used separately or in combinations such as the succulent wild lettuce cooked with lamb's quarter, or what the settlers were to call "poke salad," a mixture of dandelion, pigweed, cowslip, and cresses.

Gromwell

This member of the borage family is found in the dry soil of plains and foothills up to 7,000 feet. Many-stemmed gromwell has bright yellow flowers in the upper leaf axis. The western Indians ate the boiled roots and also used the plant for medicines.

Ground Cherries

See Chinese Lanterns.

Groundnut

The groundnut, with its almost voluptuous pink

or white flowers, grows from the valleys to the alpine. It also grows throughout the world where it is highly prized for a unique characteristic: its root is long, and strung along it like beads on a necklace are tubers the size of hens' eggs. Richly nutritious, these make good eating all over the globe.

The Indians ate every part of the groundnut—stem, leaves, taproots, corms. Corms eaten raw have a mild taste rather like a pallid radish. When boiled, they resemble a first-class baked potato in taste and texture. Indians dug the tubers in the fall and put them in baskets to dry in a warm place.

The settlers learned from them and it is said that during the first winters of near starvation, the Pilgrims would have gone hungry had not the Indians shown them the groundnuts growing near Plymouth Rock.

Gumplant

Known also as gumweed, this disheveled grindelia is found along roads and in open spaces where the soil is dry. It reaches up to 8,000 feet.

It is among the first plants to enter fire-denuded areas where, instead of brightening the dingy scene, its faded-yellow flowers droop dejectedly. The Indians made it into herb tea, chewed the leaves, and found medical uses for it. By some slightly esoteric reasoning, New Mexican Indians call it the *yerba del buey*, the "herb of the ox."

Harebell

See Bluebell, Mountain.

Haw and Hawthorn

The haw and the hawthorn have two points in

common. One is the confusing similarity of their names. The other is that their fruit is most delicious when it has been left to freeze and then is gathered and thawed. This, of course, is for winter eating.

The haw, a viburnum, is a shrub with white flower clusters that yield to sweet blue-black fruit. Hawthorns are trees, their fruit varying from dark red to black. All the fruit is edible and delicious.

The Indians collected large quantities of the berries, ate them fresh, mixed them, dried, with their pemmican, used them as seasoning, and stored the remaining dried fruit for the winter months. Unfortunately, though they make excellent eating, the berries are high in sugar, low in fats and protein.

Hazelnut

Found along the streams of the foothills, the hazelnut, though only shrub size, boasts very hard wood of great value to the Indians, who not only ate the nuts but also used them for seasoning.

Heather Flower

See Clematis.

Hellebore, False

First to flower in the high mountains, false hellebore grows up to six feet tall and is found in marshy ground where its carpet-like patches can be seen from afar. This is because of its large accordion-like leaves, ovate, strongly veined. Flowers are star-shaped, pale green to white. It has been called, but is not, skunk-cabbage.

HELLEBORE

Hellebore is a dangerous herb, containing alkaloids that lower the blood pressure and thus slow the heartbeat. The Indians discovered this quality and used it medically for this and other purposes. Here again, they were helpful to the incomers, warning them of the dangers of the herb.

Hemlock Tree

Of its many uses, the most frequent was the hot beverage the Indians made from the leaves. Lumbermen still indulge in hemlock tea. The tree is not to be confused with the poisonous hemlock plant!

Hemp

Tall-branched, high-growing hemp, with its milky sap and delicate pink flower bells is also called dogbane. Indians ate the parched seeds or ground them into flat cakes. In England, Turner (1525), possibly a first among "modern" neurotics, objected to this practice, common then in the country. He warned that "hemp seeds if it be taken out of measure, taketh men's wyttes from them." The Indians unquestionably had experimented and proved how much hemp seed they could enjoy without going beyond a sensible measure. They used hemp seeds and meal happily for countless generations and the evidence is that they had their "wyttes" about them every inch of the way.

Wherever there is hemp, ropes and cordage are made and the Indians used it for these purposes and for weaving their baskets and mats. There is no evidence that they had discovered the plant's use recorded by Parkinson in 1629 who advised that "a decoction of hemp will draw earthworms out of their holes and fishermen thus obtain their bait."

Hollyhock

The wild hollyhock grows in the moist black soil of river beds and canyons from the piedmont area to about 9,000 feet. The familiar flowers, white, pink, rose, pale purple, cling in dense spikes along the straight stalky root, not so tall as the cultivated hollyhocks but sturdier. The roots hold high nourishment and the Indians made their starchily rich flour from them.

Honey

The honey from the buckwheat flower has a reputation for delightful flavor. Honey from the sunflower is most popular with the bees, which obtain wax from the flowers as well as a great amount of nectar. White honey comes from the snowberry and a bonanza from the bee-plant. There are many other honeys, but, according to the Indians, no honey can match that from hyssop.

The settlers reduced their sweetly cooling honey drink to a recipe: To a quart of water, ⅔ cup of honey. Blend, shake, drink, and be refreshed. The Indian woman, always polite, formally thanked the bear who guided her to some hidden hive of wild honey.

HONEYSUCKLE

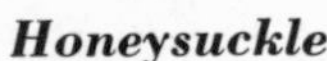

Honeysuckle

Be guided by the sweet scent of the swamp honey-suckle, leading to shady canyons or moist hillsides high in the mountains (above 7,000 feet). Like the familiar trailing or climbing vine of the lowlands, the stem of the swamp honeysuckle is woody, its trumpet-shaped flowers are yellow or orange. The Indians ate its bright red berries though they were both tough and tasteless.

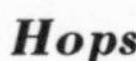

Hops

Along the Rocky Mountain streams on the eastern side of the Divide grow the useful hops. In spring, the Indians ate the buds and tender stems, either raw or cooked, just as their contemporaries did in England. The herbalist's suggestion in 1699 was that the "buds and young tendrels . . . may be eaten raw but more conveniently being boil'd and cold like asparagus." France gave the name *panicles* to the flower of the male plant. The edible tip of the *panicle* was broken from the woody stem like asparagus, precisely as the Indians did except that the thrifty Indians saved the stems and used them for flavoring stews.

No indication has been found that the Indians had discovered the principle of beer making. But they were not interested in alcoholic beverages, the use of which was limited to ceremonial ritual. The Indian was taught by the white man about beer—and the white men were delighted when they found the wild hops.

HOPS

An elderly lady near the Great Salt Lake recalls that as a child, homesteading on the Weber, she went barefoot "up the canyons to gather hops and dry them as they had begun to make beer. In the fall I sold them for fifty cents a pound and got enough to buy a piece of lawn which I made into a dress."

Pioneer women, too, rejoiced to find the hops, for hops in decoction were used with "wild yeast" to produce the raised bread and add flavor to it. In this connection, hops were of particular value because of their antiseptic qualities that prevented the yeast from spoiling.

Horsemint

More familiarly known as oregano, horsemint is delightful to look at, with its leafy bracts surrounding little purple or rose flowers. Of the several varieties that grow from the plains to the 7,000-foot level, it is the cloverhead whose leaves are aromatic. But only slightly more so than the other species. The fragrant leaves of any of the horsemints produce the oregano which the Indians had used for countless generations before the white folk discovered their use for seasoning. In New Mexico today, the Indians follow age-old tradition in the preparation of a favorite dish—a kid sprinkled with oregano leaves before and during roasting.

Horsetail

The lowly horsetail, with its hollow joint stems, is spread widely in the Rocky Mountains, notably in the foothills. The Indians boiled the tender heads exactly as Parkinson noted in 1629 that the rural English did. He noted also that "country housewives use the common weed horsetail to scour their wooden, pewter and brass vessels—even as the first Americans did and still do. The Indians had found that only the outer layer of the stems got cleansing-and-polishing results. So they obtained excellent results without knowing the reason: the stem's outer layer contains a quantity of silica.

WILD HYACINTH

Hyacinth, Wild

A close relative of the onion, the wild hyacinth's corm was gathered in quantities by the Indians and eaten either raw or cooked, being highly favored especially by the Nez Percés. This is one of the most savory of the bulbs and when boiled has the taste of sweetened nuts. The seed pods make delicious greens.

Hyssop

This sweet-scented herb is a member of the mint family, with white to pale purple flowers and stems growing up to five feet. Its leaves are aromatic, its rootstock branching. Liking the sun, it prefers the western slope of the Rockies but can be found throughout the area on open hillsides and in valleys from 6,000 to 8,500 feet.

The Indians ate the tops and flowers as salad or cooked as potherbs, and the seeds raw or converted into meal. They viewed hyssop honey as a special treat.

In England, too, the elegant John Evelyn approved hyssop. In his book on *Sallats,* written in 1699, he added a delicate touch. "The tops and flowers," he advised, "reduc'd to powder, are by some reserv'd for strew upon the colder ingredients."

I

Indian (or Prairie) Apple

See Breadroot.

Indian Banana

See Yucca.

Indian Millet

See Sand Grass.

Indian Potato

See Snowdrop.

Iris, Rocky Mountain

Wild iris looks much like the familiar cultivated flag. It grows high in the moist mountain meadows and its light-blue flowers have signified for aeons that spring has really arrived. More significantly, the sight of iris always was a cause for jubiliation in the thirsty West: a patch of iris meant that there was water close to the surface.

The Indians used iris against their enemies. The rootstocks contain irisin, a poison which they had discovered countless generations into the dim past. They ground the roots, mixed them with animal bile, put the concoction in a buffalo's gall bladder, hung it to warm for several days near the fire. Then the arrow points were dipped into the potent poison. It is recorded that many of the enemy thus were destroyed, some seemingly only slightly wounded who died after from three to seven days.

J

Jasmine

The leaves grow low. The stems are only an inch high. The four or five flowers that perch atop them are tiny, fragrant, and white with an orange center. The whole effect is delightful, like a garden in miniature. But it is seldom seen for the rock jasmine grows only on stony slopes above the timber line. Nevertheless, the Indians found and used it.

Jerusalem Artichoke

See Artichoke, Jerusalem.

Jimson Weed (Datura)

This weed, which has no justification for growing

in high country, grows in high places. I have seen it at 7,000 feet. Its qualities were familiar to the Indians, its rituals performed for countless generations. They knew exactly how much of the drug should be used under varying conditions, its beneficial properties being listed here in the "Maladies and Medicines" section. They used its quieting properties also in handling their horses. If a horse showed that he was all set to stray, he was washed with a quieting tea of jimson weed.

Joint Fir

See Ephedra.

Juniper

JUNIPER

The mountain juniper grows high up, being prevalent in the foothills. The cherrystone juniper grows at lower elevations, especially among scrub oak. Both species prefer dry, shady places. Both produce the coveted blue berry.

Indians used the berries freely for flavoring. They used the wood in fashioning bows and arrows. They made a dye. They used it medicinally for everything from hiccoughs to birth control.

The French cooks, within their métier, used juniper as did the Indians, the Liègeoise method using the mashed berries for the flavoring of kidneys and for thrush *à la Liègeoise.*

Gin entered the records early, credit for its invention going to a son of Henry II. The Indians, using juniper to flavor their buffalo stew or to soothe a stomach ache, knew nothing about gin until the white men taught him.

Kinnikinnick

Called bearberry east of the Mississippi, this prostrate evergreen with the little white or pink flowers is so named because the bears are apt to be in evidence, consuming the red pea-size berries. Equally appreciative of this all-winter emergency food were birds, rodents, and humans. The Indians ate them raw but preferred them boiled to bring out what sweetness there was in the acid fruit. Its natural habitat is in the open glades of the forest of ponderosa pine from 6,000 to 10,000 feet.

The uses of kinnikinnick by the Indians were many. They boiled the plant for tea. They used it as a cleansing lotion. They cured their pelts with tannin drawn from the leaves. But most of all, they liked their kinnikinnick because it made a good smoke. Whether by the Spanish name, *coralillo,* or by Indian language, *k'nick* or *k'nack,* they carried the herb pulverized in their skin pouches and, as they later showed the pioneers, mixed this with crushed leaves of willow, dogwood, or sumac, with or without tobacco, which gave them a satisfying smoke. The habit was rationalized—and this may have been true—that a pipe or two of kinnikinnick was protection against malarial fevers.

Lamb's Quarters

Though lamb's quarters is a pallid-looking weed with its faded leaves and numerous undistinguished green flowers, it is one of the Indians' most useful herbs.

They boiled the leaves like spinach. They ate them raw. They gathered the seeds, ground them into meal, converted it into gruel and cakes. They still do all these things. Many Indian tribes still use lamb's quarters as did their ancestors; and in New Mexico, virtually every pueblo cultivates this valuable herb. Many a descendant of pioneer settlers turns atavistic when spring comes and, strolling in the meadows, nibbles the sweet trowel-shaped leaves.

R. A. C. Prior, writing *On the Popular Names of British Plants,* suggests that the name may be a corruption of that ancient festival in Britain called "lammas quarter," and so listed on their calendar.

Laurel

In the water-saturated soil of the subalpine, from 10,000 feet to the timberline, grows the mountain laurel with its charming clusters of rose-colored blossoms. But, like so much that is beautiful, it can be dangerous. Its leaves are said to be poisonous to animals and that birds, having eaten the plant, then poison those who eat them. Observing this phenomenon, the Indians drank a decoction of the leaves to commit suicide.

Leek

It is said that the true leek has never been found in its wild state and is thought to be a "cultivated variety of oriental garlic." However that may be, an exploring expedition in 1862 recorded finding leeks on the mountainsides of Colorado's Long's Peak. Stated the report: "We often gathered them for use and they afforded quite a relish." For countless centuries before the arrival of the white man, the Indians had savored the herb whatever its English name.

Lettuce, Wild

Of the twenty species of wild lettuce growing in the Rocky Mountain area, the most common is the yellow monkey-flower, its red-spotted vivid yellow flowers resembling a snapdragon. It is found in damp to wet soil flourishing on beaver dams and near springs in alkaline soil. Around hot pools of Yellowstone Park, notably Old Faithful, it is there in profusion but only two inches high.

In spite of its somewhat bitter taste, the Indians and early settlers ate the leaves fresh like lettuce. Miners' lettuce, growing in deep shade, the Indians preferred cooked with lamb's quarters or mustard greens. Blue-flowered lettuce (chicory) was viewed by the incoming white men as a highly undesirable weed because its root-stocks, sprawling widely underground, were difficult to destroy. But the Indians savored plants and leaves and used the roots as chewing gum.

When injured, the chicory plant exudes a milky sap that the Indians caught. For though they had established the rule that plants with milky juice were poisonous to humans, they had proved chicory to be an exception; they had also found salsify to be safe.

Lettuce, whatever its species, has been the greatest of the greens for "civilized" man as, for probably aeons longer, it was to the American Indian. In 1699, Evelyn wrote that it "still continues the principal foundation of the universal Tribe of Sallets, which is to Cool and Refresh," laudable because the "effect it has upon the Morals, Temperance and Chastity. Galen (whose beloved Sallet it was) from its *pinguid subdulcid* and agreeable Nature, says it breeds the most laudable blood." And, as extra proof, there was "that excellent Emperor Tacitus being us'd to say of lettuce—a sumptuous Feast with a Sallet and a single Pullet which was usually all the Flesh-Meat that sober Prince ate of."

Lichens

Technically, the lichen is not a plant. It is "a remarkable example of a way of life"—symbiosis in which a green plant, an alga, becomes the parasite of a fungus to their mutual benefit. The alga manufactures organic material from carbon dioxide and water; the fungus draws inorganic material from the substratum. Forming a unique plant structure, the two plants live as if a single entity. They grow very slowly but reach a great age. There is a wide variety of types found on rocks and trees, the majority useful to man. We think of lichens in terms of antibiotics, perfume bases, and dyestuffs. The Indians used them for dyes and for medicine but they also used them for food.

The Algonquins as well as the western Indians made a dish of pine lichens which were boiled and stirred to the consistency of scrambled eggs. Throughout the Rocky Mountain area, the lichens that live on conifers were used especially in the autumn when most green foods were exhausted. Along the Columbia River, the Indians still use the lichens from the firs and pines, which they boil to the consistency of jelly. Even more savor is produced by making piles of lichens, sprinkling them with water, and leaving them to ferment. Then they are formed into large balls, put in hot pits with grass between the layers, and baked over a long period. The result is said to be delicious.

Licorice, Wild

This tall, weedy-looking, shrublike plant, with its painfully prickly brown burs, grows high into the Rocky Mountains. It is a perennial from one to three feet tall, rising from deep-spreading stems. Its insipid green-white flowers cluster in dense racemes. Generally in patches, it frequents the clayey and saline soils of waste places but also is at home in moist mountain draws. The Indians used it for flavoring and chewed it raw. Today, following Indian practice, commercial licorice is obtained from the rootstocks with their sugar and glycyrrhizin.

MOUNTAIN LILY

The Lily

Consider the lily of the field, from the time of man's earliest recording noted as the flower of purest beauty. Sustaining the symbol through the ages comes this from Bartholomaeus Anglicus about the year 1260. "The lily," he wrote, "is an herbe wyth a whyte floure. And though the levys of the floure be whyte yet wythin shyneth the lykeness of golde."

To the Indians and early settlers, it did indeed shine like gold, not so much for its blooms as for the life-giving gifts of the lily and its related species, the onion, garlic, and leek, the wild hyacinth, and the greatest of them all, the camas. Of the lilies themselves found in the Rocky Mountain area, there were three of especial value to the Indians.

There was the yellow pond-lily—the *wokas* of the Indians, the entire plant, seeds, blooms and particularly the roots being used. The squaws waded hip-deep into the still waters and pulled up the lilies, the roots of which were boiled long enough to become very tender, with the flavor of "sheep's liver," according to seventeenth-century naturalist, John Josselyn. The Indians dried them, roasted them like popcorn, or ground them into meal for bread and porridge.

There was the leopard (tiger) lily, also known as the purple fritillary. No other flower in the Rocky Mountains has such distinctive coloring—dull brownish-purple with green-yellow spots. The blooms tip downward on an unbranched stem that sometimes grows as high as thirty inches, beneath which rich nutriment is hidden. Western Indians and the Eskimos still eat the starchlike corms.

The Shoshones call the third of these wonderful lilies the *sego* or *segaw*. The southwestern Indians called it the mariposa lily and it is by that name that it is known officially—"perhaps," wrote Eric Stone, "the most famous life-maintaining food . . . " used alike by Indians and the white men they taught. It is a most graceful and lovely meadow flower, like a white tulip with dark splotches, almost like pansy markings, in its cup. Some white settlers called it the star tulip. Of the nine species in the Rockies, some are found in the high mountains, others in the low country.

The Indians dug the bulbs when the flowers opened. They roasted them in hot ashes or they steamed them. When boiled, this bulbous, walnut-size root tastes rather like a potato, but with a sweetness which, with its high nutrition, made it well worth the effort of grinding it into meal for bread.

After the Mormon settlers arrived in the "Promised Land," they would have been without sustenance part of those first lean years had there not been available large quantities of the bulb. It was the Ute Indians who taught these pioneers how to find and prepare the roots in "starving time." Small wonder that the state flower of Utah is the mariposa lily.

Lily-of-the-Valley, Wild

The *Smilacina stellata* of the liliaceous family is known also in the West as wild spikenard or Solomon's-plume or false Solomon's-seal. The familiar lily-of-the-valley with its unbranched leafy stem, the raceme with its bell-like white flowers, the globus berries of green or black, grows in the mountains to about 9,000 feet. The fastidious elk eat the stems and green leaves. The Indians ate the young leaves and shoots as greens.

Lupines

In the spring the Indians steamed the lupine leaves and pealike pale-blue flowers and ate them with their acorn soup. Sometimes the settlers called them wild peas because the seeds tasted somewhat like their garden peas back home. But most of all, the Indians valued the lupine seeds for which they had special bags and from which they made a tea to ease rheumatism or help urination.

In 1640, Parkinson recorded other, more trivial uses in England. Burning lupine seeds, he claimed, drove away gnats and the seeds "mixed with meal and honey take away black-and-blue spots." More than sixteen hundred years earlier, Virgil had called them "sad lupines" because the seeds were boiled and eaten by the poor.

Mahogany, Mountain

Mountain mahogany does not lend itself to arbitrary description. It is a high-altitude, drought-resistant shrub. But in Utah, the curl-leaf is a small tree. It is not deciduous but neither is it wholly evergreen. Its flowers commence life a distinct green, then turn a wan brown or muddy white or indeterminate red. But the various types have these characteristics in common. They thrive even on the barest sandstone. Their small leaves are wedge-shape, leathery, and gray. Their glory among the herbs centers in the twisted-tailed seed plumes, feathery, silver-shining in the sunlight. They have great hidden virtues, to be found listed in the "Maladies and Medicines" section.

The Indians found the hard wood perfect for making arrow shafts, fish spears, or strong, pointed sticks for digging. They found that, though brittle, this quality was excellent in making a fire. They found that the inner layer of the richly brown bark made a strong purple dye. Later, the Spanish Americans laid branches of mountain mahogany on their blanket rolls or petates or hung them from their beds to warn away bedbugs.

Manzanita

Manzanita was used by the Indians much as kinnikinnick. It is found high, in the montane region, and grows upright with weirdly distorted branches. Shrub size, it craves the sun and is therefore most prevalent on the western slope. Its flowers are pink; its fruit is hard but edible. Hence the Spanish name, *manzanita*, "little apple."

Marsh Marigold

There is only one species of marsh marigold in the Rockies and this grows high, from 7,000 to 10,000 feet, where it will be found in wet meadows and along mountain streams, made gay in spring by its large white flowers. It is an early riser, the blossoms opening wide before nine in the morning and closing in the late afternoon.

The Indians boiled the buds and used the leaves as

a potherb. Early settlers pickled the buds and flowers. In olden days in England, too, the marigold was used as a potherb. But not happily. To put it euphemistically, its principal purpose was to disguise the taste and odor of meat that was no longer fresh. To phrase it as succinctly as the partakers thereof, its presence in the pot meant that the "vittles were a bit flyblown."

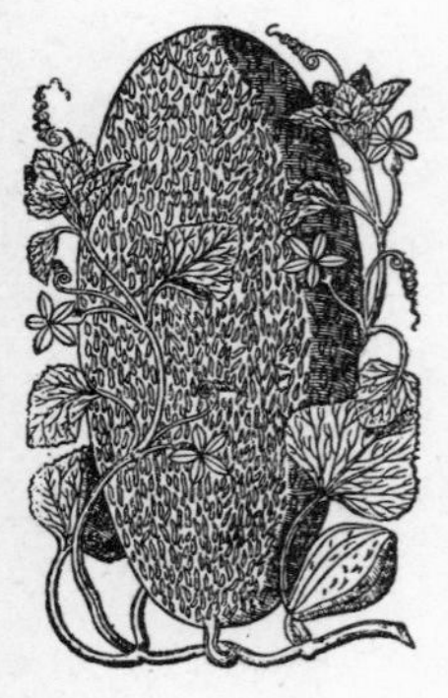

MELON

Melons

A variety of melons were found wild or were cultivated by the Indians, who also valued them as horse medicine. Hariot in 1588 recorded that the Virginia Indians planted "mellions . . . and very good."

Mesquite

Mesquite belongs to the plains and seldom climbs higher than 6,000 feet. It is a predominant shrub of the arid lands of the Southwest, but it is also valuable for purposes of trade with the Indians of the high plains. All the Indian tribes recognized the spring protuberances on the mesquite, the sweet-smelling soft-yellow flower spikes and, above all, the bumpy bean pods. All western Indians, notably the Mojave, made cakes from the sweet pulp between the pod and the seeds. All the Indians pulverized the beans into meal for cakes and porridge and savored mesquite gruel. The sharing of this gruel was part of the Yuma marriage ceremony. The Pima Indians made candy from the mesquite gum. The Opata Indians smoked the fungus clinging to the mesquite tree. The Cocopa Indians made a beverage from the inner bark that was the baby's only nourishment in its first four days of life.

Milkweed

This familiar perennial with its pink-white flowers and its three-inch-long pods holding the flat seeds and adorned with silky hairs is scattered profusely in the Rockies. The Indians have been using it medically for centuries as they have used it for food. The young shoots, the leaves, and pods all were of value. Blossoms and buds became both flavoring and thickening for meat soups. But the most graceful gastronomical gesture was their habit of sweetening their wild strawberries by shaking on them the early dew from the milkweed blossoms.

Frémont found the Indians of the Platte River country eating the young milkweed pods or cooking them with buffalo meat; today, in Taos for instance, if one is invited to an Indian home, one may dine on meat dishes to which have been added young milkweed leaves or pods cooked as we cook green beans.

Miner's Candle

The varieties of this herbaceous perennial, bristly torch, white borage, and other relatives, thrive on the dry slopes of the foothills. The Indians used the flowers and young leaves for salads and flavoring. France had made a parallel discovery, using the young leaves not only in salads but also in iced drinks, herbal tea, and claret cups.

Mint

Of some thirty species of mint, there are only eight in the Rocky Mountains. Like all *mentha,* they live in moist soil with the exception of the horsemints, which prefer sandy soil. The familiar wild mint with its pink-lavender flowers and the spearmint with its flowers clustered at the end of the stems spread their special aromatic fragrance from the valleys to about 9,000 feet. The Indians steeped the seeds for seasoning and appetizers, made hot or cooling drinks, and used the plant freely as *materia medica.*

Monkey-flower

Fortunately for the balanced diet of the Indians, both the yellow and the red monkey-flowers, along with some twenty other species, are scattered widely on Rocky Mountain hillsides. Their use as greens, and their identification by the white pioneers with lettuce, is described under that listing. The flowers resemble snapdragons and their markings give them the appearance of grinning or grimacing.

Mormon Tea

See Ephedra.

Morning-glory

This timekeeping convolvulus opens about five in the morning and closes before noon. Growing in moist soil high into the Rockies, its big, deeply sunk roots, though neither good-tasting nor highly nutritious, were roasted and used as famine food by the Indians.

Mountain Ash

See Ash, Mountain.

Mountain Bluebell

See Bluebell, Mountain.

Mountain Mahogany

See Mahogany, Mountain.

Mugwort

Mugwort belongs under the sagebrush category and it belongs where it will be found—in the medical section of this book. But it is noted here as an illustration of the differences in attitude surrounding a simple herb. To the Indians it was invaluable for the treatment of colds, fever, wounds, and other ills. This was true also across the sea, but there through the ages it became entangled in superstition.

Dioscorides claimed that mugwort dissolved gallstones; that, "made up with axungia [hog and goose grease], it took away wens and hard knots," and that "three drams of powder of dried mugwort leaves taken in wine" is a "speedy and best cure for sciatica."

Pliny advised that "if a traveller bind some mugwort about him, he will feel no weariness on his journey." As quoted by Gerard in 1597, Pliny amplified this: "He who hath it about him can come to no hurt by poysonous medicine, nor by any wilde beasts, neither yet by the Sun itself."

In ancient England, mugwort was one of the three sacred herbs, described thus in the tenth-century *Lacnunga:*

> Eldest of worts
> Thou hast might for three
> And against thirty
> For venom availest
> For flying vile things,
> Mighty against loathed ones
> That through the land rove.

Translated into comprehensibility, the Indians would have recognized its use against venomous insects. They, too, used it that way. But there is no record that they knew of the aspect given in the *Grete Herbal* of 1525–1526: "To make a child mery, hange a bondall of mugwort or make smoke thereof under the chylde's bedde for it taketh away annox for him."

Mullein

See same entry under "Maladies and Medicines" section.

Mushrooms

Indians down on the plains used mushrooms freely for there were only a few, easily identified species. These, notably the boletus, they fried, baked, or simmered into soup to which meat had been added. If there was no meat, a soup of fresh mushrooms and wild onions was equally savory.

But the Indians of the Rocky Mountain area did not use mushrooms to any extent and there is virtually no reference to them in the journals of those early explorers who partook of their hospitality. The reason is simply that there were too many mushrooms. Some species made delightful eating but some, almost indistinguishable, were fatally poisonous. The result was that numerous tribes forbade the use of mushrooms unless they were approved by the medicine men and, we are told, a few tribes forbade their use altogether.

Of some thirty-eight thousand varieties of the mushroom family recorded over some thirty centuries, a very great many are poisonous, and there was quite a concentration of these in the glades of the Rocky Mountain region. One has only to glimpse the beguiling vivid orange or yellow mushrooms on a hillside to understand why a firm taboo had to be placed on mushrooms to keep them from children's gathering or from the watering mouths of adult gourmets.

Most striking of these is the *Amanita muscari* of the foothills, its vivid scarlet cap luring the unwary as it blazes like a beacon under the lodgepole pines. So deadly is this that it is known as the fly *Amanita* since it spells instant death to flies—or mortals. A warning, this, to those unfortunate young people of today who, under the impression that some mushrooms are hallucinogenic, are desecrating the quiet little mushroom fields in an effort to find a new and potent substitute for pot.

As a happier thought, we give you from the days of the Roman Empire, the poet Juvenal: "Keep your corn, O Lybia; unyoke your oxen, provided only that you send us mushrooms."

Mustard

MUSTARD

Pink mustard with its lavender flowers prefers the sunlit western slope of the Rockies. The Indians ate the young shoots as salad and dried the seeds for seasoning.

Nettle

The slim nettle is a common weed of the Rocky

Mountain region, with green flowers, tall straight stems, and stinging hairs. It served as fresh green and potherb, especially in soups, and the Indians also gathered the tips and boiled them like spinach. The settlers learned to do the same—but they put on gloves to avoid the stinging hairs.

New Jersey Tea

This *Ceanothus fendleri* is a low shrub, with white flowers in clusters and with innumerable thorns. Aside from its medicinal value, the Indians used it to make a red dye which they extracted from the roots. It obtained its name from the soldiers in the American Revolution who, near starvation, dried the leaves as did the Indians and made an infusion that was slightly nutritious, blessedly hot, and "very palatable."

Nightshade, Deadly

There are a dozen or so species of deadly nightshade in the Rockies. It is not choosy about its habitat, growing in dusty waste places, sunlit glades, and the moist verges of streams. It is equipped with small white flowers which yield to round green berries, turning black when ripe. Every part of the plant is impregnated with a poisonous alkaloid, sotanine. Through long experiment, the Indians learned to destroy this by long slow cooking. They used the berries as the settlers learned to do; the latter became so skilled at handling them that they made nightshade jam and nightshade pies.

Onion

There are about three hundred species of onion scattered over the earth, all with the unmistakable odor and taste caused by volatile sulphur compound. In the western mountain area, there are some fifty species of this member of the lily family, a very lovely one being the red-flowered onion of the western slope. The flowers of the sand onion grow in clusters so that they look like umbrellas. Onions grow high up, especially the *Allium cernuum,* the favored pink-flowered nodding onion with its cousin the purple onion that thrive up to 10,000 feet.

Onions were used in every conceivable way by the Indians. The bulbs were eaten raw or cooked with meat. They were eaten as a vegetable and used for seasoning. The Aztecs chewed the bulbs as food and to relieve flatulence. The whole plant was used as an insect repellent by rubbing it on the body.

ONION

When onion time came, the Indians really let themselves go, not only because they delighted in them but also because their winter-depleted systems craved the vitamins and salts with which they are so richly endowed. Mountain men and explorers commented on the ease of locating an Indian encampment, especially with the Zuñi, during this season when the aroma of onions hung over the tepees and adjacent landscape like a beneficent miasma. Once their first craving was satisfied, the Indians gathered as many onions as possible. The bulbs were roasted or steamed in the cooking pits, then dried and tied into bundles for winter use.

One of the first lessons the children learned was how to find and fix the onions. They dug only the *se-e,* the little onions, rooted shallowly. Already they had made their fire so that the rocks would be hot. Now they put the onions into their pit, put hot rocks on top of them, and covered these with earth to keep them from cooling. Then, for two whole days they had to wait. When the slow time had passed, the earth was tossed aside, the rocks were rolled away with a stick, and the onions were removed to cool—but not too cool. Water was warmed, the onions stirred in, and then, at last, the small folk had a self-prepared feast.

Onions were a welcome addition to the diet of

Lewis and Clark, and Frémont, in August 1843, noted in his diary that at Medicine Butte certain "species of onion [were] very abundant." The earliest colonists to cross to America had been so concerned lest they find no onions in the New World that they had brought their bulbs with them.

Respect and appreciation for the onion has been shown from earliest times, not alone by the Indians but, for instance, by the Egyptians, who used them as a sacrificial offering, "much to the amusement of the Romans," commented Doctor Candolle. Theophrastus made numerous references to onions in his *Inquiry into Plants*, but some centuries later, in Elizabethan times, the perfumed gentlemen of the period were inclined to look down their noses at them—or pinch their noses delicately to protect themselves from the odor. Herbalist Turner, in 1525, warned that "onions eaten in meat largely make the head ache. They make them forgetfull whiche in the tyme of sykness use them out of measure."

In modern times, it has been stated that it is likely most of the virtues of the onion are "mere Old Wives' tales with no foundation in physiological fact."

Unaware of these dicta, the Indians kept right on using their onions. Neither they nor the settlers seem to have known of this seventeenth-century use of the herb: "To Write Letters of Secrets: . . . You may . . . write with vinegar or the juice of limon or onion; if you would read the same, hold it before the fire."

Orchids

Since orchids are apt to be associated in the lay mind with lush backgrounds against which move very expensive ladies in diamonds and very much less expensive ladies in grass skirts, it may seem virtually unbelievable that there are eight species in the Rockies, growing from deep valleys up to 10,000 feet. Green bog orchid can be found from the subalpine to the timber line.

The bulbs of all North American orchids are said

to be edible. But the orchid is rare, its tubers not savory. The Indians used them mostly as emergency food.

Oregano

See Horsemint.

Oyster Plant

See Salsify.

P

Parsley

The familiar word parsley has been used somewhat promiscuously in the West. Actually there are some thirty species in the mountain region, roots of many of these being used as food. Especially is this true of the *Lomatium,* the most noted members of which are the cous.

With all those that proved edible, the usage was the same. Roots were eaten baked or roasted or raw or ground into a flour.

But there is also the so-called mountain parsley which belongs to another family. It is a *Harbouria trachypleura,* with feathery leaves and small yellow flowers. The whisk-broom parsley is technically a *Cogswellia orientalis,* a fragile-appearing grayish plant with very small pink or white blooms. Neither has anything to do with the true desert parsley of the *Umbelliferaes.* But the Indians did not know about this. They enjoyed them all.

PENNYROYAL

Peas, Wild

See Lupines.

Pennyroyal

A strong-smelling member of the mint family, pennyroyal grows in the mountains, in canyons, and on dry slopes, frequently in close proximity to the catnip. It stands upright but is low, with many branches and a profusion of dead-gray hairs against which, in spring, its slender, light-pink blooms appear fragile and incongruous. Parkinson, in 1629, regretted that pennyroyal was passing out of use. "The former age of our great-grandfathers had all these pot herbes . . . but no longer." But the Indians had used pennyroyal for centuries as a potherb. They continue to do so.

Pigweed

Two kinds of pigweed were used by Indians and settlers as potherbs and seasoning. There was the prostrate with quantities of desirable shiny black seeds, and there was the redroot pigweed, tough, stout, rough of stem. That was unimportant. What mattered were the plump, fleshy taproots that stretched to gratifying distances.

This, according to an old-timer, was what "Aunt called a 'fat hen.'" There is no record of what the Indians called it but the succulent taproots were among their favorite greens.

Plantains

The rattlesnake plantain stays close to the earth, growing not more than eight inches high. It is an orchid, with pale green-white flowers. Find it nestled in the moss in the chilly high forests. The *Plantago major* is a weed with veined leaves and long spikes that hold the seeds. A favorite dish of the Indians was corn salad made with plantain leaves.

PLANTAIN

Plum

The plum is not an herb and purists would not list it here. But it was fruit and edible and mingled with those plants of more lowly stature. It is a shrub or shrubby tree, depending on environment, and grows in thickets up to about 5,000 feet. It was much sought by the Indians and by the incoming whites. George Catlin, for example, wrote in 1837, "Oftentimes [we] find our progress completely arrested by hundreds of acres of small plum trees."

Plumes, Pink

A sturdy, straight-standing spring plant with pinkish-purple flowers followed by conspicuous and lovely plumes, by reason of which the plant is known as "old man's whiskers." The Indians found them valuable as a skin softener.

POPPY

Poppy

Though the great worth of the poppy for the relief of pain cannot be overstated, it appears that the Indians, though using it, never did so to its full potential. When the settlers arrived, they found the Indians using poppy seeds much as they did, for flavoring. The Indians also extracted a useful oil from the seeds and since these have no physiological action, the oil was used with impunity.

Potatoes

The "Indian potato" is not a potato. It is *Orogenia,* a member of the parsley family. The Indians ate the tubers cooked or raw and in the latter case, as the pioneers discovered, they have a potato-like taste.

The "trail potato" is a *Canum gairdneri.* The Shoshones used a shorter word, *yomba,* a term that became part of the settlers' vocabulary. It is found on mountainsides and is distinguished by white flowers. When these fall, the potatoes are ripe. The Indians dug them, washed them, cooked them like Irish potatoes. Some they dried in the sun and then stored. After this process, they are pale yellow inside like sweet potatoes. As a lifesaving and life-giving tuber, the Indians held the potato in highest esteem and, centuries after they had begun to do so, one of the great French chefs, André L. Simon, wrote in agreement. The potato, he asserted from the background of his expertise, is "full of everything that is good for good people, that is, normal people who do not suffer from diabetes or the craze for slimming."

Primrose

Under their demure demeanor, the primroses delight by their surprises. There are twenty-five species in the Rocky Mountain area, unfolding sweetly in unexpected places such as disturbed soil or the middle of roadbeds. It is the evening primrose that intrigues the most. It does not have a stem, its leaves being bunched about the root crown. Its white flowers turn pink and then, as the plant matures, red. They open at sundown or after and generally do not close until the following noon.

The yellow variety is even more exciting to watch. Its evening ritual is one of nature's choice treats. The intensely yellow blossoms appear dormant, then suddenly they open wide with an almost audible "pop." Very shortly after that display, the evening moths arrive and hover.

Primrose seeds were eaten or ground by the Indians but it was their roots that were most cherished. Supplying sound nutrition, they generally were boiled. Doctor Charles F. Millspaugh, highly critical of native plants though he was, in 1892 corroborated that the primrose's "young roots are said to be pleasant, edible, either pickled or boiled."

Pumpkin

Though probably indigenous to tropical America, the western Indians of North America were cultivating the pumpkin long before the arrival of the Spaniards. It was used in a variety of delightful ways, and the delicately seasoned pumpkin soup was a gourmet's delight.

Purslane

Reddish, fleshy, branched, an annual creeper with infinitesimal yellow star-flowers that open early in bright sunlight, purslane has closed shop for the night by four in the afternoon. It is an annoying weed but its young leaves are pleasant greens or potherbs, either as a vegetable or as an addition to soup.

The Indians had used the herb for centuries before

John Evelyn advised his aristocratic readers in 1699: "Purslane . . . whilst tender, next the seed leaves with the young stalks being eminently moist and cooling, quickens Appetite, assuages Thirst and is very profitable for hot and Bilous Tempers as well as Sanguine, and generally entertain'd in all our Sallets, mingled with the hotter herbes. . . . Some eat it cold, after it has been boil'd which Dr. Muffet would have in wine for nourishment."

Pussytoes

Pussytoes is a plant noteworthy because many species produce seed without being fertilized. From the plains to the heights at 9,000 feet, the Indians ate the seeds and chewed a gum made from the stalks.

Rabbitbrush

Rabbitbrush spreads like a golden blanket over considerable areas of the foothills and tells the knowledgeable that the land it covers is poor, eroded, or neglected. It is a late-blooming shrublike plant often found among the sage. It contains rubber but not enough apparently to be profitable on a commercial basis. Having discovered its latex content, the Indians processed it into chewing gum. They also made it into a dye.

Rabbitguts

Rabbitguts was so named because, viewed from beneath, its undersides look like an opened rabbit, as can be seen by those whose imaginations run in that direction. Its leaves are as sweet raw as cooked and were much used by the Indians.

Raspberry, Wild

Of the hundreds of species of *Rubus*, fifteen are found in the Rockies, of which the American red raspberry, in particular, has brought joy to hundreds of generations of Indians and whites. It is particularly common in the foothills from 6,000 to 8,000 feet, and is often found on disturbed ground.

WILD RASPBERRY

Such, it seems, was not the case in England. Gerard, in 1597 wrote, "Raspis groweth not wilde that I know of. . . . I found it among the bushes of a causey neere unto a village called Wisterson, where I went to school."

The Indians pressed the berries into cakes before drying them for future use. They savored these as well as the fresh fruit, particularly when boiled with meat. They also made a cooling raspberry drink. The settlers, when they arrived, favored hot raspberry tea.

Reeds

There are many species of reeds, so similar that it is difficult to differentiate. In the Rocky Mountains, the most common are the pond reed and the bur reed. Which of these the Indians used as *be-ha-bee,* a source of sugar, is not known. We know only that it was the reed whose stems and leaves become heavily encrusted in autumn with a gray-toned exudate. The Indians beat and shook the plants over a cloth, the sap oozed out through aphid-punctured holes, and the Indian children ate the hardening exudate as candy.

Rice

Rice is not native to the Rocky Mountain area's higher reaches. But it was one of the great trade commodities.

In the lakes and streams, and even in the sluggish waters of wide and shallow rivers, there grew this precious grain. It belonged especially in the land of the Dakotas and of the Menomini, whose name means wild rice. In that region, cut by the line of 50 degrees north latitude, the September moon is "rice-is-ready-to-dry moon."

Rice gathering was and is work for the Indian

women, paddling their canoes, using their crooked sticks to pull the bunches forward, binding them, leaving the waters "filled with shocks like giant herons, bill downward." Mountain tribes had their bags of herbs ready for trade and by snowfall the western Indian world had its provisions of rice for the winter.

This wild rice is a North American perennial grass (genus *Zizania*), bearing vast quantities of the hard seeds that were cooked like rice. The Indians used it precisely as we use our familiar varieties, even to making wild rice stuffing for their turkeys.

Peter Pond, fur trader, recorded this touch: "When it is Cleaned fit for youse Thay Boile it as we Due Rise and Eat it with Bairs Greas and Sugar."

Roper's Relief

Paiute-Shoshones still use the raw leaves and stems as applications to rope burns on the hands of the Indian vaqueros.

Rose, Wild

Over a hundred species of wild roses and considerable numbers of escaped cultivated types are spread over the earth, making it difficult for even the professional botanist to be sure of his ground. But it is simple in the Rockies. There are ten species, all easily identified.

The familiar wild rose *(Rosa woodsii)* is a shrub with pink-to-red flowers, growing in clusters. It likes open places, growing on hillsides and in draws, and is found in the valleys up to 10,000 feet. Often it forms its own thickets. Sometimes it keeps close company with other growing things. The so-called native rose *(Rosa arkansana)* is so similar to this that differentiation seldom is made, as is the case also with the *Rosa cicularis* of the plains.

WILD ROSE

All the Indians and many wild things—black bear, pheasants, grouse—ate the fruit of the rose, the round or pear-shaped hips, from which the settlers made their jelly and wild-rose tea. The Warm Springs Indians gave the rose an affectionate name, "mean old lady, she sticks you." Indian women always formally thanked the bear whose paw tracks guided her to hidden rose hips. She could not have been more appreciative had she known that rose hips contain more vitamin C than oranges.

Rue

Listed by Hippocrates as a "soothing herb," meadow rue was used by the Indians long before that time. They chopped it finely for seasoning—and there are hostesses today in the West who use finely chopped rue in brown bread and butter sandwiches. Though it is supposedly limited to the foothills from 6,000 to 8,000 feet, this delicate fernlike plant with its miniature green-brown flowers was collected by early explorers high in the Sangre de Cristo range of New Mexico. It was—and is, perhaps—used as a ceremonial tea drunk after the Navajo War Dance. Altogether a valued and respected herb in contrast to the Shakespearean symbol of "Rue and magic and witchcraft."

Rushes

The true rush, the *Juncus balticus*, with its variations, can be found from the plains to about 9,000 feet. Of some 225 species spread over the earth, some 40 appear in the Rocky Mountains. The Indians ate the leaves and young spring shoots as greens and cooked the fleshy roots with their high starch content. These were used best as potherbs. Under the shadow of the mountains in New Mexico, children still make whistles from the *cañutillo del llano,* the "little tubes."

Rushpink

This rushlike plant with its pink flower heads grows in dry open places in the mountains. The Indians boiled the leaves with their meat.

Rye

Great Basin wild rye grows from three to six feet

high in bunches, hence is known as "bunch grass." It is found in the Rockies up to about 8,000 feet, three species being quite common. A close kin to cultivated rye, the Indians and settlers used it as such, pounding or grinding the grain into meal.

S

Sage

Wormwood is another name for this *Artemisia tridentata,* the familiar silver-leaved sage that spreads over wide areas of the foothills and plains and shows by its presence that the soil on which it grows is fertile. Pioneers learned early to settle where the sagebrush grew. This big sagebrush is gray-green, many branched and, to Frémont's surprise, as much as eight inches in the diameter of its branches. The leaves are evergreen, their aromatic odor increased by and after rain into one of the most stimulating scents in nature. It flowers in early spring, but the blooms are small, inconspicuous, and inconsequential.

There are over a hundred species of *Artemisia* with more than twenty in the Rocky Mountain area. They reach almost to the timber line and down to the dry prairie floor. Parenthetically, it has nothing in common with the garden sage which is salvia.

"Pathfinder" Frémont recorded in 1842 that the wild sage began to make its appearance near Fort Laramie and that at the point where the coming Oregon Trail would leave the Platte and cross to the Sweetwater River the "absinthe has lost its shrub-like character and becomes a small tree six to eight feet in height." He noted also that, as is true of many plants, "the *Artemisia* has its small fly accompanying it through every change of elevation and latitude."

After rain or when it is used as fuel, its volatile oils spread the scent of sage that to countless thousands of generations of Indians and latecomers spelled rest and food and warmth. In many parts of the Rocky Mountain area, sage is the only fuel, even the green plants burning rapidly and throwing out strong heat. It also throws forth the symbol of home and rest, in the most exciting odor in the West.

The Indians had numerous other uses for the sage. It was a yellow dye. The seeds of the sweet sage were steeped for flavoring. The white sage leaves made a delightful beverage called *sissop,* and the same decoction was used to wash the hair. Its greatest value was, of course, medicinal.

Wild life shared the Indians' appreciation of sagebrush. It has been pointed out that, being high in fat content, "it undoubtedly saved many animals from being winter-killed."

The word sage, it is said, was a time transmutation of *salveo,* "I save," and that its great virtues were bestowed on it by the Virgin in gratitude for its shelter on the flight into Egypt.

Aside from absinthe, which civilized men have always deplored, there was in ancient times a wine called *abrotonito,* the basis of which was in infusion of *Artemisia.* Through the centuries various other uses appeared. A fourteenth-century record, *The Goodman of Paris,* advises: "For washing hands at table," boil sage in water, pour off, and "offer it to the diners lukewarm."

Like the Indians, John Evelyn advocated sage tea and in 1699 wrote: "Sage, hot and dry, the tops . . . well pick'd and wash'd—with the flowers retain all the noble properties of other hot Plants. . . . In short, 'tis a Plant endued with so many and wonderful properties, as that the assiduous use of it *is said to render men immortal:* We cannot therefore but allow the Tender Summities of the young leaves, but principally the Flower in our cold Sallets; yet so as not to domineer."

Salsify (Oyster Plant)

Down on the plains, the flowers of the salsify plant are purple. In the high mountains, they are a delicate yellow and remain open only until about noon. The seed heads are brownish fluffy plumes like an oversized dandelion and, like the dandelion, the plant contains a milky juice that the Indians coagulated into chewing gum.

One of the most reliable winter vegetables, the large fleshy taproots of the salsify were enjoyed by the Indians, either as a potherb or in soup. When cooked, the taste is somewhat like that of parsnips but the more imaginative among the whites claimed the flavor to be similar to that of an oyster. Member of the chicory group, the young leaves are delicious as salad.

It has been claimed that early American colonists introduced salsify from Europe where it was cultivated for its thin white roots. If so, despite the prevailing westerlies, it spread with phenomenal rapidity for it is deeply rooted in the cuisine and pharmacopoeia of the Indians of the mountain West.

Saltbush ("Chico")

This sprawling shrub grows on alkali soil on the plains and up into the foothills. It is a dreary-gray plant, growing from one to five feet tall. Its flowers are gray-green. Its leaves are coated with tiny white hairs and scales. It often spreads over extensive areas and usually can be found mingling with sage and creosote.

But its seeds are rich in starch and sodium and other salts. The Indians ground the seeds for meal, ate the leaves like spinach, used the *chamiso* in numerous other ways. They stirred saltbush ashes into their water-bread batter to change the color of the meal to a blue-green. They chewed the seeds. The Zuñi still attach prayer plumes to the bush to draw from their holes the cottontail rabbits. There are plenty of these plumes; under government supervision, the saltbush is being planted in many parts of the Southwest below the mountains, to decrease soil erosion and increase range vegetation.

Sand Grass (Indian Millet)

The round black seeds of the prevalent sand grass are an important food for animals and man. The Indians ground them into meal, especially used in cakes, and were particularly fond of this meal made into mush or gruel. The white newcomers mixed the seeds with cornmeal to make their dumplings.

Sandroot

In arid areas, the sandroot is the most useful fruit of the rose family. It is small, leafless, and almost wholly root—a big fat root to be eaten raw or roasted over coals, the taste then being somewhat like a sweet potato. It thrives best under blazing desert sun where the Papagos used it as a staple, sometimes grinding the root and mixing it with mesquite beans to create a kind of pinole. It does not confine itself to the plains but is found high in the foothills but only on the western slope where it sucks in the sun.

The lifesaving quality of the sandroot lies in its root juices which in emergency can be used to quench the thirst.

Sassafras

Sassafras is included here not because it grows in the Rocky Mountain area but because it does not. By one of nature's outstanding oddities, its absence dramatizes the distribution of herbs. We are indebted to Doctor Rutherford Platt *(The Great American Forest)* for the explanation.

Sassafras was part of a "motly forest congregation" that came from Asia and soared over the entire North American continent until it was caught and held by the Appalachian Mountains. Why had this not happened in the West? Because when this migration occurred, there were as yet no Rocky Mountains. They had not as yet been spewed from the depths of the upheaving earth.

SASSAFRAS

Wrote Doctor Platt, "Convincing evidence indicates . . . that the Appalachian forest of the eastern United

States did, indeed, come from Asia many millions of years ago."

Carried by the strong westerlies, these forest seeds did not stop there. Some were carried much farther east, crossing the Atlantic Ocean to the next great land mass. This became known when Doctor Platt received a letter telling of how "on the mainland of Greenland facing the north shore of Disko at Aternakerdluk lay the site of the 'earliest hardwood forest known to have grown on earth.'" Older than the Appalachian? Doctor Platt discussed the subject with Admiral Donald B. MacMillan. An expedition was formed. The site was located. "The sledge was swung, the rock loosened . . . and there lay revealed the tip and lobes of sassafras."

The East Coast Indians of the United States ultimately found sassafras bark one of their most valuable trade commodities. In view of the claims that the herb moved west in spite of the strong winds, the only remaining mystery in this saga of the sassafras is why the seeds did not blow farther west than Ontario and Iowa whence the bark was traded to the western Indians.

Sedge

Bluish-green, grasslike sedge, with its waving white plumes, is common in the Rocky Mountain area, notably in the forests of lodgepole pine where it spreads a dense cover. In the foothills it is found in moist meadows and is popularly called cottongrass. The Indians ate the young shoots and leaves as greens. Today, hunters value sedge as an emergency food and the outdoors man makes himself a comfortable and insulated bed of comfortable clumps of sedge leaves.

Serviceberry (Sarvis Berry)

The most widespread early blossoming shrub, the serviceberry blooms along the verge of streams and in moist areas of the mountains well above 7,000 feet.

White flowers are so closely crowded that the effect is of a white frame enclosing the green bush. After the blooms, the berries. Purple or dark blue, not more than a half inch in diameter, growing in profusion throughout the region, the serviceberries are edible and wondrously sweet. There were plenty of berries to be eaten fresh and still leave an abundance for the Indian women to crush and dry and make into cakes. These were round and flat, like disks, and sometimes weighed up to ten or fifteen pounds. Pieces of these cakes were broken off during the winter to be added to soup or vegetables. Mainstay of men on the move, the classic pemmican was considered at its best if made by pounding the dried serviceberries and dried buffalo meat together, adding fat and forming it into cakes.

Frémont noted in his journal for August 23, 1843, at the Shoshone village in Bear River Valley: "We obtained from them a considerable number [quantity] of berries . . . among which the service berries were most abundant," and, shortly thereafter, "From the Snake Lodges on the Bear near Great Salt Lake . . . we purchased almost a bushel of service berries." *Voyageurs* and mountain men favored them as flavoring for their *pommes blanches.*

When the settlers arrived they found that serviceberries make a sweet and delicate jelly, a juicy pie, and a delicious wine. The difference between this and other berries lies in the fact that technically the serviceberry is not a berry. It is, in the botanical sense, a core fruit, a *pomme,* cousin of the apple and pear and of similar consistency.

Shooting Star

This member of the primrose family flaunts brilliant rose-purple flowers which droop down in terminal umbels. There are five species in the Rocky Mountains and all of them were used by the Indians who ate the green leaves and roasted the roots and found them good.

Skullcap

A member of the mint family and a close associate

SKULLCAP

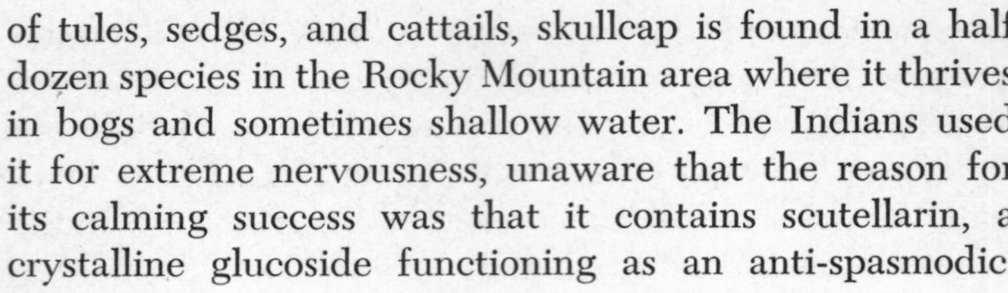

of tules, sedges, and cattails, skullcap is found in a half dozen species in the Rocky Mountain area where it thrives in bogs and sometimes shallow water. The Indians used it for extreme nervousness, unaware that the reason for its calming success was that it contains scutellarin, a crystalline glucoside functioning as an anti-spasmodic.

Skunkbush

The berries of the skunkbush are red and sticky and the Indians ate them with relish. It derives its name from the smell of the wood—dank, strong, antiseptic, but useful to the Indians who split the stems of this drought-resistant plant and used them to twine their baskets. *Brooks Botany* states that astringent properties make skunkbush valuable in tanning leather, but we have found no evidence that the Indians used it for this purpose. (They probably did.) Now, "old-fashioned" housewives of the West put skunkbush in wardrobes and chests to keep out moths.

Skunkcabbage, Yellow

The single species of skunkcabbage found in the Rockies is easy to identify since it is the only plant with one upright blossoming stalk atop which perches a vivid yellow, partially rolled flower covering known as a spathe. It is among the first of the mountain plants to flower, the blooms appearing before the leaves start their growth.

Centuries ago, the Indians learned not to satisfy their spring hunger for greens with the yellow skunkcabbage. The whole plant contains calcium oxalate crystals which cause a burning and stinging sensation in the mouth. But those indomitable experimenters also discovered that by roasting and drying the root they destroyed the unpleasantness and that a satisfactory meal could be made therefrom. Throughout the world there have been equally hungry native peoples who have proved that members of the arum family such as this can be rendered stingless to the taste if boiled and dried.

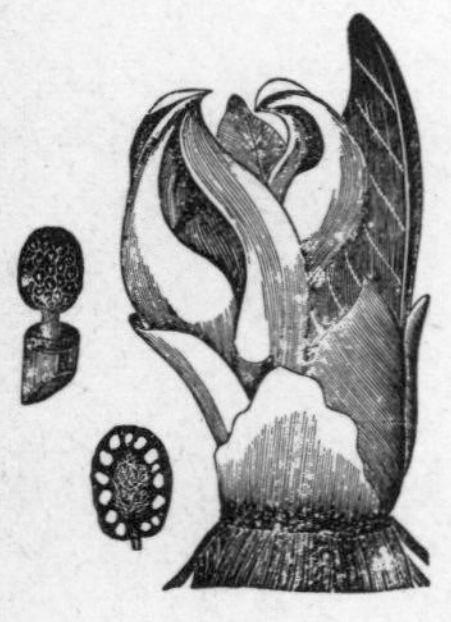

SKUNKCABBAGE

The staple food of the Polynesians is taro, cousin of the skunkcabbage.

Sneezeweed

Also known as sneezewort or western orange, sneezeweed is appropriately named. A sturdy plant of the sunflower family it has numerous yellow-centered heads of gold. It is common at heights from 7,000 to 10,000 feet, wherever it gets the sun. Indians ate the greens, not objecting to the bit of a bite in the leaves. In England this was even approved, the *Simmonite-Culpeper Herbal* commenting that sneezeweed "has a biting taste in salads that corrects the coldness of the other herbs."

Snowberry

This charming plant, with its purplish flower clusters and white berries, belongs high in the mountains, in the foothills and montane. A low, erect shrub, it is important to wildlife as protection for birds in winter and for the berries which remain on the bushes through the cold months.

Since it produced a white honey, the Indians called it the honey plant and also used the sturdy wood for the making of bows and arrows.

Snowbush

In spring the snowbush is so covered with minute white flowers that it looks like the victim of an out-of-season snowstorm. Its shiny leaves are evergreen. It exudes a delightfully aromatic aroma. Numerous species of the *Ceanothus* have a poisonous glucoside called saponin which contains the qualities for soap. As such, the Indians used the flowers and showed the settlers how to make a soap substitute. The latter therefore endowed the lovely plant with the prosaic designation of soapbloom.

Snowdrop

There are two species of snowdrop, members of the parsley family and known also as Indian potato and turkey peas. These are found in mountain valleys, diminutive herbs never more than half a foot high, with an umbel of little white flowers before the leaves come. The tubers made good eating for the Indians, the flavor when eaten raw being somewhat like that of a potato. Indian women used the snowdrops as cosmetics.

Soapweed

See Yucca.

Solomon's-seal, False

SPIKENARD

Known also as wild spikenard, this plant looks like a lily, to which family it belongs. It has a thick cluster of very small white flowers and strong, ovate leaves. Its berries are round and juicy. Its real gift to man, however, is the rootstock, heavy, branching underground to form dense and spreading growths. It flourishes particularly in the foothills. The Indians cooked the fat, starchy rootstock with its parsnip-like taste and ate the slightly bitter berries—but not too many at once since if taken in quantity they have a cathartic effect.

Sorrel

The popular herb called sorrel flourishes on mountain slopes from 6,000 to 11,000 feet, where it blooms throughout the summer in the woods and open places. Its flowers are small, sometimes green or red but usually yellow. The brightly green leaves resemble clover. The fruit is flattish with encircling wings and of a vivid rose color. In the Rockies, there is only one species of *Oxyria,* the name deriving from the Greek *oxys,* "sour."

It *is* sour—but pleasantly so. The slightly acid leaves were and are savored by the Indians both as salad and potherb. They ate as much sorrel as they could, as a fundamental base of their green diet. They did not know that the reason for doing so lay in its rich content of vitamin C, but they had proved it as a scurvy preventative.

Sorrel often grew around the mining camps in the

Rockies and miners welcomed its coming after their winter fare. They learned from the Indians that a touch of sorrel made an otherwise monotonous soup delicious. They drank the lemonade-like drink the Indians made and watched them make their dyes.

A friendly-to-man plant, sorrel—but now, to obtain it, one has to go where the sorrel grows. André L. Simon, the famous gastronome, recently complained, "Take greengrocers. How many bother to stock sorrel? Very few. Sorrel is really a weed, which can be grown anywhere, at all times and at very little cost. It is excellent in soups and sauces and it is very good with tasteless white fish or with poached eggs. . . . But it is too cheap; it does not pay to sell it, so one cannot buy it in the shops."

Spikenard, Wild

See Solomon's-seal, False.

Spirea

Spirea grows sturdily and tall in the Rocky Mountains where there are some half dozen species. Some have white flowers, some pink, some a combination from the crossing of the species. All are lovely and delightful when made into an Indian tea from flowers, leaves, and stems.

Squash

Squash, pumpkins, and their kin probably have no legitimate place here since certainly they were introduced from tropical America. There even is evidence that their origin may have been in Asia. Be that as it may, squash and pumpkins became basic foods of the western American Indians, ranking next to corn. Though there was a good deal of escaped wild squash throughout the West, it was a valuable trade commodity to the sedentary or partially settled tribes who cultivated it.

The Indians baked squash whole in the ashes of their fire pits. They ate all of it, including seeds and shells. They simmered it into a subtly sweet stew flavored with squash blossoms. These lovely blooms when fried are still considered a gourmet dish and rightly so, especially if prepared by the Zuñi who select only the largest male flowers to fry and serve as an appetizer at the beginning of a meal or to season their stews and soups.

Squaw Apple

See Apple, Squaw.

Squawbush

This member of the sumac family is a relative of poison ivy. To many, this tall shrub with its shining leaves, small oyster-white flowers, and depressing fruit is poisonous even to the touch. But to those not allergic to it, squawbush juice from the berries makes a pleasant drink and westward-bound pioneers learned from the Indians of this and of the relief that came from sucking the acid berries to relieve their thirst.

With the exception of certain willows, squawbush was chosen by the women to weave their baskets. It was used as a strong dye. A decoction of the roots was and is used as a rinse following a shampoo, to make the hair grow.

It was food. One early arrival in the West recalls, "In my youth I saw Apache squaws make bread out of ground *lemita* berries," and today the Tewas, among others, so use the ground fruit—or eat it whole.

Squawgrass

See Wheat, Wild.

Star-flower, White Evening

The stars, the delightful *Mentzelias,* are alive only briefly, opening from about five to half-past seven on summer and early fall evenings. The bees come then and their honey was considered choice by the Indians. The large evening star *(Decapetala)* is a twilight joy, its ten white petals nearly two inches long, its fragrance exquisite.

Stinkweed

See Beeplant, Rocky Mountain.

Storksbill

See Geranium, Wild.

Strawberry

"Doubtless God could have made a better berry but doubtless God never did." How many centuries of grateful people, in how many parts of the world, have echoed William Butler's piety? There are only two species in the Rocky Mountain area but these are prodigious and prodigal.

WILD STRAWBERRY

The Indians went on veritable strawberry sprees, eating the delicate berries, seasoning their meat with them, drinking strawberry soup or a tea made from the leaves. They made strawberry bitters "for the good of the stomach."

In Elizabethan England, the wife appears to have viewed the fruit with something less than enthusiasm. An annoyed husband is recorded as having prodded her with the words, "It's four o'clock. By the time you get your clothes on, it will be light enough to pick strawberries." A 1557 English book on gardening offered this for September:

> Wife into the garden and set me a plot
> With strawberry roots, the best to be got;
> Such growing abroad among thornes in the wood,
> Well chosen and picked, proved excellent good.

The 1530 expense account book of the royal household of Henry VIII lists "small basket of strawberries at 10 pence."

The Indians did not need to be wakened. They rose in time to welcome the rising sun. Without paying tenpence, and viewing their picking not as a job but as a joy, they had their strawberries for breakfast. But, being gourmets, they sweetened their berries with the early morning dew shaken from milkweed blossoms.

Sumac, Sumach

There are many varieties of the familiar sumac and the Indians put them to many varied uses. The berries were gathered in the early fall for winter use and as a trade commodity, this in the Canadian West being called *sacacomi.* Numerous western Indian tribes smoke equal parts of tobacco and the roots and leaves of sumac. Rafinesque in his *Medical Flora* called this *kinikah* and stated that it was supposed to break the smoker of the habit of tobacco smoking. An infusion of sumac berries was held unbeatable as a black dye for wool.

A cooling drink was made from the crushed berries of the sumac, one of these, *Rhus integrifolia,* being known by the incomers as the lemonade berry. The *Rhus ovata* was called the sugar sumac because of the berries' coating of a sweet waxy substance gathered by the Indians to make sugar.

Sunflower

Of approximately fifteen species of sunflower, four are spread throughout the Rockies. The little sunflower is little and grows from the valleys to the timber line where it is joined by the alpine sunflower that is found from 10,000 to 12,000 feet. These latter are particularly wonderful. They seem to grow from utterly barren stone crevices, and they always face the east. It is a truly thrilling sight to see massed hundreds of them, from their great heights greeting the rising sun.

The common sunflower is a composite, so called because in the botanical sense it is not a single flower but a grouping of numerous small flowers. Once native only of the West, it has almost literally covered the country.

The Indians parched the highly nutritious seeds and ground them into meal for gruel and cakes. Frequently, they added water to the meal as a drink, and crushed roasted seeds made a drink like coffee. Marrow grease mixed with the meal acquired the consistency of dough and, commented a nineteenth-century traveler, "This last composition we preferred as a very palatable dish."

There were other contributions on the part of the sunflower. Purple and black dyes were extracted from the seeds and yellow dye from the flowers. Fiber came from the stems. The seeds contained an oil, extracted by boiling the flower heads; this was used by the Indians to grease their hair. Today the same high-grade oil is expressed for use in paints and margarine. To top this munificence of gifts, the sunflower is an excellently inviting plant for the bees which collect great quantities of honey and wax.

French explorers found the Indians along Lake Huron cultivating sunflowers which, they testified, grew up to twenty feet with flower heads a foot across. Lewis and Clark noted in their journal, July 17, 1805, the prevalence of sunflowers along the Missouri in its upper reaches. Frémont's journal for November 8, 1842, comments on the many spots of yellow—"deep warm colors"—along Lodge Pole Creek. He noted that the sunflowers "seem to love the sandy soil."

Swamp Potato

See Arrowhead.

Sweet Cicely

See Cicely, Sweet.

Sweet Pea, Wild

See Vetch.

Syringa

Hillsides up to about 7,000 feet look, in the Rocky Mountain spring, like snow, so densely covered are they with the multitude of syringa blooms. The air is filled with their delightful fragrance and brought joy to the hearts of the Indians. But they were practical, too, and for them the plant served a necessary utilitarian purpose. Its long straight stems were the preferred wood for making their arrows.

Syringa first was found, collected, and recorded by Captain Meriwether Lewis in 1806. It is the state flower of Idaho.

T

Thimbleberry

The berries of this member of the rose family look much like raspberries. But though they are juicy, they are almost tasteless. The Indians found them in profusion from the 6,000- to 10,000-foot level in the Rockies and ate them like raspberries.

Thistle

Thistles are our only plants whose leaves are covered in long spines. Of about two hundred species in the North Temperate Zone, some fifty inhabit North America and twenty, the Rocky Mountains.

Indians ate the young shoots as salad, the peeled stems having a "sweet, delicate taste," according to one old-timer, especially when cooked as a green. So, too, in many of the world's areas, thistles have been eaten, and it is believed that the peeled stems and roots of any of them make safe and succulent eating. This stands also for the milk thistle which is not a thistle but a composite, a weed used as greens and potherbs by many peoples including the Indians, after it had been brought over by the first white comers and spread by the winds.

Frémont recorded that in the Platte Valley "among the roots we obtained here . . . a large root thistle now in abundance," and near Great Salt Lake on the Bear, he noted that Snake Indian "squaws had just gathered about a bushel of roots of thistle . . . about the size of carrots, sweet and well flavored, requiring only long preparation."

In England, John Evelyn wrote of thistles: "the young Stalk about May, being peel'd and soak'd in Water to extract the bitterness, boil'd or raw, is a Very Wholesome Sallet, eaten with Oyl, Salt and Peper; some eat them sodden in proper Broath, or bak'd in Pies, like the Artichoak; but the tender Stalk boil'd or fry'd, some preferr, both Nourishing and Restorative."

Nearly two centuries later in the great unknown western wilderness, Truman Everts, member of the first group to make a careful examination of Yellowstone National Park, became separated from his party, was hurt and would have starved had he not sustained life for nearly a month by eating the thistle's fat root.

Mountain men, explorers, pioneers, knew the secrets of the life-sustaining thistle, and a taxi driver in Denver told me how his grandparents on the westward trail had made the refreshing thistle tea and of how, in the evening at home, his wife still makes this welcome brew for her husband when he returns from work. It has a slightly relaxing effect, as the Indians found, among other medical properties.

Tobacco

There is no argument whence came the name tobacco. It derived from the word the Carib Indians called their pipe. There is much controversy today, as we all know, on the subject of tobacco. But in the mid-sixteenth century, there was unanimity in England, Europe, the newly discovered America, and wherever the big-leafed herb was introduced. It was wonderful. It quieted. It stimulated. It healed wounds. There never had been anything in nature like tobacco.

TOBACCO

The first authentic account on record of the impact of tobacco was written in 1569 by a learned doctor named Nicolas Monardes and translated into English eight years later, in 1577, by "John Frampton, Marchaunt." The book was entitled, *Joyfull Newes out of the Newe founde Worlde wherein is declared the rare and singular vertues of diuerse and sundrie Hearbes . . .*" The second part of this study is given to the "first written acc't and illustration of the 'hearbe tobaco.'" Wrote the translator, "The Red Indians called it '*picielt.*' The name tabaco was given it by the Spaniards either from the island which still bears the name Tobago as Monardes declares, or from a native word connected in some way with the use of dried leaves for smoking."

It was the "Indian pastime to smoke tabaco," and the book contains not only the first description of the peace-pipe ceremony but also the first known record of tobacco chewing: "Red Indians also use the herb if obliged to travel several days . . . in a dispeopled countrie where they shal finde neither water nor meate." They rolled the leaves into small balls which they put "betweene the lower lippe and the teeth whiche they chew and swallow down and in this sort they journey three or four days without having neede of meate or drink, for they feel no hunger nor weaknesse nor their travel doth trouble them."

Pipe smoking became the fashion in England through its popularization by Sir Walter Raleigh and Pocahontas' husband, John Rolfe. Already tobacco had been introduced into France by Diplomat Jean Nicot for whom it was given its generic name, *Nicotiana,* whence the noun, nicotine. Doctor Monardes gave the details:

"Nicotiana was so-called after Nicot, my very friend ye first author inventor and bringer of the hearbe into France. . . . Maister John Nicot, being Embassador for his Maiestrie in Portugall, in the Yeare of our Lorde 1559, went one day to see the Prysons of the King of Portugall, and a Gentleman being Keeper of the said Prysons, presented him with this hearbe as a strong plant brought from Florida."

This, we must remind ourselves, was not only the Age of Exploration but the dawn of its corollary and successor, the Age of Enlightenment, when every enlightened man studied, observed, and compared notes with others on all discovered natural phenomena. Nicot made experiments with tobacco as a drug, but it was Doctor Monardes, the physician and scientist, who worked incessantly to establish its medicinal properties, as will be told in the section of this book on medicines.

Once discovered by white men, the use of tobacco spread rapidly; by 1617 in the Virginia colony, the raising of tobacco had become the prime occupation of the plantation owner. Tobacco leaves were used as money, precisely as for centuries the Indians had used them as an exchange commodity.

The use of tobacco had spread early among the Indians, being introduced into the Temperate Zone by various tribes and by the Spanish conquerors, and bartering for its acquisition was an established trade procedure. Thus, the Sioux did not raise gardens of corn, squash, and tobacco. Their deadly enemies, the Crow, however, cultivated the land. But the Sioux had developed a commodity coveted by the Crows—tobacco pipes made of black or red stone (almost certainly hardened clay). These were decorated with rings of lead or eye-dazzling shiny tin. The Sioux demanded a high price. The Crows paid in corn and tobacco. Crow, Blackfoot, Hidatsa, Mandan, Arikara, and Pawnees were among the tribes in the West to raise tobacco.

The pipe was, of course, vital to the Indian mores, both as utility and symbol. Women smoked only to cure a cold. Men carried their pipes with them and smoked them for pleasure or in ceremonial conference. A. C. Seward recalls, writing in 1911 on *Links with the Past in the Plant World,* "I was asked to contribute to makings for a long pipe. I reached for a plug of tobacco that I carried for such emergencies and, cutting it in two, gave half to the pipe-holder who shaved off the necessary amount to mix with proper quantities of Indian tobacco. This was of two kinds:—The bark of the red willow or kinnikinnick, a low creeping plant with glossy dark green leaves, found in some locations in the mountains, known as 'larb.'" They mixed equal amounts and the result was a "mild and fragrant smoke."

Though kinnikinnick was preferred, the Indians approved other mixtures, always, when possible, in equal amounts. There was red-osier dogwood and magnolia bark, said to help break the habit of tobacco chewing. There was a fungus from the mesquite, favored by the Opata. There was sandwort and the "quinine bush." There were mullein and ceanothus leaves, these often used if tobacco was not available. There were the leaves of sumac after it had turned scarlet. The daring young sophisticates of my generation were not the first to hide behind the barn and roll pulverized leaves in corn husks. The Indians had been doing it for centuries. The preferred technique in acquiring tobacco was to gather the leaves when they were green but not until the seeds were ripe.

In England, too, blends and substitutes became the order of the day, though centuries after the Indians had approved the procedure. The reason was this: In 1878, 960 tons of cigars were imported into England, nearly one-half Cuban or West Indian. The remainder came from the United States. Import duties kept the price high. Summarized a news story of the day: "The high duty on foreign tobacco has led to various plants being substituted, as leaves of cabbage, rhubarb, dock, etc., which are soaked with tobacco liquor," so flavoring them that, when dried, they emerged as cigar-tasting cigars.

We conclude with the words of Monardes:

"Loe here you have the true Historie of Nicotiane of the which the sayde Lorde Nicot, one of the King's counsellors, first founder out of this hearbe, hath made me privie, as well by woord as by writing, to make thee (friendly Reader), partaker thereof, to whome I require thee to yield as harty thanks as I acknowledge myself bound unto him for this benefite received."

Tobaccoroot

Tobaccoroot is a valerian and like others of its kind, the roots give forth an offensive odor, like something foul or rotten. The Indians learned by practice how to handle these roots, collecting them in the spring and baking them to remove the bitter taste. Highly nutritious, the roots, thus treated, became sweet and pleasant to the taste. Growing in high altitudes and thriving in the moist black soil of conifer forests, the plants are leafy with infinitesimal pale-pink flowers.

Kooyah, the Indians called it, as Frémont recorded, his journal note being made at "3 a.m. from Smith's Fork near Beer Springs": "I ate here for the first time the Kooyah or tobaccoroot *(Valeriana edulis),* the principal edible root of the Indians . . . of the upper water, on the west side of the mountains. It has a strong and remarkably peculiar taste and odor . . . characterized by Mr. Preuss as the most horrid food he had ever put in his mouth. . . . To others it is agreeable, full of nutriment, poisonous unless baked in the ground for days." Near Great Salt Lake in the vicinity of the Bear, Frémont "by gift of a knife . . . prevailed upon a little boy to show me the Kooyah plant. . . . The root which constitutes the Kooyah is large, of a very bright yellow color."

Turkey Peas

See Snowdrop.

Twisted-stalk

Twisted-stalk is a charming member of the lily family, its small white flowers jointed so that they droop downward, almost hidden by the proportionately large, ovate leaves. It likes the shade, growing in moist places in the woods up to about 9,000 feet. The Indians ate the vivid red oval berries.

Vetch

"By the time it blooms in the mountains, bighorn

sheep have moved their lambs to the lush alpine meadows." A team of botanical experts made this happy picture, and vetch is a happy plant for man and for the wild creatures, especially mountain goats and white-tailed deer.

There is the purple vetch, sometimes called the wild sweet pea. There is Drummond's milk vetch with its dangling black-haired pods. Parry vetch is dwarf and very hairy. Looseleaf milk vetch is a common locoweed as is the Hayden poison vetch. About a hundred of the fifteen hundred species grow in the Rocky Mountain region.

After centuries of experiment, the Indians were expert in differentiating between the vetches that were helpful to them and the locos with their poisonous alkaloid. This knowledge they passed on to mountain men and pioneers who, like them, gathered the nourishing roots in early spring or in the autumn. These roots, with their taste of licorice, were boiled, as were the pods, the latter being eaten also raw. The delicate starch seeds like small peas, and the tender stems were savored as spring greens. The fragrant violet vetch, in particular, while fulfilling these functions, delighted the senses with its massed blue flowers and sweet aroma.

Violet

Scattered over the mountains and deep in the canyons, half hidden by other foliage in moist or boggy places, are the exquisite violets of the Rockies. Of the twenty-five to thirty species to be found there, probably the most familiar is the dogtooth, with three closely related species, which climb all the way to subalpine cirques and canyons.

VIOLETS

The Indians boiled the bulbs or dried them for winter use. They ate the leaves as greens, and added them to their soups. They made violet syrup, turning the simplest gruel into an epicurean treat.

W

Wake-robin

Eagerly awaited in the Rockies, wake-robin (trillium) breaks from the earth the moment the snow melts. In a week or less, it is in bloom, with its single three-petaled flower that turns from white to pink to rose, and its three broad leaves near the stem's top. Three leaves—three-petaled blooms—the trillium. Spring is here.

There are twenty-five species, all natives of North America, but only two in the Rockies where it climbs to about 7,000 feet. All the trilliums make excellent greens when cooked, and so the Indians savored them. The heavy rootstocks were valuable in childbirth as the settlers were shown. They called it birthroot.

Wallflower

This member of the mustard family grows from the plains to the alpine, and everywhere it is a delightful sign that winter is behind. It prefers open hillsides or meadows where its vivid yellow flowers, sometimes orange-touched, form fields of captured sunshine. The Indians used the seeds of this, as of other mustards, for seasoning their soups and meal cakes.

Wapato

See Arrowhead.

Watercress

Another mustard, its acid sap with its sulphur compound as familiar to the Indians as to the latecomers, bites and delights the taste. Find its ten Rocky Mountain species where it would be found elsewhere, beside cool streams or pristine springs, anywhere from low country to some 8,000 feet, its dense clumps of leaves forming a mat in which the modest white blossoms are all but invisible. The Indians, even as you and I, ate the leaves and the young stems. They do not seem to have discovered the property claimed by the Romans, that watercress was good food for those of deranged minds.

Waterleaf

The plant gets its name from one of nature's most accommodating arrangements. There is a heavy root system that holds a food and water supply in reserve. So the plant, with its bell-shaped blue flower clusters, grows early when the spring rains afford ample water. This is caught and held in well-engineered leaf cavities whence it is sent downward. Flowers appear and die, seeds form and are blown away, the plant withers, but the fleshy roots remain, fed by their built-in water supply. The next spring the shoots reappear to be eaten by the Indians either raw or cooked. The cooked roots were particularly desirable.

Western Orange

See Sneezeweed.

Wheat, Wild

WHEAT

The squawgrass of the Indians, the grains were gathered and ground into meal for cakes and porridge. In New Mexico today, as for centuries with all western Indians, the roots of the wild wheat are boiled and heads are washed in the resultant tea to promote the growth of hair.

Willowherb

Willowherb is a slight plant with minute pink flowers and unique seed pods, four-angled, with silky tufts appearing as they open. It grows in the foothills where Indians and incomers gathered it to burn in the lower elevations where they were beset by bugs. A species of the plant was used similarly in England, Parkinson in

1629 advising, "Willow-herb, being burned . . . driveth away flies and gnats and other such like small creatures . . . which in the night season sting and bite."

Windflower

See Anemone.

Wormwood

See Sage.

Wyethis, White

Rising from a thick, woody taproot, with coarse stems and flower heads like white sunflowers, they look like what they were called by mountain men and miners —white mule-ears. Wyethis is showy, destructive, found on the West Coast and in Montana and Wyoming. Indians ate the plant if they had to, first processing it by boiling and fermenting.

Y

Yampa

Yampa, the wild carrot of the settlers, is one of the three great plants of the Rocky Mountain Indians, both for food and for trade. This member of the parsley family grows from its priceless tubers, the slim stems crowned with long-stemmed compound umbels of small white blooms. Found on open hillsides, in meadows, and in stands of aspen, it flourishes wherever the spring soil is damp.

It was in the spring that the Indians took the two finger-like roots from the ground, washed them, and removed their brown skins by trampling them with their bare feet. Then the roots were washed again and scraped. Eaten raw, they had a parsnip-cum-nuts flavor. But more generally the little tubers, shaped like a sweet potato, were boiled the same way. When cooked until mealy, they were served as a vegetable or the cooking was continued to make yampa soup. The seeds were used to flavor other soups. Some roots were dried and stored to be ground into meal and made into cakes. At remote Indian rodeos today, yampa root, sold by the tin-cupful, is eaten like popcorn.

Sacajawea, the "Bird Woman," showed Lewis and Clark how to boil the yampa and eat it like potatoes. Frémont liked yampa cooked with wild duck and he was able to achieve this along the Snake where it "grows much." It also grew much in the vicinity of Bear River and the Great Salt Lake where, he recorded, "Among the roots we obtained here, we could distinguish five or six kinds; and the supply of the Indians whom we met consisted principally of Yampa."

Yarrow

Widespread in the foothills, yarrow is odd to look at, flat-topped, with clustered white flowers and leaves almost invisibly separated into divisions. It is aromatic and its two species in the Rockies grow from the plains to the timber line and above.

Though primarily of medical value, it was eaten by the Indians who enjoyed the young tops as salad just as, in England, the young leaves were chopped and substituted for chervil. The Indians, however, knew a few other surprises about the herb. They had proved to their satisfaction that yarrow oil stopped falling hair, and to this day the Zuñi maintain that yarrow leaves create a cooler sensation to the skin than any other plant.

Yarrow, known in England as tansy, was also one of the country's aboriginal plants. It was one of the witches' herbs, used in incantations and brought by well-intentioned superstitious friends to weddings to insure the couple of seven years of love. Even at the present time, it is viewed as a very potent love charm, especially if it has been plucked by some lovelorn maiden from a young man's grave. Country folk in England still hold it to be one of the priceless herbs.

John Evelyn urged that tansy be used sparingly when "mixt with our cold Sallat and much fitter (tho' in very small quantity) for the Pan, being qualified with the juices of other fresh Herbes, *Spinach, Green Corn, Violet, Primrose . . . leaves etc.*, at entrance of Spring and then fried brownish and eaten hot with the juice of Orange and Sugar as one of the most agreeable of all boil's Herbaceous Dishes."

Yerba Mansa

Called Apache beads, yerba mansa is a marsh plant with hollow rhubarb-red stems and tailed flower heads, somewhat resembling anemones. The herb has a spicy, sometimes heavy odor. The Indians prepared the rootstocks in the usual way and pulverized the seeds into meal for mush or for bread cooked in hot ashes. According to one authority, yerba mansa means "Herb of the Tamed Indian."

Yucca

The yuccas, in particular soapweed and Indian banana *(Yucca glauca and Yucca baccata)*, dominate the dry plains and dry mountain slopes. Soapweed, with its speared leaves, is breath taking when its masses of white bell-shaped flowers burst into bloom along their thick supporting stalks. The Indian banana was valued especially for its edible seed pods.

The Indians savored the yucca flowers and stalks which are rich in sugar, and the fat pulpy fruit which they ate raw or roasted or dried for winter. Leaves became fiber for baskets and mats and for producing skinny yucca dolls and horrendous masks for the children.

The roots were made into soap for cleansing the hair and often whole tribes indulged in a simultaneous shampooing party. In some groups, this fun was absorbed into the marriage ceremony when big bowls of suds were (and are) set before the bride and groom who washed each other's hair. Reversing the picture, young yucca shoots were boiled and mashed, the juice then being poured back into the steaming pot and cooked until it became a winelike liquid, red in color. This was drunk by *los hermanos penitentes* as a stimulant to make them *muy bravo y valiente* during their Good Friday ordeal.

Part Two
Maladies and Medicines

It is the medicine man to whom tribute is due for this section, he who for countless centuries has experimented with the herbal uses in medicine. The genuine and great contribution of the Indians' medicine man has been obscured by his obscuring magic, ceremonials, and ritual. But beneath that, he was actually a hard-working scientist doing his business with imagination, patience, and dedication.

It was he who found new methods of staunching a wound. He may even have found a cure for syphilis. He worked alone. But he met others of his kind whenever possible and there were regular convocations of medicine men, drawn together from many tribes and distant places. Knowledge was pooled, herbs exchanged, formulae improved. The result was that, though basically tribal, the Indian pharmacopoeia in the West was more or less universal and unified by the time—at the very moment of the Indians' fullest development—the white men came.

It will be noted that for almost all the ills there are a half dozen or more recommended remedies. This was necessary because if one needed remedy was not to be found in the immediate area, there would be another herb that could be used for almost any contingency, and to meet the current crisis and anticipate those that might occur, there were herbs that, when found, were dried and stored for later use.

Alcoholism

The Indians, after the white man had brought

them this problem, faced it as they did other of his vices, by trying to find a cure. Hop tea was recommended to stop the craving.

Alder

Widely used as alterative and astringent as well as for its tonic properties, the Indians also made a decoction applied externally for skin irritations. The berries provided a cathartic and vermifuge, and a decoction of the leaves was used on burns and inflamed wounds.

ALDER

Though the black alder was used, it was the white that served the Indians better. Widespread and common along streams high in the mountains, it was easy to locate with its conspicuous white-to-gray bark and its green hanging catkins and diminutive cones. Its dried bark in decoction furnished medicine to check diarrhea, induce circulation, allay an upset stomach, or check hemorrhage. The medicine man made an infusion of alder bark as eye drops or mixed the bark with Indian tobacco to induce vomiting. It was, and still is, of recognized assistance in facilitating childbirth.

Alfalfa

The first Americans knew the value of alfalfa long years before the white men discovered the vitamins, organic minerals, and trace elements contained therein. The Indians made an infusion for rheumatism and arthritis and, where it was plentiful, drank alfalfa regularly as a medicinal tea.

Anemone

The Indians attributed potent healing properties to the delicate little anemone, using the roots especially in the treatment of wounds. I have found no record that early English herbalists had discovered this significant "vertue," but they advocated sniffing the juice to "purge the head." They made an ointment to "cleanse malignant and corroding ulcers," and they even claimed that if the patient's body was bathed in a decoction of anemone leaves, it "cures the leprosy."

Anesthethics

Yarrow roots were the traditionally accepted and commonly used local anesthetic of the Indians tribes in the West. That it is still so used is recorded in two examples cited by the Research Service of the United States Department of Agriculture.

A Nevada Indian was in intense pain from a deep cut in his thigh where foreign matter had entered the wound. A dressing was applied of fresh yarrow roots mashed to a pulp. Within a half hour, the anesthetic had taken effect and it was possible to open and cleanse the wound. In another case, a deeply embedded splinter was similarly extracted after a preliminary soaking of the afflicted part in a solution of yarrow root. This was done by members of the family.

The medicine man was called in only in cases of extreme illness. For the rest, every Indian was his own doctor and the women were as knowledgeable in the uses of herbs as medicine as to be almost professional doctors themselves.

Angel Stem

With what success is not recorded, angel stem was administered in cases of syncope.

Angelica

In the autumn, angelica was collected in anticipation of the inevitable winter ailments. For influenza: a tea from the roots. For head colds: the roots dried, shaved fine, and smoked as a cigarette. For bronchitis: the roots scraped and soaked but not boiled. For sore throat and cough: small bits of the root. For chest pains, rheumatic pains, pneumonia: poultices from the larger roots. For kidney troubles, the roots were boiled in a gallon or so of water and drunk instead of it. The root was mashed and smeared on sores and cuts. When whatever ailment finally had been brought to an end, a good strong tea was made from angelica roots and drunk hot several times a day to rebuild the depleted system. It was inevitable that, after the coming of the white man, the Indians experimented with *Angelica ampla* as a cleansing wash for venereal disease.

Anodynes

Wild lettuce was recognized throughout the Indian world for its excellent quieting effects. Mullein also was used frequently and sometimes henbane, with care.

See also Sedatives, Narcotics.

Antelope Brush

High in the Indians' pharmacopoeia, the widespread antelope brush was used as a remedy for a dozen assorted ills. The leaf decoction was prescribed for liver complaints and as a blood tonic, for colds and tuberculosis and pneumonia, though in the last instance a tea was preferred made from the inner white bark. Boiled young branches or leaves, sometimes with the flowers added, were deemed helpful in cases of measles, chicken pox, and smallpox. If the smallpox was severe, twigs were boiled with this decoction to which was added a "chunk of dried rat-urine."

A boiled handful of leaves or ripe unground seed provided physics or emetics, depending on the dosage. A wash was made for rashes, itches, and bug bites, and green leaves were mashed as a wet dressing for sores or dried leaves were applied to them in powdered form.

It was only a small step, therefore, to the most important function of antelope brush, the treatment of venereal disease. A decoction of boiled leaves taken as tea, ranked high as a specific for gonorrhea. The inner bark of the trunk was preferred by some tribes, by others, the boiled roots. But that antelope brush had value in the treatment of this dread imported disease was claimed by Indians throughout the West.

Antiseptics

Easily available antiseptics were in general use, four in particular. Balsam, with root base, was deemed excellent. Milkweed was antiseptic and healing. The liquid from the soaked and mashed roots of Solomon's-seal was administered as an antiseptic in cases of blood poisoning as was also yarrow, an antiseptic wash from which being applied while still warm. Boiled leaves and sometimes stems went into this wash.

Anti-spasmodics

Mullein, skunkcabbage, spearmint, and rue quieted the spasms as they do today. The Indians favored in particular the *Grindelia squarrosa* or gumweed and it was they, almost certainly, who instructed in its use the vanguard of the Jesuit missionaries. Now, as then, the flowers and young leaves are dried and decocted into anti-spasmodics. Sometimes the Indians chewed the leaves or drank a mildly quieting leaf tea.

There were the skullcaps also, with a crystalline glucose; the Indians used this, too, though they did not know, of course, why the plant quieted their nerves. There was valerian, which is still used, and there were intestinal anti-spasmodics: clematis, decocted by the Apaches; greasewood bark, drunk in mild decoction by the Pima; corn meal, steeped in lye, used by the Sioux, Cheyenne, and other western tribes.

Appetizers

Though the Indians depended on tonics rather than appetizers, one of the latter, apparently universally popular as a pre-dinner teaser, was a bowl of tea made from the seed heads of horsemint.

See also Tonics.

Arnica

The plant that somewhat resembles a sunflower was cherished by countless generations of Indians, as it has been valued by innumerable late-arriving whites. The arnicas grow under the protection of the lodgepole and ponderosa pines of the high Rockies and beneath the quaking aspens of the upland valleys. On stiffened Indian muscles arnica was rubbed in to avoid infection and speed healing, and on open wounds and gashes it was applied as a salve.

To the Indian, there was nothing more healing than arnica for chapped lips or dust-clogged nose. The arriving settlers decorated the formula by making their own salve—one ounce of arnica flowers heated for a while with an ounce of lard. For open cuts and small wounds, they followed the Indian precept—two heaping teaspoons of flowers to a cup of boiling water. Steep and apply cold.

Arnica today is an officinal drug plant. But for fifteen thousand, or fifty thousand years, the Indians have used arnica and have known the potency of the big yellow flowers that hold high their vivid heads to glimpse the sun through stately lodgepole pines.

Artichoke, Jerusalem

To relieve rheumatic pains, the heads were eaten in the usual way or the leaves and stalks were made into a tea and drunk twice daily.

Ash, Prickly

Prickly ash was the basis of a widely prescribed Indian medicine called *hantola.* The decocted roots were recommended for stomach upset, rheumatism, and gonorrhea. The Indians chewed ash for toothache. They made poultices, combining the decoction with bear grease, and applied it to sores and ulcers. A decoction of the bark served as a diaphoretic (they had discovered that it excited most secretions). It was a strong stimulant in healing wounds. Decocted root bark was helpful for rheumatism and for colic. An infusion of the berries was soothing in cases of bronchial diseases. The pioneers, having learned from the Indians, adopted it for many of their purposes. Ash was still officinal in the United States pharmacopoeia as late as 1892.

PRICKLY ASH

We have found no evidence of the uses of ash that reached down the centuries from Pliny to Gerard. But the latter was fluent on the subject. He claimed that, if taken in the morning fasting, the water distilled from the top leaves of the ash would "abate the greatness of those that are too gross and fat."

Straddling the centuries, both he and the great Greek scientist agreed that "the tender tops and leaves" of ash should be used "inwardly and outwardly for the bite of an adder, viper," or other snake, and Gerard restated what Pliny had enunciated, "that there is such an antipathy between an adder and an ash tree that if an adder be encompassed around with ash-tree leaves, he would sooner run through the fire than through the leaves." To which Shakespeare's neighbor added caustically, "the contrary to which is the truth as both my eyes are witness."

Asparagus

The Indians used asparagus for kidney and bladder ills. They had proved that it promotes secretions of urine, as the settlers discovered from them. In the Sheridan *Wyoming Post* of February 28, 1889, its readers were reminded that asparagus "purifies the blood and especially acts on the kidneys." Today we state succinctly that it is "rich in mineral salts, stimulates the bladder, and contains vitamins A and B."

Elizabethan Gerard elaborated. Young asparagus "buds or branches boiled in ordinary broth maketh the belly soluble and open." For kidney stimulation, he recommended that the asparagus be boiled in white wine and declared this prescription to be beneficial also for gout. According to this famous herbalist, a decoction of the roots "boiled in wine, clears the sight" and that this, held in the mouth, "eases toothache." Since he must always have the final word, he produced this for his punchline: "Being taken fasting several mornings altogether, [asparagus] stirreth up bodily lust in man or woman."

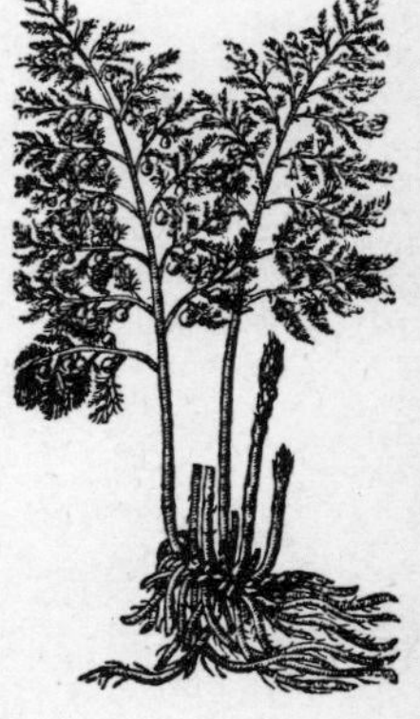

ASPARAGUS

Aspen, Quaking

A spring tonic tea was made by the Indians of quaking aspen bark and wild grape root. But with aspen, there appears again the tragic groping for relief from their most vicious physical enemy. Recent studies show that the Paiutes and Shoshones, over a long period of time, experimented with aspen bark boiled into a tea as relief from venereal disease.

Aspirin

All western Indians knew that if you decocted willow bark the welcoming tea relieved headache and fever and eased the aches and pains. From the Potawatomi to the Mandan to the Sioux to the Nez Percé, they knew that a tea made from wintergreen leaves broke a fever or made bearable the throbbing of sore muscles or rheumatism.

In 1763, Reverend Edward Stone noticed willows in a damp region where rheumatism was common among the settlers. He had heard of the Indian success with willow bark, so he tried the decoction on the local sufferers and eased their pain thereby, thus proving to the white men the effectiveness of salicylic acid (*salix,* "willow"). But it was three-fourths of a century later before the drug was put on the market, longer than that before it was discovered that wintergreen leaves, too, contain the substance that is an integral part of aspirin.

Aster

Victims of rheumatism welcomed the sight of the early fall asters, for their stems and flowers became an easing wash when soaked. Countless generations ago, the Indians proved that a tea from the dried stems (without leaves) provided an excellent blood tonic.

Asthma

Skunkcabbage, onion, and honey were deemed an excellent brew to relieve asthma, the Indians sometimes varying the formula with garlic. A more cautious early nineteenth-century settler used skunkcabbage alone and approved its efficacy. The Indians also used jack-in-the-pulpit, snakeroot in decoction, and lobelia which, when tested by a white man in 1817, was commended. The bruised leaves of yerba mansa were said to bring relief. Sage tea was extensively used. Popularly known as *romerillo,* it was taken morning and evening for forty days and at night a sage poultice was applied to chest and back. Even *maíz* flour boiled in a cup of water was acceptable.

But, America's first medical practitioners largely recommended inhalations for asthma. The dried leaves of jimson weed (datura) were smoked like tobacco, as was pulverized balsam root sometimes mixed with tobacco. A variant of this was to inhale the fumes of the root while it was burning in a bed of live coals. When pitch was available, it often was added. The patient inhaled with a cloth over his head—even as you and I did as children. Mullein leaves were inhaled but today the New Mexican Indian sufferer has been known to soak the leaves first in *mula blanca,* which is a very potent local corn whisky. Few asthma victims these days would employ the ancient Indian remedy of swallowing a handful of spider webs rolled into a ball. But perhaps they should. For, in 1882, the substance arachnidan was isolated from them and proved "a remarkable febrifuge."

Astringents

Bistort and blackberry, hemlock, nettles and trillium, St. Johnswort and the milder curlydock and avens —"an excellent astringent"—all these were used by the Indians. Also excellent, as noted by an 1840 settler, was an Indian favorite, raspberry leaves. This pioneer, like the others, had learned from the Indians who had proved the properties of the herbs without knowing why they were successful. Thus, prince's pine contains a volatile oil still used in medicine as an astringent, as also is cinquefoil with its tannic acid content—still an Indian favorite.

Druggists still use kinnikinnick and countless families still gather the low-growing shrub for medical purposes. Goldenrod still is decocted, too, by the Indians as an astringent and old-timer Priddy Meeks's experiments with cinquefoil and chokecherry paralleled the Indians' use of them. Most highly prized for its astringent properties appears to have been wild geranium, as attested by Charles F. Millspaugh who noted in his book on *Medicinal Plants* (1892), that the "American aborigines value the root [wild geranium] as an astringent in looseness of the bowels and exhaustive discharges of all kinds."

Avens

As noted above, avens formed the base of one of the best astringents. It was employed commonly as a styptic for uterine hemorrhage. But its claim to fame was as "Indian chocolate," so named by the settlers as they followed the Indians' precepts and took a dose of decocted avens mixed with honey (to which the white people added milk) for diarrhea and dysentery.

B

Backache

In New Mexico today, the Indians still use the traditional remedy for backache, a plaster of pitch and powdered verbena.

Balm of Gilead

See Poplar.

Balsam

Indian *toza* was one of the most widely employed medicinal herbs in the West and it has been said that "of all the ailments to which the Indian was heir, probably there is none which has not been treated one way or another, by remedies prepared from the [balsam] root."

It came to the attention of Europe almost immediately after the white man first encountered the dwellers of the New World. In his first report of Indian medicinal imports, sixteenth-century Spanish Doctor Monardes wrote:

"That licour most excellent whiche for its excellencie and maruelous effects is called Balsamo, an imitation of the true Balsamo that was in the lande of Egipt . . . carrieth leaues like to Nettles." The "Red Indians" cut incisions and let "clammish licour, of colour white but most excellent and very perfite," run out, or cut up "boughs and branches of the tree into very small pieces, boiling them in cauldrons," then skimming off the oil. "The use of them is only in things of medicine. . . .

"The Spaniards had knowledge of it because they did heale therewith the wounds that they did receive of the Indians: beying advised of the vertue thereof by the same Indians and they did see the saide Indians heal and cure themselves therewith." When this new precious balsam was first brought to Spain in the mid-sixteenth century, it sold for ten ducats an ounce in France and in Italy for a hundred ducats an ounce.

This was no universal panacea. It was and is a drug. It worked and it works. The Indians still use it constantly. For instance, in a study of medical herbs in Nevada it was found that *all* the Indians try to maintain a stock of balsam sufficient to last through the winter, peeling and slicing the roots and laying them away to dry.

Over the centuries, the Indians had tested and proved the value of this priceless root for coughs and colds, bronchitis and influenza, tuberculosis, pneumonia, and even hay fever, a tea from the boiled dried root being used. For sore throat: raw root, chewed. For asthma: pulverized roots smoked or fumes inhaled.

The roots, boiled to the consistency of yellow soup, were administered for severe stomach or bladder upsets. The decoction became an eyewash when, as the dried roots boiled, the oil was skimmed from the water. One drop of this oil was used for eye infections, trachoma, and gonorrheal eyes.

For swellings, sprains, and rheumatism, the root was crushed and, raw or boiled, made into a poultice, this being highly regarded also for skin rashes, cuts and sores, and for mosquito bites. The water from the boiled roots was used as a wash, this being standard procedure in bathing a smallpox patient or in other illness where an antiseptic was indicated. After severe illness, the dwelling was fumigated by burning balsamroot. In former times, possibly even now in remote regions, the Indian women ground the fresh root to a pulp and applied it to the umbilical cord of the newborn baby.

Inevitably, in their frantic efforts to combat venereal disease, experiments were made with balsam. *Hiza* was drunk daily, a half cup of tea decocted from the boiled roots. When *hiza* was not sufficiently potent, other roots were added. For syphilitic sores, mashed or dry powdered balsam was applied.

The use of the wonder drug was not limited to humans. Many Indians today cure the distemper of their horses with balsamroot. The horse is run first to quicken its breathing. Then it is led to a bucket of smoldering roots, its head is covered, and it inhales the healing fumes.

Barley, Wild

Roots, boiled to a yellow solution, were administered to stop "bloody flux"—dysentery. The decoction was given also as a blood tonic and so, logically, it was tried out for possible value in treating venereal disease.

Basil

The Indians used this American dittany for everything from snakebite to consumption.

Bedstraw

This tall slender plant belongs to the madder

family whence, among other properties, come ipecac and quinine. The Indians used it primarily as a healing agent for wounds and burns. Back in England, there is no evidence that herbalist Culpeper discovered these qualities. He advised his readers only that the herb or flower, when bruised and put in the nostrils, would stop nosebleed, and that a decoction of them was "good to bathe the feet of travellers and lacqueys."

Beeplant

Indians still place the crushed leaves of the beeplant on swellings and the like to reduce inflammation, notably in the case of bites of poisonous bugs. They still eat the leaves as a green remedy and still boil the leaves in barely sufficient water to cover, and drink the tea for stomach upsets.

Betony

This coarse many-spiked plant of the montane appears to have been tested, then discarded, in the fight against venereal disease. Though we are without record of it, it is probable that it was used for generations for other purposes such as were proved abroad. In Italy, a proverbial compliment (recorded in 1876) flatters that "you have more virtues than betony." Certain it is that the Indians did not try it, as recommended in the *Grete Herbal* of 1525–1526, "for them that be ferfull."

Birch

Birch is a diuretic and was so used by the Indians who instructed also that a strong solution will break stone and remove gravel from the kidneys. A milder solution was used for a sore mouth. Birch sap or the juice of the young leaves or the water distilled from them was used externally for skin irritations and scurvy.

Birth Control

In a life of continual food shortages and hunger

crises, it was reasonable for a realistic society to arrive at the concept of birth control, to evolve it, and to practice it as a normal phase of life. For countless generations, all the western tribes have done so, and the fact that all the Indians have used the same herbs and practices indicates the unanimity of their approval. There was no question or doubt as to its morality. It was the thing to do and it was done.

False hellebore was perhaps the most widely used contraceptive. Indian women daily drank a tea from its fresh root. This had to be prepared, however, in careful doses; too much would result in sterility for life.

Juniper berry tea taken on three consecutive and appropriate days was considered effective, or the boiled leaves of Solomon's-seal taken for a calculated week, or the dried boiled roots of the mountain hollyhock.

If the medicine man decided that in an individual case permanent sterility was advisable, stone seed *(plante aux perles)* could be used, a handful of the chipped dried root being boiled in water to cover and the resultant tea used daily for six months. The same procedure was followed with gromwell roots except that the infusion was drunk cold. Skunkcabbage appears to have been effective more rapidly, the boiled root being taken in small amounts three times a day for three weeks. In one locality, it was found that both the man and woman took this dosage.

The use of yarrow (tansy) was no more limited to the Indians than the age-old practice of abortion, as Doctor Charles F. Millspaugh noted in his 1892 book on *Medicinal Plants*. The dosage was recorded as ten drops or more of the oil. Of the herb, he commented: Yarrow is "one of most frequently used abortives among ignorant people—not so dangerous generally as that following the use of nutmeg but very often serious." Other abortifacients of the Indians included decoctions of kinnikinnick, hops, and cedar sprouts.

The practice of abortion probably increased greatly after the coming of the white men. The delivery of infants of mixed blood is difficult, especially so in the case of the Indian woman who is built to bring forth safely only the very small babies of her own pure blood.

The health of the Indian mother frequently was protected by a year of birth control after the arrival of her baby, and this still is done. In Elko, Nevada, for instance, when the baby is a month old, a trench is filled with warm ashes and the mother lies down in them, relaxing and drinking a tea made of wild geranium. By doing so, it has been proved for centuries, she will be safe from pregnancy until the baby's first birthday.

Birthroot

See Trillium.

Bistort

Familiarly known as snakeweed, this member of the buckwheat family contributed roots which, when boiled by the Indians, served as astringent, diuretic, and alterative. In Elizabethan England, experiments seem to have been carried further, Culpeper recording that the distilled root induced vomiting and therefore "expelleth the venom" of smallpox, measles, and the plague. The distilled water from leaves and roots had proved to be a "singular remedy to wash the sting of venemous creatures . . . to fasten the gums and take away inflammation in the jaws." The leaves were declared to kill worms in children and a decoction of the root in wine "hindereth abortion or miscarriage."

Bites and Stings, Insect

The Indians, like the rest of humanity, suffered from insect bites and, like the rest of humanity, had their favorite amelioratives. The crushed leaves of the beeplant reduced the inflammation of all poisonous insect bites. Mashed balsamroot was effective as was tobacco, "mashed and bound on the swellings, especially of spider bites." Sarsaparilla was cooling and a wash of the leaves, young branches, and/or flowers of the antelope brush were recommended. Hot dressings of piñon resin drew out the poison of more serious infections and for ant bites, the Zuñi still follow the prescription of their ancestors by applying the blossoms and ground roots of the saltbush, moistened with saliva. Garlic juice was commonly used on bites as were wintergreen and other herbs. We have no evidence that they used pennyroyal which, in Elizabethan England, was first steeped in wine.

See also Mosquitoes.

Bitterroot

The roots *were* bitter but, ground fine, they were chewed by the Indians for sore throat.

Bitters

The bitter herbs were as well or better known to the Indians than to their European counterparts, and for the same purposes. Cranesbill, dandelion root, sassafras, the "spring bitters" comprised the Indian tonics and blood purifiers after the long winter. Other plants used for the bitter infusions and decoctions included hops, wild parsley, lichen, quassia, and bitter ash. A highly favored prescription, taken in small doses, called for a combination of quaking aspen bark, roots of Oregon grape, columbine, dandelion, and chokecherry. Dandelion bitters were held valuable also in cases of yellow jaundice. The docks were used and blue gentian, "one of the simple bitters."

Many of these herbs were adapted by the incomers, red clover tops being highly favored. According to an old recipe, the roots and flowers were washed and put in an earthen vessel where two quarts of boiled and cooled water were poured over them. After standing overnight, the crock was set on the back of the stove and steeped five hours. "It must not boil but must be nearly ready to boil. When ready, strain and add a half pint of good gin and keep in a cool place. Dose: one-half wineglass twice a day."

According to Mrs. F. L. Gillette and Hugo Ziemann, the White House Steward, in the 1889 edition of the *White House Cookbook,* "This is better than all the patent medicines that are in the market—a superior blood purifier." The Indians' blood continued to be purified without the gin.

The old-time pharmacopoeia listed as major bitters the roots of asparagus, fennel, and parsley and the minor bitters as the roots of couchgrass, fern, maidenhair, strawberry, and thistle. All these the Indians had used for centuries.

Currently, the word bitters is associated only with certain bottled mixes or with *apéritifs* which are designed to stir the appetite. Their base is largely hops, gentian, bitter orange, or wormwood.

Blackberry

The blackberry root, decocted, was used by the Indians as an eyewash and cure for sore eyes. There are several tribes that still mash the blackberry roots and apply them when a poultice is called for. There still are those who use the bitter brew as an astringent, a variant of which was that astringent familiar and famous among the settlers and their offspring, known as blackberry cordial.

Blackthorn

See Snowbush.

Bladder

See Kidney and Bladder.

Bladder Pod

This, too, was used in treating a sore throat.

Blood

In a nomadic life of hunting and fighting, the stopping of the blood flow from wounds was of vital importance and for centuries the Indians had experimented with possible coagulants. They had found ceanothus valuable in stopping excessive bleeding and still use it. Tobacco was favored and nettles, willow, plantain, and wintergreen were applied according to their availability.

No Indian family was without Solomon's-seal. The slim round root was gathered in the autumn and cut crosswise into small rings. These were threaded and hung up to dry. When a cut or wound would not stop bleeding, rings of the herb were pounded into powder and poured into the gaping hole. It is testified that the "blood clots almost immediately."

But the most generally used herb to stop the blood flow was yarrow, its leaves steeped in water. In 1840, a white physician admitted in writing that it was a "good styptick." Being used for everything from a pricked finger to a spear-torn thigh, the settlers came to call the yarrow by the affectionate nickname of "Nosebleed."

The Indians recognized the signs of high blood pressure and probably taught the pioneers the value of false hellebore in combating it. As blood purifiers they used their bitters and decocted teas of sage, red clover blossoms, yerba mansa leaves, borage, paintbrush root, flowers of the mountain cottonwood steeped in cold water, or a tepid tea of Oregon grapes.

As the settlers found, nettle juice was a "wonderful blood cleanser," and to "clear the blood" there was nothing better than scurvy grass tea. Explorers, mountain men, and miners would have disagreed. To them, there was no blood purifier to match Mormon tea (ephedra). They took it every spring. The Indians favored hops, the blossoms made into a tea. In 1669, England caught up with them, the herbalists recommending hop tea to "depurate the blood."

Rue tea was taken by the Indians to stimulate the circulation of blood, and the root of the mountain grape was decocted into a blood tonic. There were also many other herbs that in decoction were calculated to correct the depletion of a long winter without green things. The dried stems of asters (without their leaves) were a blood tonic as were decocted wild barley roots. The young twigs of juniper or juniper seeds eaten daily were used for this purpose or the berries were made into a tea and taken cold every day for a week. This was recommended also for the lumbago sufferer.

For blood poisoning there were two herbs preferred as antiseptics, the mashed soaked roots of Solomon's-seal and the mashed raw root of skunkcabbage. Ashamed to admit that there is venereal disease among them, it is said that today the Shoshones claim that the tea of the scarlet gilia they sometimes drink is to "clean blood."

Blueberry

A "very pungent aromatic," blueberry tea was a widely recognized anti-spasmodic among the Indians, used commonly by the women at the birth of their babies. This practice was adopted also by the settlers' wives, as attested by a medical book of 1813.

In Culpeper's England, the berries were used as the Indians used them, to "bind the belly" and "cool the liver and stomach." Blueberry juice and syrup were used for "old coughs" which, in their own tongues, the Indians called tuberculosis. One species, referred to as the red whorl, was employed to "stop women's courses" even as for centuries Indian women had used blueberry tea to control excessive menstruation.

Boils

If you have boils in the country where the Shoshone live, ask for *saga donzia,* the boiled leaves of phlox which they apply to the swellings. Crushed leaves of (sour) dock were widely used also, bound on the boils to draw out suppuration. They also used warmed fir pitch or a poultice of mashed clematis leaves. A dressing of heated piñon resin to which might be added terminal juniper twigs was used and is used by Paiutes and Shoshones as a drawing agent. Other poultices for this purpose included one of the mashed raw roots of skunk-cabbage or the fresh roots of Solomon's-seal. Cottonwood bark burned and the ashes mixed with corn meal and water was made into a poultice as were the boiled young shoots of white pine or the fungus galls of wild roses. After the boil had opened, the Shoshones reapplied the boiled leaves of the strawberry phlox.

Bones, Broken

Most preferred by the Indians for fractures was cottonwood bark. A large quantity was simmered for an entire day in a big tub over a low fire. The liquid was strained and again there was cooking until the consistency of honey was reached. When the broken bone had been set, this thick syrup was spread on a cloth and wrapped tightly about the fracture. Added bandage was not needed. The syrup hardened into a splint and wrapping and "such was the nature of this remarkable cast that it remained in place about two months, only disintegrating after the bone had ample time to knit. A drop or two of oil aided removal." We are indebted to L. S. M. Curtin of the Laboratory of Anthropology at Santa Fe for the above description.

Sometimes the Indians placed a poultice of crushed roots and leaves of thistle around the broken bone. Sometimes ground dandelion leaves were reduced to a paste and spread over the fracture, bound on with fresh dandelion leaves and rags. Sometimes a poultice made of the entire yarrow plant was used and sometimes, the crushed roots of Solomon's-seal. Over in England, a famed herbalist also approved Solomon's-seal, writing, "There is not to be found another herb comparable to it for the purpose of knitting bones." In 1587, Thomas Hill recommended an internal treatment which we have not found in the Indian pharmacopoeia, "The distilled water of valerian drunke vnto the quantities of foure ounces at a time, both morning and evening, profiteth the creature having any bone broken."

Bowel Disorders

See Stomach and Bowel Disorders.

Brain

The Indians used white hellebore in treating mental derangements, even as had been done part way around the globe from ancient times. It appears that they knew also the properties of wormwood as a strong stimulant to the brain. But there is no record that they paralleled seventeenth-century England, which was advised that "drye roses put to ye nose to smell do comforte the brain."

Bright's Disease

The Indians have known for generations of the value of hemp and still use it in combating Bright's disease.

Bruises and Sprains

For so many bruises, so many remedies: hyssop, plantain and poplar, mullein and pennyroyal, sage and wormwood, sometimes in decoction as with everlastings and mountain grapes, sometimes as poultices as with yerba mansa and yarrow. A poultice of the entire yarrow plant was used for sprains as, similarly, was mullein. The yerba mansa poultice was made only of the leaves. Pulverized dandelion leaves were mixed with dough and applied to a bad bruise. Crushed daisy leaves were so popular for bruises and the like among the mountain men and miners that they called the daisies "bruisewort."

The inevitable balsamroot, raw or boiled, applied as a poultice was effective, as was water from the boiled root used as a wash for sprains.

For bruises, pulped root of curlydock could be

used as dressing or poultice. For black-and-blue spots, Parkinson (1640) elaborated on an Indian practice of centuries: the use of lupine of which "the seed, with meal and honey" take away the discoloration. Preferred by the Indians was a poultice of the fresh roots of Solomon's-seal or its dry material soaked in hot water.

Buckwheat, Wild

Buckwheat was used extensively by the Indians. The stems and leaves were made into a tea for bladder trouble. The roots and sometimes the tops were decocted and drunk for colds, tuberculosis, and diarrhea. For rheumatic pains the whole plant was boiled and the solution used as a wash.

Bur, Sand

A decoction of the whole plant was given nursing mothers to increase lactation.

Burdock

BURDOCK

Of all the docks, burdock appears to have been recommended for the most Indian ills. It had been used for centuries as a tonic and diuretic, the Indians finding it to work powerfully on the urine. Diaphoretic, aparient, sudorific, burdock soothed the pains of rheumatism, sciatica, and gout as well. It was of value in a salve for wounds and as a wash for skin irritations and burns. Combined with bean pods, it was applied in cases of erysipelas. A fast rule was that only year-old roots should be used and that these should be dug in the early spring or late fall.

Burns and Scalds

With the Indian cooking ritual, there must have been burns and scalds to be doctored almost daily, and the list of remedies employed is correspondingly long. The following were the most widely accepted: poplar, hound's tongue, gumplant, alder, bedstraw, burdock, linseed oil from the wild flax.

The root of sand dock was dried, powdered, and sprinkled in burns. The inner bark of the elderberry was stewed and mixed with fat as a salve. Onions were bruised with salt and laid on fresh burns to draw out the heat and prevent blistering, a treatment that still is applied in the West by both Indians and white inhabitants.

The inevitable yarrow plant was ground and mixed with water before its application. The powdered roots of yerba mansa made an excellent poultice. In New Mexico, and, I have been told, in Arizona, a strong tea made from the leaves of the creosote bush was and is mixed with badger oil and formed into an ointment for burns.

In an 1813 publication entitled *The Indian Doctor's Dispensatory,* the Indian use of pine bark was recommended. This was boiled, the soft part stripped out and beaten to a poultice. Moistened in its own liquor, it was applied to burns and scalds. The book's author, one "Fr. Smith," assured that the "new skin will come quickly without a scar."

If one needed herb was unavailable, another would be at hand. Pink sand verbena was mashed into a poultice for burns, or, similarly, ripe wild mustard seeds. The dried bark of mountain mahogany was made into a paste or powder. Clematis seed, mashed and moistened for severe burns, is still in use today. The poisonous iris seed proved its worth as a paste for burns and mashed young juniper twigs were available for a poultice, the same being true of the pulp of the curlydock root.

Farther to the south, the Maya treated their burns with egg yolk and lime juice and the Aztecs made an unguent of thistle juice and honey, with egg yolk as a binder. In England, more limited in its choice of herbs, Parkinson in 1629 made only one recommendation in this category: purslane for "blasting by lightening, or planets or for burning by Gunpowder or other wise."

C

Cabbage, Wild

See Prince's Plume.

Cactus

There are those who see in the prickly pear only an annoying thorn-spiked desert growth. There are those who gush over it as "decorative" and "exotic" and plant it near, but not too near, the primroses. And there are those who recognize the great values that lie within those spine-studded green discs, virtues assiduously hidden from the intrusive eyes of the ignorant.

To the Indians the prickly pear was one of nature's great gifts. They used the thorns for needles and the like. When there was no water, they drank the thirst-quenching liquid. But, above all, they saw in the common ugly-appearing cactus a plant to be cherished for its properties of healing.

The stems were peeled and the mucilaginous juice bound on wounds as a dressing. In more serious cases, pulpy poultices were applied to the festering wounds of man or horse. The lobes were and are viewed as most helpful in cases of rheumatic inflammation. A decoction was much favored as a diuretic though a white doctor who tried it in 1892 commented that it "renders the urine a bloody tinge. . . . The taste is acid and cool." In cases of mumps, the spines were removed from the big green pancakes and roasted; these were then bound below the chin and on the side of the neck to reduce the swelling. It is reported that this practice is continued today among the New Mexico Indians.

Indefatigable investigator into Indian herbal usages, C. S. Rafiniesque, recommended in 1892 the split joints of the prickly pear as a good emollient for acute rheumatism and these joints, when baked, for recent wounds, chronic ulcers, and gout.

Calcareous Affections

The Indians called them hard swellings, Rousseau called them calcareous affections. Both Rousseau and the Indians found it helped to eat plenty of wild strawberries.

Calendula

The medical use of the "Marygold" has been recorded since the earliest days of writing and from their earliest times the Indians recorded it by word of mouth. The aromatic content of the calendula was widely recognized, the leaves and flowers being steeped in boiling water. Fresh leaves or, in winter, the dried flowers were mixed with buffalo fat to provide a highly valuable salve.

Callous

For callouses elder tree ointment was used.

Camas

Camas were mashed and formed into a poultice for a dozen ailments and, in case of crisis, were given as a carefully measured emetic.

Cancer

During the last months of his illness, the late Secretary of State John Foster Dulles received more than six hundred letters suggesting the use of fifty-seven different plants. The National Cancer Institute published an analysis of these in a May 1960 report. This points out that a number of the remedies were folk therapies dating back to Egypt, Greece, and Rome which now have received scientific approval. The search for plants to be screened for cancer is currently the largest drug-plant project of the United States Department of Agriculture. In this, the folklore clues are assiduously pursued.

The Indians, of course, did not recognize cancer as such. But follow-ups are being made on hosts of the herbs they used for stomach pain and the like. Thus, a decoction of autumn crocus eased acute stomach spasms and was widely used by the Indians. Dioscorides, physician with Nero's army, likewise recommended it. Today, an alkaloid from this plant is used to treat chronic granulocytic leukemia.

Mistletoe, recommended by Plinius the Elder, was investigated by the Roswell Park Memorial Institute of Buffalo. It had been used by countless generations of Indians who could not have known that the pressed juice of the *Viscum album* species was to be found to yield the most active material that caused more than 50 percent of the tumor inhibitions in mice.

The May apple, applied for untold centuries by the Indians to their sores and warts, after experiments of recent years is now the basis for treatment by some cancer specialists for certain skin growths. The extract podophyllin was the result of a five-year investigation by scientist Hartwell of the use of this plant by the Penobscot Indians. For years, it had been in disrepute as a quack remedy.

There is the melon and the cucumber and the periwinkle whose leaves yield vinblastine proved valuable in Hodgkin's disease. These are known but the field is still practically untouched.

The Indians tried every herb at hand and found at least amelioratives. For all we know, they may have found cures for some types of cancer in their early stages. Thus, sorrel was thought to be effective in some instances, and the newcomers to America, likewise groping, tested this and found it good. Thus, in 1813, it was recorded that "cancers have been cured by common snails." The settlers' adaptation of the Indian procedure was to "dissolve them in salt in pewter plate set on coals. . . . Apply steam and ointment via tent."

More than forty years later, in 1858, the Indian Medical Institute of Boston claimed that by its herbal cures, "hundreds and thousands of men and women are now rejoicing in health who were supposed to be beyond the reach of medical aid from any of the other systems of medicine known to man," a statement reminiscent of the claims of the itinerant so-called Indian medicine men.

But this type of phoney claim was not characteristic of the researcher Indian any more than it is of the researcher of today. Though more than fourteen thousand plant extracts have been tested in institutions throughout the country since 1960, we know that the field is still almost unopened. Perhaps, though he treated the symptoms rather than the cause, the Indian's pharmacopoeia may yet be found to contain some of the secrets for the cure for cancer.

Carminative

To dispel flatulence, expel gas from the bowels, and so on, the Indians drank tea made from mint leaves, pennyroyal, fennel, sweet flag, and others. Their favored remedy was a decoction of yarrow. But elsewhere this fell into disuse, an English comment in 1892 pointing out that tansy (yarrow) had been used since the Middle Ages but now is "almost entirely laic among country folk."

Carrot

The wild carrot seed, when ground, produced a diuretic and remedy for colic. The roots made an excellent poultice.

Cascara

This age-old Indian remedy grows on the sides and at the base of the Rocky Mountains. The early Spanish settlers learned from the Indians of its superlative medicinal properties and named it *cascara sagrada,* the "sacred bark." They watched as the Indians made their vertical cuts, peeled off the bark and dried it. They learned that the bark should be gathered in early spring or in the autumn and that it should be aged for at least a year before using. They learned of other herbs that the Indians combined with it as a purgative and found that, alone, it was an excellent cure for constipation. Like the

Indians, they drank a large mouthful at intervals during the day, the total dosage being about a modern cupful. The procedure was to cut small or to granulate about a modern teaspoon of the bark, pour over it the boiling water, and drink it cold. A small piece of bark soaked for twelve hours in cold water was used for a tonic.

Catarrh

Catarrh appears to have been prevalent and virtually omnipresent, for remedies are found among nearly all the western Indians. Kinnikinnick was widely accepted and was recommended to and by the settlers, as also was skunkcabbage. Similarly, lobelia had been tested successfully. But the choice of many tribes was a powder of dried and ground yellow nettles blown into the throat.

Catharsis and Cathartics

For a quick bowel movement: gentian or the dried roots or rhizomes of Indian hemp. The latter is still used. For cathartics: a small dosage of hemp or milkweed or the sap of sugar pine or gentian or cascara or the fruit of the snowberry. A large dose of snakeroot was recommended to the settlers as noted in 1817. The root bark of the Oregon grape was used in infusion and the leaf and buds of the elderberry, described by an incoming white as a "violent unsafe cathartic." The ripe berries of Solomon's-seal had to be taken in quantity. The inner bark of the elder was found valuable especially for intestinal obstructions. Rocky Mountain iris was used carefully since, though the Indians did not know the reason, it contains the poison irisin.

See also Laxatives; Purgatives.

CATNIP

Catnip

Catnip was drunk as we drink it, as a tea to quiet us for sleep, to help during fever, to soothe during colds. For the last, however, the Indians preferred to smoke the dried leaves, this being known as shinnecock. Catnip tea was drunk by the womenfolk for their periodic discomforts and headaches. A catnip poultice was deemed valuable for painful swellings. The tea was widely held as a cure for scarlet fever and smallpox.

Cattail

Eat the flowering heads of cattail to stop diarrhea. That would have been the Indians' advice and they do so now as their ancestors did for a thousand years.

Ceanothus

With medicinal properties that are serviceable today, ceanothus had a wide following among the Indians. It was used for failure to assimilate food properly. It was regarded as beneficial in serious inflammation of the liver and spleen. One species found widespread usage as a blood coagulant, and, since it stimulates the mucous membranes, for severe coughing.

Cedar, Red

Wherever cedar grew, the Indians boiled into a decoction its fruits and leaves and drank it for coughs. But there is one record of its value that seems to stand alone. In 1849–1850, there was an epidemic of Asiatic cholera among the Teton Dakotas. Many died and others panicked and fled. Famous Chief Red Cloud, then a young man, tried every treatment for his people that his desperate medicine men could contrive. It is attested that, the remedy that, proved successful was a decoction of cedar leaves. This was drunk and also was used to bathe the patient. It is said that this cedar tea and bath "provided the cure."

Chapping

See Arnica.

Cherries

There were many medicinal remedies made from

the cherry and its tree. An infusion of wild cherry bark, or a syrup from it, was a recommended sedative. Decoctions of the berries and inner bark were drunk for diarrhea. To relieve nervous tension, a decoction was used. It was accepted among most western Indians as a blood purifier and for stomach inflammation and for rheumatism. For tuberculosis, a tea was administered that had been brewed from the leaves or bark, or the dried roots were boiled. For coughs, a tea from the boiled root shavings or peeled bark was drunk. For head colds or headache, the pulverized bark was smoked. A decoction of the bark was drunk for indigestion. There were many cases of snow blindness and recently two tribes have reported that they still follow the precepts of their fathers in treating it by holding the head over a vessel of boiling cherry bark which thus is steamed into the eyes.

Since an absorbent powder from the pulverized dried bark had proved successful with sores, it was logical to use it also in cases of venereal disease. For syphilis, the cherry bark was combined with lobelia.

In due course and to a limited degree, England, allowing for regional eccentricities, caught up with the Indians. In Elizabethan times, dried cherries soaked in wine were advocated to "bind the belly" and "provoke the urine." Cherry gum was dissolved in wine for coughs and hoarseness and this "likewise . . . mendeth the color of the face and provoketh the appetite." The roots or "bark of the body" turned into "an excellent stimulant, black cherries being recommended" as, no doubt, they are today.

Chía

After the white man came, the seeds of the chía were used for gunshot wounds. Fresh chía leaves were chewed for stomach trouble, often a bit of salt being taken simultaneously, or, as in New Mexico today, a decoction of green or dried chía leaves was drunk. It is said that, following the practice of centuries, if something gets into the eye, a chía seed placed therein will quickly remove the offender.

Chickweed

The whole herb was a cooling demulcent. The fresh leaves were bruised and applied as a poultice which was changed several times a day. The bruised leaves combined with animal fat became an ointment for skin irritations.

Childbirth

The nomadic tribes, we are told, paid small attention to the pregnancies of their women. It was a normal process and was viewed as such. But the Indians settled in villages, the Pueblo Indians and others, permitted pregnant women no overexertion. Frequent warm baths were prescribed and their abdomens were kneaded regularly to keep the fetus in its proper position.

Among the majority of tribes, the Indian woman, about a month before her baby was due, began drinking a half cupful or so of tea made from boiled juniper twigs. She did this every morning until the labor pains began. If there had been the slightest indication of miscarriage or premature birth, she had drunk a decoction of black haw, described as a "powerful" counteractive influence.

When her time came, most tribes led the mother-to-be to the family lodge and left her only when the labor pains began. The Plains Indians, however, built an enclosure of bushes away from the village and near a stream. In most tribes, the woman was left alone with a woman relative or friend or two. But among the Brûlé Sioux and the Paiutes, family, friends, and distant relatives assembled to witness the event.

When labor pains began, there were relaxing or pain-easing drugs, notably trillium, the thick rootstocks of which were decocted in a practice so common that it was adopted by the settlers who called it birthroot.

Basil was used as a tea and fennel, lupin, elder,

mugwort, skeleton weed, and the mints, peppermint being preferred. To speed labor, a tea was administered of the blossoms or seed of Indian corn or a decoction of ground cedar berries, the inner bark of pine, or the inner bark of fir. Tobacco was frequently taken as snuff. If the season was propitious, a tea brewed from raspberry leaves was favored and, if available, watercress was eaten. Hops were applied to "relieve cramps and pains of the womb, when put on the belly in a sack in a hot condition."

There was a difference of opinion as to which was the more effective relaxant, lobelia or blueberry tea, the anti-spasmodic being made from the root and said "to be *the* great medicine that squaws use at the birth of their children."

The blueberry tea was welcomed by the white women, this description being given in 1813: "Take a handful of fresh or dry roots . . . take fresh tea every ten minutes until effective" and labor comes "easy and well." When "her time has come," delivery will be facilitated "so it is seldom slow." But the great benefit is the "state of safety and speedy and sure recovery that the mother experiences afterward."

Labor *was* relatively short with the Indians, about three hours, and was said to have been only a little painful. In many tribes, a squatting position was maintained, but among the Apaches, Navajo, Nez Percé, and Utes, the woman was recumbent. Among the Warm Springs and Brûlé Sioux, the woman stood until her delivery, made kneeling, then rose again to deliver the placenta. There were some fantastic deviations, of course. But these *were* deviations, not to be considered here.

If the labor was slow or protracted, the Dakotas placed a wide strap, the "squaw belt," around the patient. But the maternity belt was not confined to them, though it was they who seem to have dramatized it. Both practical and mythological, it was used throughout the western Indian world. It was usually put on at the start of labor and, by tightening it as the expulsion progressed, it was thought to hasten delivery. This is still done.

It is believed that the magic qualities of the belt will prevent or remove the chance of unfortunate accidents during the birth. Its potency lies in the selection of the skins which are chosen according to the location of the tribe. Since there is a fixed belief that some of the properties of the animal involved will become manifest, the antelope and mountain lion, the black-tail and the white-tail deer and the snake yield their skins for the maternity belt since they are the creatures that, claim the Indians, bring forth their young without delay or pain.

Meantime, while all this was going on and the tea was being drunk and the climax was approaching, the mother-to-be's friends were praying her prayer for her:

"We are your children. When you gave birth to your children, it caused you no trouble. Make me like yourself." Or, another prayer, "Help my babe soon to be born, to come as you did, quickly, easily and without pain."

The baby came and all was well; mortality was low among both mothers and babies. Then came the delivery of the placenta, for in no tribe was the cord cut until this had been done.

Sometimes the squaw belt was used again but it is noteworthy that all American Indians practiced Credé's method of expelling the placenta more than a century at least—more likely innumerable centuries—before he published his procedure.

When all was accomplished, the Sioux woman was up and at it again, unless there was hemorrhage in which case sumac fruits were boiled as a styptic wash. Kiowas, Comanches, and women of other tribes rested a few days and most wore abdominal binders. Pueblo women remained on their pallets for four days and then were ceremonially purified. Among the Yavapai of Arizona today the woman, four days after childbirth, is steamed with an infusion of the leaves and twigs of the creosote plant.

In other tribes, purification did not take place until

the termination of the menses and if there was any delay in that function a juniper decoction promoted its cessation. In New Mexico, there was a fumigation ceremony on the fourth day, with branches and leaves of juniper placed in a vessel on hot coals. Sage branches also were burned as a fumigant and the baskets and blankets used during the birth were held to the smoke.

Then came the rebuilding process. A decoction of yarrow plant was taken twice daily as a blood tonic. Or the whole sage plant was decocted and taken, as a tonic, three times a day for a week. This sage tea was in high favor throughout the Rocky Mountain area as was also piñon resin tea.

When the baby was born, puffballs ("prairie mushrooms") had been placed on the umbilicus or the pine powder or dried willow stems or, perhaps the most widely favored, balsam root ground to pulp and applied to the severed cord. During its first four days of life, the Cocopa baby was fed only a beverage made from the inner bark of the mesquite tree. But, otherwise, almost universally, the baby was nursed and there were the usual nursing problems.

For dry breasts, there was skeleton weed, the infusion favored by the Pawnees, or there was a decoction of the entire sandbur plant which was widely used to increase lactation. The Tewa women of New Mexico still favor a decoction of milkweed which they use also for sore breasts. But suppose the mother had no milk and there was none available. Then the "life of many an Indian baby has been saved by feeding it pine-nut [piñon] soup used as milk."

Chilblains

The best cure for chilblains, according to widespread and still current Indian practice, was to apply hot roast onion cut into small sections. This was repeated twice daily. They, of course, used the universal treatment of rubbing snow on the afflicted parts, but they preferred fat—rabbit fat smeared on thickly. After learning the lesson of chilblains for the careless, the victim thereafter wore a bit of fresh rabbit skin next to his feet.

When a baby had stomach ache, it was given fragments broken from dried cherry cakes. For skin irritations, especially on baby's bottom, a strong decoction of dried evening primrose was applied externally. Teething babies, as now in New Mexico, chewed on onion stems and leaves and, provably, the pain and swelling of the gums was thus dramatically reduced.

For baby's cough, juice roasted or fried out of onions and sweetened with honey was deemed "one of the best." For croup: flaxseed tea or, as is still used over the Indian world, a poultice of lightly fried onions.

In New Mexico, little ones who are frail and puny and do not grow properly are still helped (the word is used advisedly) by the use of tobacco. This is smoked or chewed and, demonstrably, aids digestion. According to L. S. M. Curtin of the Laboratory of Anthropology at Santa Fe, it "may have more positive effects against whatever is preventing growth."

Tobacco was used also for baby's colic, the smoke being blown under its clothes. Also for infant colic were yerba mansa roots boiled until a red liquid resulted. This was taken at intervals until it brought relief, the treatment being administered also to older children.

For childhood stomach aches, there were numerous remedies: tea of the boiled white pentstemon plant, a cold-water infusion of phlox which had been ground with carrot seed, and, of course, the universal catnip tea.

Fever was treated with small doses of those herbs used by adults, decocted wild licorice roots being held in high regard for fever in children. Laxatives generally were likewise modified doses of adult treatments, licorice root being in universal favor.

Lupine seeds destroy worms, for which there are so many suggested Indian remedies that they are listed in a separate category.

For serious influenza or blood-tinged diarrhea, what approximates a tablespoon of wild-rose tea was given. Elderberry tea was used in all manner of childhood diseases. Fennel seeds were chewed or decocted for cramps. A strong infusion of red clover suspended spasms in whooping cough. Powdered lichen, black, orange, or green, was applied to children's mouth sores. Breaking out on the head was washed with spearmint water.

The Indians herbal heritage, passed down through the centuries, was practical and proved medical practice. But in England, in matters relating to children, there was a smothering patina of cherished folklore. Thus, the famous fourteenth-century Albertus Magnus, describing the virtues of verbena, stated, "Infants bearing it shalbe very apte to learn and louing learnyng and they shalbe glad and jouous."

Children

If the juice of sarsaparilla is given a newborn child, it shall never be hurt by poison. That was an English superstition enunciated by Culpeper. We can find no parallel in the Indian pharmacopoeia. They used only what for centuries had been tested and proved for their children.

Chills

Chills were treated by the Indians much as by people elsewhere. The patient was wrapped in a blanket, hot stones were placed at his feet (or, in some groups, all around him), and hot drinks were administered—decocted leaves of the creosote bush or sweat-inducing teas made of steeped peppermint, pennyroyal, sage, or yarrow.

Chinaberry

The rootstalk was used when needed as a violent emetic and irritant. But, to the Indian, the primary value of the chinaberry was external and these uses continue to this day. The roots were ground, mixed with wild tobacco, and rubbed dry on rheumatic limbs. New Mexico Indians still advocate the chinaberry for neuralgia. For this "air in the head," the ground seeds are mixed with piñon pitch to form a plaster which is placed behind and in front of the ear.

Cholera

There was cholera and there were experimental medications by the medicine men. Cranesbill was found to be a powerful astringent. Horseradish from the high, dim woods was an attested cure as was a cedar-bark tea or one from steeped rushes. The last was adapted by Mormon settlers into Brigham tea but, for cholera, the Mormons and other early settlers preferred a tea made of cayenne pepper.

Cicely, Sweet

Highly approved and widely used even today, sweet cicely adapted itself to numerous uses. Pieces of the fresh root were inserted into the nostrils to relieve headache. The root was chewed for sore throat. Decocted, this was said to cure colds, influenza, and pulmonary disorders. Pulverized, it was smoked to clear a running nose. The decocted root drunk as a hot tea still is a standard remedy for fever, diarrhea, and for the regulating of menstrual irregularities.

The raw root reduced toothache pain and, heated after pulped, became a wet dressing for cuts and sores, swellings and snakebite. Externally, too, it was used, notably as an eyewash. It seems to have been proved as a lice killer among humans. On the introduction of fowl, it became a dip for chicken lice.

It had proved itself in treating skin rashes. Hence, when the time of crisis came, experiments were made in its use for the treatment of syphilis and gonorrhea. The root of sweet cicely became highly important in the fight against venereal disease, the dosage being a half cup a day over a long stretch of time.

Cinquefoil

Though the Indians did not know this to be the

reason, the tannic acid in cinquefoil made it a valuable astringent. It was a cooling agent in fevers and infections. The boiled roots were said to ease toothache if held in the mouth. The powdered bark was adapted to many ills, from nosebleed to kidney ulcers. A decoction of the bark was said to be excellent for inflamed eyes.

In England, the roots boiled in wine were an amelioration for gout. Among the first settlers in the Mormon area, Priddy Meeks put together a Rocky Mountain herbal in which the use of cinquefoil closely paralleled that of the Indians.

Circulation

To induce normal circulation, the Indians used the dried bark of the white elder.

Clematis, Wild

WILD CLEMATIS

Western Indians and early western settlers chewed wild clematis as a remedy for sore throats and colds, and as an anti-spasmodic for these ills and for fever. Mashed clematis leaves, brought to a boil, reduced swellings. There is known to be one Indian family today, and no doubt there are hundreds of others, who prepare poultices of mashed and moistened clematis seed and put them on severe burns. Inevitably, the leaves were dried, ground to powder, and applied as a healing agent or a solution of the boiled leaves was made as treatment for syphilitic sores.

Clover, Red

The red clover blossoms, drunk as a tea, cleansed the blood in springtime. A strong hot tea made from the blossoms or a strong syrup mixed with the juice of roasted onions and strained honey was excellent for coughs, hoarseness, and the like. Either as salve or extract, it was approved for sores and ulcers, "to whiche," it was noted in 1892, "it proves particularly soothing." The soothing qualities of a strong infusion of red clover also were tested and applauded by the white men as a means of suspending spasms in whooping cough.

Colds

From the list of remedies, it may be deduced that colds were as common among Indians living in the open as among current city dwellers.

There were flax and iris, gumplant and hyssop, and horehound, linden, milkweed, mullein, oak, white pine, skunkcabbage, slippery elm, bilberry, cinquefoil, bistort, wild cherry, columbine, honeysuckle, and spearmint. There were daisies, onions, poppies, roses, strawberries, vervain and nettles, parsnips, purslane, and sarsaparilla. The leaves of the everlastings in decoction were drunk for pulmonary and catarrhal infections. A decoction of mugwort leaves was recommended for bronchitis.

Parkinson commended the Indians' use of yampa seeds for colds. The Shoshone still use *wungobe*, a tea made from the needles and resinous blisters of balsam fir. They gave their children a tea from the blue gilia. Like the Shoshone, the Blackfeet made cough medicine from the upper third of the gumplant, especially the sticky buds. Elsewhere, in Nevada today, tea from the roots of wild buckwheat is a popular remedy, as is tea from the leaves of the creosote bush.

Most Rocky Mountain tribes regarded balsam tea as the big medicine for coughs, but if that was not available there was tea from the root of meadow rue or from the seed heads of horsemint. Everywhere, of course, there was elderberry syrup, sage tea, or a tea made from the roots of the wild rose. Basil (American dittany) was a remedy as was a decoction of the pounded and steeped roots of the snowberry.

Juice of pounded primrose roots was sniffed to clear the head or dried catnip leaves were smoked. Root tea of the mountain grape, bark tea of the mountain mahogany, and the decocted stems of the skunkbush helped produce perspiration.

Dried yarrow flowers swallowed with water were also favored for coughs as was ceanothus, especially for tonsilitis, since it is a stimulant to the mucous membranes. Dried elderberry flowers were used similarly. Milk of the wild lettuce was approved by the settlers as an allaying treatment for "coughs and irritability." For chronic coughs, skunkcabbage.

The whole yarrow plant was decocted and taken twice a day and yarrow root was chewed to break up a cold. "Hysop" was noted by the white newcomers to be good for all cases of influenza. Flowering pentstemon tops were boiled and drunk for colds in the chest.

Angelica was favored, a decoction of the roots being drunk for colds and chest congestion, its root dried and scraped, then soaked, for bronchitis. If rabbitbrush was available, the steeped leaves became a tea for colds. If ephedra was present, Mormon tea was made; if spirea, the stems were used. Both Paiutes and Shoshones still are partial to juniper tea made from the young terminal twigs and/or berries. Tea from boiled peeled chokecherry bark or root shavings was approved both for colds and for tuberculosis. Other plants had to be added to boiled piñon resin to make it palatable. This was done also to make the tea from the inner white bark of the antelope brush. An excellent cough syrup was produced from an exudate of Solomon's-seal. Pine cough syrup still is made and in New Mexico sweetened boiled ocote wood is used.

The Aztecs advised that "he who is troubled with a dripping nose" is to sniff *atochizti* which is pennyroyal and *tzompilihuitl* which, so far as we know, is unidentified but means "cold-in-the-head plant." Farther north, to relieve rhinitis, the Zuñi still crush the rays of fleabane blossoms between their fingers and insert them up their nose to induce sneezing. Other tribes used garlic, especially for bronchitis.

There were mustard plaster and mustard baths and baths medicated with a large amount of sage leaves to relieve the aches and pains of colds.

But most of all there was, and is, the onion. For influenza, the body was covered in ground onions and wrapped in blankets. All Indians everywhere used onions, raw or cooked, to cure colds. Onion gruel, too, was administered, a practice adopted by the settlers who elaborated: "A shawl around the shoulders, mutton tallow on the chest and a large bowl of onion gruel."

An excellent cough syrup was derived from strong red clover syrup mixed with the juice of roasted onions and strained honey. The accepted method of obtaining onion juice was to bake the onions—and squeeze. Onion poultices were always used, apparently by all the Indians, but if the chest congestion or bronchitis was deeply rooted, the poultice was covered with a sack of hot ashes, the treatment being repeated until it brought relief.

For head colds, smoking was the accepted cure. Juniper leaves were smoked or their fumes inhaled. The pulverized root of sweet cicely was smoked or the pulverized bark of the chokecherry or angelica roots, dried, finely shaved, and rolled into a leaf for smoking.

Perhaps in this day of adverse publicity one should refrain from mentioning it, but the fact remains that the most widespread and approved treatment for a cold was tobacco. For nose colds, it was inhaled. For chest and lung infections, a distilled water of tobacco leaves was used. Still favored for a chest cold, a few tobacco leaves were ground, mixed with a little fat, put on the chest, and covered with a piece of wool.

Thought for the day: The only time that Indian women smoked was to cure their colds, bronchitis, and lung infections.

Columbine

As useful as it is beautiful, the coming of the columbine in the spring was welcomed by the Indians.

COLUMBINE

They boiled the roots for a tea to stop diarrhea. Fresh roots were mashed and rubbed on aching joints. Roots and leaves were boiled together and doses of the decoction given several times daily for dizziness and biliousness. Tea from the boiled roots eased coughs and stomach ache. In England, it was said that columbine "seed in wine causeth speedy delivery of women." But it was not the wine; it was the seed that did the trick, as Indians had proved for generations. We find no evidence of success in their desperate attempt to halt or cure venereal disease with small doses of the whole decocted columbine plant.

Coneflower, Purple

A universally used herb among western Indians, the coneflower was held in high esteem as an antidote for the bites of snakes and other venemous creatures. Juice of the plant was applied to burns and the finely powdered root was placed on an aching tooth, the throbbing being then reduced. Today Spanish-Indian New Mexicans still attest that if there is painful rheumatism, or if there are pustules on the body, an armful of *yerba de la tusa* ("herb of the prairie dog") should be boiled in enough water for a bath, after which the patient should wrap himself in a blanket and go to bed. In the morning, the rheumatism will have eased or the angry spots disappeared.

Contagious Diseases

The Indians had no racial immunity to the white man's epidemics. They had no precedent for treating them and were so hopelessly terrified of them that, when the preliminary symptoms occurred in the 1875 outbreak of smallpox among the Dakotas, the victims committed suicide by jumping into the Mississippi River.

In time, the Indians had taught themselves these things:

Many tribes discovered that incineration of everything contacted by the diseased slowed the spread of the epidemic. The Apaches and Pima-Utes burned all the patient's property as soon as he died. The Navajo buried his property with his body and burned his lodge. Other tribes took similar measures.

It must be emphasized again that in this category, as in others, the Indians were treating the symptoms rather than the disease. Familiar febrifuges were employed and familiar sponge baths and cooling drinks. Especially favored was a tea made from the boiled leaves and young branches, with or without flowers, of the antelope brush. This was given in cases of measles, chicken pox, or smallpox. As attested by a medical man in 1817, the Indian use of wild tobacco was to "some degree" efficacious against the "contagions of epidemics."

Contraception

See Birth Control.

Convulsions and Cramps

The Indians used decocted mullein roots for convulsions just as Dioscorides had recommended to Nero's Roman world.

Corn

As long as there has been corn, corn has made a medicinal contribution. The Indians used dry corn in pneumonia and as a diaphoretic in other cases. Boiled cornflowers were taken twice daily for asthma. Boiled corn silk, with sweetening added, was commended as a diuretic. The Comanches and their kin took ground corn meal steeped in lye as an intestinal anti-spasmodic. Mush made from blue meal was applied hourly to bullet wounds. In the San Ildefonso pueblo, corn pollen still is prescribed for heart palpitation and the Maya still use their *maíz,* soaked in water, for blood in the urine. In many parts, black corn with a slight streaking of red is by associative signature deemed good for women during their menstrual periods.

CORN

Corn Smut

Chapetes, growing on corn stalks, are most prevalent in the upland valleys beneath the shadow of the great mountains. The black powder of the smut was mixed with water and spread on a compress for a sore throat. The Zuñi used the fungus as a parturient and as a remedy for post-parturient hemorrhage.

Cottonwood

In the spring the cottonwood flowers were steeped, strained, and the decoction taken as a blood purifier. The bark was burned and the ashes mixed with water and corn meal as a poultice for boils. The boiled leaves in decoction were administered for dropsy. The bark was used in decoction for tuberculosis. It was favored also as a splint for broken bones. But, most of all, the black cottonwood bark was considered an *unfailing cure* for syphilis.

Counterirritants

The Indians believed in the efficacy of counterirritants, the two most commonly used techniques being the scarification of the abdomen and applied powdered ragweed for acute nausea, and the striking of painfully aching parts with nettle branches.

Cow Parsnip

This sturdy, woolly herb with its big white flowers was easily located in the swamps and bogs of the mountain area. It was in constant demand. The Indians used the raw root, mashed and soaked, as a poultice for sore throat and, in infusion, as a gargle. Today, in some tribes, the ground root is placed on a leaf or paper and blown into a diphtheritic throat.

Two Indian tribes report that, as in all their yesterdays, pieces of raw cow parsnip root are put into cavities to stop toothache. Powdered root was rubbed on the gums where teeth had loosened. For rheumatic pains or for paralytic patients, baths of a solution were recommended. For heart tremors, the roots were ground, mixed with fat, and rubbed on the chest, or the powder was used alone. As alternative, the roots were boiled and the afflicted part bathed. Dried roots expelled gas.

The juice was used in ear infections as it was in Elizabethan England where, it was advised, "The juice of the flowers dropped in ears that run and are full of matter, cleanses and heals." No record has appeared that the Indians had experimented in a direction similar to that of Gerard who in 1597 advised, "If a phrenticke or melancholicke man's head by annointed with oile wherein the leaves and roots have been sodden, it helpeth him very much, and such as bee troubled with the sickness called the forgetfull evil."

Cowslips

Their principal use was as a soothing bath in cases of paralysis.

Creosote Bush

Many desert tribes below the big mountains or on their lower slopes regard the creosote bush as their cure-all. A strong tea was taken as a tonic. Mixed with badger oil, it became an ointment for burns. A sweetened decoction of the dry or green leaves was good for the kidneys. Internal chill was taken care of by a decoction of the leaves, this being used also for colds.

The leaf nodes of the creosote bush are swollen into small growths like warts and are highly resinous. The Indians steeped them all in water that was kept boiling and applied it to bruises and wounds. Indians and whites alike, out where the creosote is available, consider this a most effective treatment.

The Pima chewed and swallowed the creosote gum as an anti-dysenteric. The Maricopa took a weak solution of the bark for intestinal trouble. The Apache used the tops as a poultice for rheumatism. The Yavapai of Arizona steam a woman four days after childbirth with decocted leaves and twigs. Today, many Indians sprinkle the insides of their shoes with powdered creosote leaves to ward off rheumatism in their feet. It is considered a first-rate treatment for snakebite, tetanus, and sores. It was therefore logical to experiment with it in the treatment of venereal disease.

Croup

Two of the most effective remedies for croup are listed here for emphasis. Others will be found under children's diseases. One of the most widespread treatments, dating back through the centuries, was a poultice of lightly fried onions. And, in 1817, it was recorded that, following the Indian pattern, the use of snakeroot in croup was "introduced into notice by Dr. Archer of Maryland. He speaks with much confidence of its utility in that disease."

Cucumber, Wild

Cucumber was used by the Indians for the kidneys and also as a tonic. Its merits had in due course been discovered too in England where the elegant herbalist John Evelyn wrote in 1679 that cucumber was "the most approved Sallet . . . to sharpen the appetite and cool the liver."

Currants

Poultices from currant roots were used for a dozen purposes.

Cuts

Wash a cut with a decoction of mountain grape as the Indians did, or of steeped yarrow leaves which also disinfect, or with balsam root, raw or pulped and boiled into a fine healing agent. Or make a warm wet dressing of the pulped raw roots of sweet cicely. Or make a hot dressing of piñon resin or of the inner bark of wild-rose stems. Or apply a dry dressing of pounded raspberry stems or use the fresh pitch of the white fir or mashed angelica root or the dried bark of mountain mahogany, usually as a powder, sometimes as a paste.

Inescapably, there was tobacco. All western Indians chewed wild tobacco leaves and then applied them to cuts or small wounds. It was a large wound, an oversized cut, that was described by "Maister Nicot" who gave his name to the plant. Tobacco was growing in his garden. He had proved to his satisfaction a number of cures with it when, one day in 1559, came his masterpiece. One of his own cooks, "hauing almost cutte off his thombe with a great Chopping Knife, ran unto the said nicotiane and healed it."

See also Wounds.

D

Daisies

The uses of the daisy by the Indians correspond so closely with those developed later in England that we quote Gerard:

"The Daisies do mitigate all kinds of pains, but especially in the joints and gout, if they be stamped with new butter unsalted and applied to the pained place. . . . The juice of the leaves and roots snift up into the nostrills purgeth the head myghtily and helpeth the megrim. The same given to little dogs with milke, keepeth them from growing great.

"The leaves stamped take away bruises and swelling proceeding of some stroke, if they be stamped and laid theron; whereupon it was called in old time Bruisewort.

"The juice put into the eies clearest them and taketh away the watering of them.

"The decoction of the field Daisie (which is best for physicks use) made in water and drunk, is good against agues."

Dandelion

The large fleshy root, collected when the plant is flowering, is officinal. Among the Indians, it was viewed as "strong medicine." This root was made into spring bitters prescribed as a tonic, stomatic, and blood purifier as well as for yellow jaundice and liver and kidney complaints. These bitters or a fluid extract were widely used as a diuretic as they had been from ancient times elsewhere.

The young plant was known to possess some slight narcotic properties, and a handful of flowers boiled until the water was yellow, then cooled overnight, became a before-breakfast dosage for heart trouble, effective, it was claimed, if taken daily for a month.

All these remedies still are used and there have developed numerous embellishments such as that at San Ildefonso where ground dandelion leaves are reduced to a paste with water and spread over fractures, fresh leaves being bound over all.

At Santa Clara, the pulverized leaves are mixed with dough and put on bad bruises. Distilled dandelion-root water was used as a wash in pestilential fevers or for sores. Experiments, apparently unsatisfactory, were made in this treatment for venereal disease.

Deliriants and Depressants

The dried leaves and/or flowering tops of jimson weed were used to lower the vital activity.

Diagnosis

If the Indians' family did not recognize what was the matter, the advice of the medicine man was sought. If *he* did not recognize the symptoms, the patient was given a diagnostic tea from the leaves of mountain balm.

Diaphoretics

Diaphoretics causing a perspirable discharge by the skin were used freely by all the western Indians who believed in the value of sweating in almost all illnesses. In their *materia medica,* lobelia ranked high to induce perspiration, with balsamroot a close runner-up. Goldenrod was widely approved or sage tea or an infusion of everlasting leaves steeped in cold water. Yarrow was used similarly and pennyroyal tea or a warm infusion made from dried elderberry flowers.

Small doses of snakeroot were approved and, when available, arborvitae was infused. A decoction of very little hemlock flowers and twigs was approved in 1840 by a white doctor who found it good. Yarrow he called a "good sudorifick." Ash tree bark also was good and by 1892 the white community had reduced this to the formula of an ounce of bark to a quart of water.

Diarrhea

The universal problem of diarrhea was treated by all-Indian accepted remedies, the choice of herb depending on the season and the location of the tribe. To control diarrhea, there were mullein and nettles, raspberry root and cinquefoil, wormwood and peppermint tea. There were boiled columbine roots and those of the dwarf purple aster. There was the boiled black seed of the poppy or a decoction of the dried bark of the white alder or of the inner bark and berries of the chokecherry. The action of the chokecherry was viewed as that of an intestinal tonic, the system then checking the diarrhea.

Thistle roots were drunk in decoction, as were rose roots, sage, and the ripe or dried fruits of nightshade. Wild geranium was valued and an infusion of the bark and roots of sumac. An infusion of the dried elderberry flowers was much used and a tea from the root of the white pond lily.

Dried strawberry leaves were somewhat astringent, a decoction of the yarrow plant much more potent. The flowering heads of cattail were eaten. A tincture of the whole rock-rose plant was deemed efficacious. The boiled ripe seed of curlydock was eaten or, burned in a pan, was mixed with resin. Lichen was scraped from the rocks, cooled overnight, and the cold water solution taken internally. Charcoal was mixed with herbs and used because the Indians had discovered that charcoal lined the intestinal walls, soothed, and healed.

Piñon resin was taken in the form of pills or was boiled into a tea. Sweet cicely tea or a cold infusion of mashed phloxroot proved helpful.

For bloody diarrhea, there was rabbitbrush tea or, still used by the Shoshone, gromwell root either boiled or soaked. Willow roots were burned to charcoal, powdered, and added to other mashed roots. For the most severe cases, some Indians still claim to be cured "*poco* soon" by putting a bunch of fresh marigold leaves into a cup, filling it with boiling water, steeping a quarter hour, straining, and drinking hot.

The settlers followed some of these procedures or made such adaptations as "Indian chocolate," a decoction of water avens made palatable with sugar and milk. But the advice of Utah's old-timer, Charles Musig, was strictly individualistic. Claimed he: There is nothing better for diarrhea than a twice-a-day half-spoonful of gunpowder

Digestives

Though the more complicated ones fall into the category of stomach disorders, there were two used everywhere by the Indians for simple indigestion: well-flavored mint tea or plenty of onion soup.

Diphtheria

During an epidemic of diphtheria some years ago, the Indians found that, of their many treatments for sore throat, that which best relieved the congestion and eased the pain, was a poultice of prince's plume. The ground root of the cow parsnip was, and among many tribes still is, used either as a gargle or an application placed on a leaf and blown into the throat. Those who came in contact with the patient wore a string of garlic around their neck to prevent contagion. This is still a common practice.

Diuretics

In lands of heat and dust or biting winter winds

and always of chronic water shortages, diuretics, to increase the flow of urine, were in constant use, and the list of the herbs utilized for this purpose is long.

Kinnikinnick, found on almost every mountainside, was the outstanding remedy. The Indians did not know the reason for its efficacy, that it contains two glucosides, arbutin and ericolin, and tannic and gallic acids, because of which the plant is used today in American drug establishments.

Wild onion probably ranked next followed by burdock, a proved and widespread remedy.

Other diuretics: ground carrot seed; ephedra boiled in water and cooled overnight; amole; yerba mansa tea; hops boiled and eaten like asparagus and approved in England in 1699; corn silk boiled in sweetened water, the *piloncillo* of the Southwest tribes; snakeroot, St. Johnswort, or juniper berries distilled in oil and noted as effective by the settlers in 1817; an infusion of elderberries or a cold infusion of elder flowers; a decoction of fleabane; a tea from green parsley root drunk freely and called by the settlers a "splendid cooling diuretic."

Prickly pear was a "pleasant diuretic . . . though it renders the urine a blòody tinge." This comment, made in 1892, added that the "taste was acid and cool." In 1880, the Indian use of raspberry leaves was approved by the white community as an "excellent diuretic." More than a half century earlier, in 1817, an experimenting physician applauded the Indian use of wild iris for its "stimulating properties. I know of no purpose for which it is better calculated than as a diuretic."

Found helpful when there was a scant supply of urine, but not so popular, were mullein, bearberry, strawberries, thistle, and horsetail. In choosing among them, Priddy Meeks, that indefatigable investigator of his new western environment, commended the Indian use of elder, milkweed, mullein, parsley, and sumac. In the ancient Codex pharmacopoeiae, the diuretic plants followed the Indian pattern, recommending the use of dried roots of asparagus, fennel, holly, and parsley.

So, at last, we come to the inevitable tobacco. Tobacco was used as a diuretic throughout the western Indian world and by the mountain men and explorers they instructed and by the settlers who learned from them. To relieve the burning and irritation, local applications were made of tobacco leaves and an early nineteenth-century physician tested and found to his satisfaction that tobacco "in doses so small as not to offend the stomach" had a "very good effect."

Dock

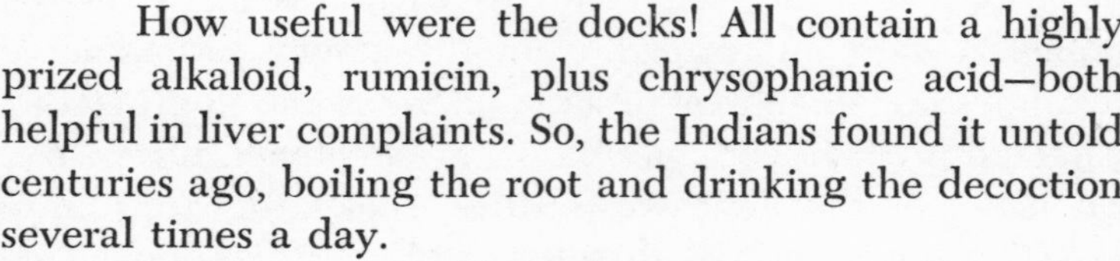

How useful were the docks! All contain a highly prized alkaloid, rumicin, plus chrysophanic acid—both helpful in liver complaints. So, the Indians found it untold centuries ago, boiling the root and drinking the decoction several times a day.

DOCK

The root was administered as laxative and tonic, the roots being cut and steeped in boiling water, and this was used, too, as a stomach remedy. For bruises, burns, and swellings, the pulped root was applied as a poultice. The leaves were crushed and bound on boils to draw out the suppuration. Burdock roots and seed were used for cleansing cuts and wounds, a practice recorded in 1840 as approved by the settlers. For skin spots and freckles, there was the distilled water of the roots and herbs. The washed roots were applied to swellings and sores and the boiled root was taken internally for venereal disease.

It was used as a palliative for rheumatic pains, a practice approved by Priddy Meeks, among the first Mormon settlers, who recommended dock especially for inflammatory rheumatism. Other white arrivals developed their own variants. Discovering the Indian success with dock as a tonic, they stated that it "promotes general action for the entire system," their prescription being to take the green root of the yellow dock, cut it up fine, put it in a bottle, and fill this with "good whisky. Let it stand 14 days." Dose: a tablespoon two or three times a day.

Dioscorides, an army doctor under Nero, had recommended that the roots be eaten to mitigate the pain of scorpion sting. In the France of Louis XIV, *herbe aux teigneux* leaves were used even as the Indians then were using them for certain kinds of sores.

Dog, Mad

For the bite of a mad dog, burdock, spearmint, nettle, or onion.

Dogbane

See Hemp.

Dogwood

Cornine, the active principle of dogwood, was the reason why the Indians used the plant for malarial fevers. For other fevers, a decoction was made of the leaves and bark, the bark being favored also for colds. It was a mild tonic and, with fat added, a very useful ointment. In 1840, a physician approved the Indian prescription of the flowers and root bark decocted into a "powerful astringent."

Down

We find no record of the use of the down of the cotton thistle but since the Indians had proved that they kept pace with or were a step or two ahead of the ancients, they quite probably had paralleled the advice of Pliny and Dioscorides and had drunk a decoction of the strained down for a severe crick in the neck.

Dropsy

Dropsy was quite common among the Indians who combated it with their favored diuretics. Vervain, milkweed, and decocted cottonwood leaves were prescribed and a tea made of hemp root boiled a long time with wild-rose berries. The decocted root of snakeroot was applauded also by the white settlers.

Drowning

For person nearly or seemingly drowned, many recoveries were made through the use of tobacco smoke injected as an enema.

Drunkenness

See Alcoholism.

Dysentery

Dysentery was all too common among the western Indians as attested by the widespread use of their proved remedies. Wild geranium, of course, was the strongest astringent, a green broth being made from the geranium powder. A decoction of oak bark was a substitute or a solution of avens ("Indian chocolate") or the bruised leaves of yerba mansa or its powdered root in water.

For bleeding dysentery ("bloody flux"), the yerba mansa decoction was most highly recommended or wild barley roots boiled into a yellow solution. This was considered a preventive, as was the chewed and swallowed gum of the creosote bush, still used by the Pima as an anti-dysenteric.

These proved Indian remedies were fairly simple of acquisition, preparation, and application. Not so in England, according to the ancient and famous tenth-century *Leech Book of Bald*. The only way to avoid the debilitating difficulty of dysentery was to undertake an elaborate maneuver. "Against dysentery," it stated, "a bramble of which both ends are in the ground earth, take the newer root, delve it up, cut up nine chips with the left hand and sing three times the Miserere Mei Deus and nine times the Pater Noster. Then take mugwort and everlasting, boil these three worts and the chips in milk till they get red, then let the man sip at night fasting a pound dish full. . . . Let him rest himself soft and wrap himself up warm."

E

Ear Disorders

It appears that there was much and widespread ear infection. To combat it, the Indians used a score of remedies: mullein flower oil, yarrow leaves, flowers, and pounded roots. Elderberry juice boiled in honey was dropped in the ears to help the pain. There was the essential oil of sarsaparilla and a decoction of parsley. Hops were mixed with coarse salt and heated. A few leaves of rue were warmed with a few drops of oil. Thistle roots were mashed and the juice warmed as was the pulped root of yellow prince's plume, or a little boiled iris root. Pulped material of Solomon's-seal was forced through a cloth into the ear.

As always, there was the onion, hot and roasted and held against the ear, or roasted until it cracked, the insides taken out and put on a compress covering the ear. Garlic and salt on wool was and is put into the ear.

There was tobacco, of course, the smoke blown into the ear which then was covered with a woollen cloth. Doctor William Thomas Corlett recalled that when he was a small boy, the relief from earache lay in a green limb from an ash tree. One end was put in the fire. As the sap was driven to the fire end of the stick by the heat, it was allowed to fall drop by drop into the patient's upturned ear.

For a serious ear infection, a practicing medicine woman dropped a strong solution of white pentstemon into the offending ear three times daily. For a broken eardrum, the widely used remedy consisted of puffballs, powdered and placed in the ear on a bit of soft material.

There was nothing better for deafness, claimed the Indians, than crushed leaves of rue made into a cigarette, the smoke then blown into the ear. A jingle about it handed down by the southwestern Indians sings, in translation, "To cure the ear there is nothing like rue. And as a way to say no, there is nothing like silence."

Eczema

Powdered green pentstemon leaves were made into a poultice for eczema, or, more favored, a poultice of wild tobacco leaves. A more elaborate treatment was to "get a wildcat, extract his fat, mix it with ground rose petals and apply as an ointment several times a day."

See also Skin Irritations.

The Elder and the Elderberry

ELDER

There are so many and various medicinal uses for the elder and its berry that it is almost certain that some have been missed here. These, however, are the ones recorded over the whole range of the Rocky Mountain Indian world.

For promoting the action of bowels and kidneys, a decoction of the bark or of the berries was routine dosage. In 1840, white Americans approved the flowers as a good laxative. The Indians kept right on preparing flowers and/or berries in a cold infusion as both laxative and diuretic.

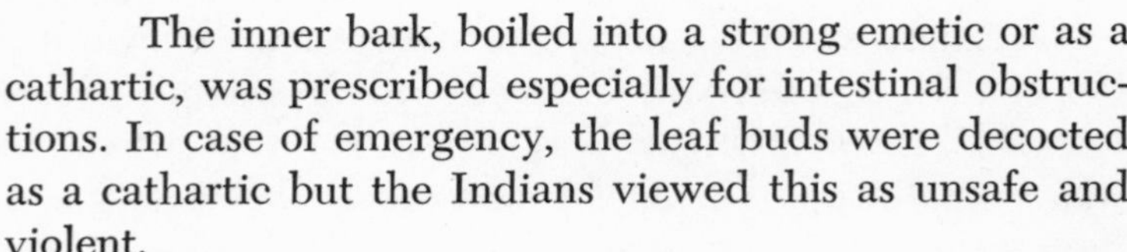

The inner bark, boiled into a strong emetic or as a cathartic, was prescribed especially for intestinal obstructions. In case of emergency, the leaf buds were decocted as a cathartic but the Indians viewed this as unsafe and violent.

The first shoots and young leaves and stalks were used for dropsy and stomach disorders. Decocted berries were taken for colds and fever, or the dried flowers which were made into a sudorific and were used similarly for bronchitis and throat inflammations. Modified, this was used for children. Boiling water, poured over the dry flowers and brewed, was added to the bath of a paralytic to bring relief, and an infusion of the dried flowers was given for diarrhea. Pith and leaves were used as a cataplasm for hemorrhoids.

As a purge, the *voyageurs* learned to use the elder, their *rob de sauce,* but only in small doses. Otherwise, there was narcotic reaction. This, the Indians had taught themselves, making a warm infusion of the flowers as a stimulant.

To relieve a headache due to a cold, bathe the head in an elder decoction, and for a dozen miseries, drink elderberry tea, or use a decoction of the root for snakebite or the bite of mad dogs. Women drank hot elder bark tea for cramps in the womb during menstruation. (In Elizabethan England, this was recommended to "bring down their courses.")

Elderberry syrup, then as now, was drunk for coughs and the juice was boiled with honey and dropped into an infected ear to ease the pain.

The "manifold properties of the elder tree," included external as well as internal medication and so universally was it used that in 1876 England, "in some remoted country places, it supplies the place of both the surgeon and the druggist, it furnishes ointment, infusions, decoctions for all ailments, cuts or bruises. Every part of it serves some useful purpose. . . . Its narcotic scent makes it unwholesome to sleep under its shade."

For cuts and wounds, the Indians used a decoction of flowers and leaves or an ointment for large wounds. This was recommended to the white population which, in 1892, added its own elaboration. The decoction was prescribed in treating wounds "to prevent the deletorious consequences from flies."

It was used for snakebite but not with the surrounding superstitions of the England of the Middle Ages —and doubtless later:

"For rent by snake, take this wort and ere thou carve it off, hold it in thine hand and say thrice nine times, '*Omnes malas bestias canto,*' that is to say, 'Enchant and overcome all evil with deer; then carve it off with a very sharp knife.'" This complicated advice can be found in the *Herbarium of Apuleius,* preserved in the British Museum.

Resuming the recording of Indian practicality: The juice of green elder leaves was dropped into inflamed eyes. This was held to be of value also if snuffed up the nostrils to purge the "tunicles of the brain." For burns, a stew was made of the inner bark in fat. To cleanse the skin and for sunburn, the distilled water of the flowers was cooling and beneficial.

So, at last, to the record of failure. In distillation, the elder had proved itself as a wash for sores, especially for "old sores and ulcers." The berries had proved of value in gout and rheumatism. Adaptation of these prescriptions were tried for syphilis. No record has been found of any success.

Emetics

Indians took emetics as frequently and casually as white folk take a laxative. More so, in fact. Many tribes "took an emetic daily as a matter of common decency."

Rocky Mountain iris was found to be a violent emetic and cathartic. Why? It contains irisin. Gentian still is used, as is saltbush. Throughout the area, teas were drunk from the roots of balsamroot, death camas, wild cherry, celery, and false hellebore. When available, antelope brush tea produced the desired effect. The Shoshones made lobelia tea, and vervain tea was held to be "one of the best."

The inner bark of the elder was a "strong" emetic. Hellebore was used and wild cabbage. Many tribes still use large quantities of warm water to empty the stomach several times.

Powdered violet root was "superior to all others," but, since this was frequently unobtainable, there was always tobacco. A decoction of powdered tobacco leaves was the Indian stand-by as an emetic.

Emollient

There were a dozen or more emollients but the almost universal Indian remedy to render body solids soft was hollyhock.

Ephedra

Ephedra was prescribed for headache, fever, and

skin eruptions. The white explorers adopted its use as a blood purifier and for kidney and bladder difficulties and *anglos* of the Southwest have followed the Indian usage of taking quantities of tea for arthritic and rheumatic pain.

These uses for kidneys, colds, blood purification, and for difficult or delayed menstruation are still part of the Indian pharmacopoeia, the Mescaleros also decocting the entire plant as an anti-blenorrhagic and the Pimas, a decoction of the stem as an anti-luetic. As diuretic and anti-pyretic, the Indians decocted the whole plant, cooled it overnight, and took it as long as needed in amounts approximating a glassful a day. This is still done but today the principal value of what was to become known as Mormon tea lies in its importance in the treatment of venereal disease.

Ephedra is an ancient medicinal plant. It was used by the father of Chinese medicine, Shen Mung, about the year 2698 B.C. Coughs, colds, headache, and fevers thus were treated with dried roots and stems in decoction. These are still sold in Chinese stores under the name *Ma-Huang*. It is the Chinese variety from which the alkaloid ephedrine is extracted. The American variety contains a high percentage of tannin. Botanists in the United States suspect, but so far as we know without proof as yet, that the knowledge of the "peculair properties" of the ephedras by Indian-Americans may be due to Mexican trade contacts, notably in the Southwest, with the Chinese long before the United States came into being.

Erysipelas

For this dread disease, especially in the face, the boiled plant of scarlet gilia was drained, mashed into plaster, and applied. Burdock and bean pods were accepted remedies. So also were hops, the efficacy of the last being tested and accepted by the settlers as early as 1817.

Everlastings

The modest and common everlasting was used by the Indians for dysentery. The leaves brought relief in catarrhal infection and their decoction was recognized for bruises and for pulmonary and similar disorders. It was deemed valuable for intestinal infections. The leaves steeped in cold water (infused) increased perspiration and the bruised plant helped to heal wounds.

Expectorants

The Indians believed in expectorants, the favorite in the Rocky Mountain area even now being an extract of gumwood. Lobelia was an acceptable runner-up, with skunkcabbage a close third.

Eyes

Because of dust, sun glare, and snow blindness, the Rocky Mountain Indians suffered from pervasive and perpetual difficulties with their eyes. How widespread the problem was is demonstrated by the fact that we have scores of recommended remedies from all parts of the western Indian world.

As an eyewash there were steeped flax roots or the whole flax plant mashed and soaked in cold water or the leaves boiled and steeped.

There was steeped alumroot or turtle back (toothache plant), or tea of boiled pink plumes' roots. Still used by the Blackfeet, these are highly regarded by numerous tribes. There was a decoction of wintergreen, one of blackberry root, and one from the boiled inner bark of the serviceberry. There were boiled yarrow leaves in solution and a decoction of balsamroot or of the inner bark of mountain mahogany. Scarlet gilia was dropped into the eyes in hot or cold decoction. Sandwort roots were decocted and spurge tea was made from the whole plant. A liquid from the mashed roots of Solomon's-seal was favored.

A tea from the leaves of the little sage bush was

adopted from the Indians and became the standard eyewash of the United States Army in the West. Fennel-seed oil was sometimes available. Many tribes today parallel the Paiute preferences—the decocted leaves of the pink and white pentstemon or of the Stansbury phlox, or antelope brush or the root decoction of sweet cicely or a solution of boiled pentstemon.

For inflammation due to dust, vaqueros still carry acacia seeds and put four in each eye on retiring. For opthalmia: tincture of the whole plant of the rock rose. For trachoma: balsamroot boiled and the oil skimmed off and used, one drop in each eye said to be efficacious. To dilate the eyes, jimson weed was the accepted mydriatic. For granulated eyelids: locoweed roots in decoction.

A chía seed placed in the eye is said to remove quickly an offending particle therein. A flax-seed poultice was recommended for sties. Parkinson endorsed the Indian use of a poultice of yampa seeds as strengthening to the eyes. For watering eyes: cucumber or blue flag. Willow decoction drops eased burning eyes. Reasonable, as willow contains the basic ingredients of aspirin.

For snow blindness, the green inner bark of the serviceberry boiled with sweetening was said to be effective, or a solution of the boiled roots and inner bark. Tribes report today that they still use cottonwood bark steamed into the eyes with the head under cover.

When an Indian could not stand the strong sunlight, the medicine man used an infusion of alder bark which he blew or rubbed into the open eyes. A variant was to chew the bark and blow the juice into the eyes. Both practices still are used.

In their often gray climate, the English did not have such problems and their recommendations regarding the care of the eyes are few, coming from the "Olden tyme." Perhaps that is just as well for here is one that has come down to us: "Daisy juice put in the eies cleaneth them and taketh away the watering of them." That may be well and good but we are dubious about this one: A "well-known cure for stye in the eye" is to stroke it with a black cat's tail.

Fainting

If an Indian fainted, pennyroyal was held to his nostrils. For anyone prone to fainting, the advice was to eat plenty of strawberries. For the weak or convalescent, apt to faint from debility, red rosewater was given in broth or stewed with the meat.

Fatigue

When overweary, the Indian drank broth or mugwort tea or a cooling herbal drink. That seems sensible and familiar to us all. But should we take the advice of the ancient herbalist Pliny, who wrote that "if a traveller bind some of the herb [mugwort] about him, he will feel no weariness on his journey"?

The Aztecs breathed flower fragrances for fatigue and recommended the scent of "trees and flowers for the lassitude of those administering the government and those holding public office."

Fear

Like all mankind, the Indians sometimes experienced fear. To combat this, they preferred sweet flag. The majority drank this in decoction but the Teton Dakotas chewed its rootstock to a paste which they rubbed on their faces to avert excitement or fear in the presence of the enemy.

Worthy of note was this coincidence: Betony was recommended as a "remedy for fear and faintheartedness" in the Badianus manuscript which was a church-supervised Aztec herbal of 1552. In sixteenth-century England, the *Grete Herbal* prescribed "Betony for them that be fearful."

Feet

The care of the feet was of prime importance to a nomadic people. Alder leaves were "put under bare feet galled with traveling," just as in *moyen âge* England. Mashed wild geranium root was spread on swollen feet or a solution of boiled pentstemon plants, this being used also for swollen legs and veins. If these herbs were not at hand, there were others also acceptable. Ground nettles were recommended, especially if the feet had become numb. The leaves and flowers of bedstraw or, used today, St. Johnswort, were boiled and the medicated water so made ready for soaking aching feet, as, similarly, was that from yerba mansa leaves.

The Aztecs answered the problem of swollen feet by making a plaster of pine resin and Sahagun recorded that they favored the pulverized grain of datura. This was a common practice also farther north.

For injuries to the feet, the Aztecs made a plaster of witch hazel, resin, and sage mixed with cochineal wax. But both they and the Rocky Mountain tribes had many remedies for this contingency. Iris was used and the approved treatment was a large leaf of horseradish, wild cabbage, mullein, or burdock, the hard fibers cut out before boiling or, better, placed on a hot stone to soften. The leaf then was folded and fastened with a bandage to the hollow of the foot. This was done to relieve pain and the same procedure was followed with pounded hot garlic.

The Indian treatment for frostbite was described in his diary by nineteenth-century pioneer Howard Egan. He told of how a companion had been so badly frostbitten that hope had been given up of saving one of his feet. The "Indians buried him to the waist in snow and soon he was better."

For athlete's foot, the Paiute still use a wet dressing of wild tobacco leaves mixed with a mountain grass.

Ferns

Some ferns have active principles valuable in medicine, notably the male fern long used by the Indians to expel tapeworm. A decoction was used for rickets in children. By associated signature, most ferns were supposed to cause sterility.

Fever

From the number of remedies, it may be deduced that fever was prevalent among all the western Indians. Without, of course, knowing about the bacterial causes, they recognized the syndrome of hot dry skin, aching, and so on. They understood the prognostic meaning of cessation from thirst, abatement of discomfort, and a cooler, moister skin. Their formula from one condition to the other was rest, a purgative, sweating, and a liquid diet.

First choice of an antipyretic was a willow decoction as, centuries later, white Americans were to use aspirin and its derivatives. A decoction of quaking aspen was next in line or dried elderberry infusion, burdock, sage tea, mugwort leaves decocted, the steeped white bark of clematis, ephedra tea or that of rabbitbrush or juniper. Aconite was used carefully. The Spanish mission fathers adopted the Indian procedure of an infusion of chía leaves.

Yarrow tea, the dried leaves placed in a bowl and boiling water poured over them, was of course the tansy tea of England and the colonies which, with sage tea, was advised since they "form good fever drinks for the poor." Boiled piñon resin was drunk, and the root of sweet cicely in decoction. This is a standard fever drink today especially among the Paiutes.

A cold infusion of sumac berries became a household remedy with the settlers. When it was available, dogwood was chosen above others, the Indians recognizing the results without knowing that its value lay in its cinchona content. But equally valued though harder to find than the willow was the wintergreen, the leaves being made into a tea to break fever. The reason lay in the parallelism that wintergreen, like the willow, contains the basic substances of aspirin.

There were adaptations according to need. A tea of bride's bouquet slowed down a child's heartbeats during fever. The Paiutes used a basket to steep wormwood leaves and put it next to the baby's skin to reduce fever. Emily Stewart Barnes, who crossed the plains in 1851 as a Mormon "plural wife," had eight children. Her remedy for fever was wild sage tea. "Drink plenty of it and bathe in it but be careful. It can be powerful."

Sliced onions were placed on the soles of the feet to reduce fever and were kept there until they turned black at which point they were renewed. This treatment is still widely practiced as is that of mashed wild onion soaked in water, strained, and drunk.

A remedy still used was that of mixing four o'clock's powdered leaves with grease and rubbing the whole body with it. Vaseline now supplants the fat. Another external application was ground dried horsemint (oregano) rubbed over the body. This is common practice especially among the Indians of New Mexico. The settlers adapted the pennyroyal formula by mashing the whole plant with vinegar and salt and spreading it over the entire body. A solution of boiled yarrow leaves was widespread as a wash and, of course, there was garlic.

Captain Bonneville, immortalized by Washington Irving, told of how he treated fever. He came on an Indian girl with an alarmingly high temperature. He gave her a vapor bath and a dose of gunpowder dissolved in water. She went to sleep and next morning, being much better, was given colt's head broth.

A widespread Indian belief was that the powdered leaves or bark of kinnikinnick, either alone or in combination with willow, was said to protect from malarial fevers.

The Aztec approach to fever was a charming combination of grace and the application of "modern" methods. Because of its psychic effect, the fragrance of flowers was wafted over the fever patient and fragrant juices were mixed with other ingredients and used as a body lotion.

Fiddleneck

See Scorpion Weed.

Fir

Fir was recognized for its healing properties in treating wounds. It was a recommended diuretic. A boiled fir-bark infusion was given to tubercular patients. Fresh pitch was applied to cuts and boils. Warmed pitch was made into a poultice for sores and gonorrhea.

The Indians used the young treetops in decoction as the excellent anti-scorbutic it was. In this connection, it has been pointed out that on the plantations of the early white Americans there was no scurvy. The reason given was that, in default of hops, fir tops were used to make the beer.

Fits

The technique commonly used as likely to help those afflicted with fits was to have them take up the practice of smoking tobacco.

Flag

Most of the Rocky Mountain tribes used the rhizomes for stomach upsets. Pulverized and mixed with water and sometimes saliva, the resultant infusion was dropped into infected ears. It was equally adapted to medicate watering eyes. Made into a paste, it was applied to bruises and sores. For severe stomach cramp, the root was regarded as "powerful medicine" and a milder infusion of the root was given to children for flatulence. The root was chewed to relieve dyspepsia.

The calamus (flag) was widely regarded as a stirring physic for the entire system, this being approved by a nineteenth-century white scientist who wrote that "sweet flag roots possess carminative and tonic properties" with "a taste which is not unpleasant."

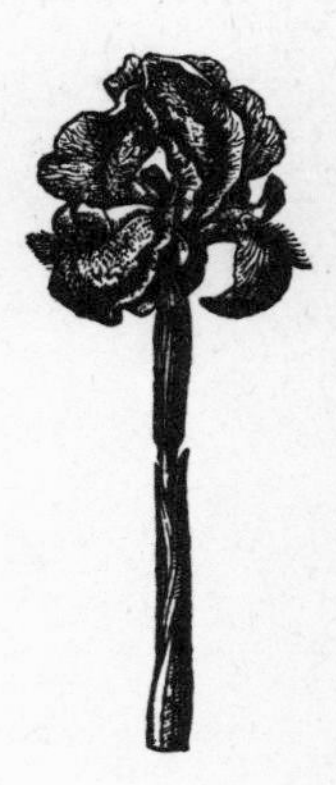
YELLOW FLAG

Approbation in lighter vein emanated from L. I. Lighthouse, self-entitled "Great Indian Medicine Man," who in 1883 contributed this thought:

"Oh! Iris Versicolor, King David needed you
To heal his sores and cleanse his blood,
The Bible says its true.
In David's psalms called thirty-eight
You'll find it so at any rate."

Flax

Flax-of-the-hundred-uses, appreciated throughout the western Indian world, contributed these remedies:

The seed was used for coughs and colds and lung congestions. The steeped stems were drunk for stomach disorders. It was a laxative, and a dose of flax seed relieved earache.

Poultices were applied, especially for goiter or to reduce swelling or for burns and scalds. To make these, flax leaves or stems and leaves were crushed. The same applied to sties. Another school of thought recommended the poultice of ground seed, it being contended that the oily matter served to retain heat and to moisten, as well as make a soothingly soft application. The poultice relieved the pain of gout, inflammation, and rheumatism.

The settlers elaborated the poultice by forming powdered seed, corn meal, and water into a paste applied to wounds or the swellings of mumps.

The Paiutes and Shoshones use flax still for sore eyes, there being several methods of treatment. The whole plant is mashed and soaked in cold water or it is boiled. Or the tops are soaked in cold water or the leaves are boiled or steeped. Or the roots are boiled into a decoction.

Flax was extensively favored by the Indian world in gall bladder cases, fresh leaves being crushed to form the poultice. At Austin, Nevada, the Shoshones call the flax the "gall medicine."

The Roman physician Dioscorides covered, to a limited degree, the same area, stating that flax "mortified all inflammations inward and outwardly by being sod [boiled] with honey and oil and a little water." Flax mixed with honey and pepper "doeth also provoke venery."

Fleabane

The daisy called fleabane was used in decoction as a diuretic, a tonic, stimulant, and astringent. It was a palliative for sore throat, hemorrhoids, rheumatism and gonorrhea. In fact, wrote Doctor Charles F. Millspaugh in 1892, it was so "well known to the aborigines" that there are "too many uses to list."

Twenty years before, in 1872, Doctor Gilbert Smith, having experimented with this Indian remedy, introduced the decocted fleabane into the New York Almshouse for treatment of "the type of diarrhea often prevailing there." He "met with very great success."

Fleas

Did the Indians have fleas? There does not appear to be a record of them. But if they did, it is almost certain that they had anticipated the recommendation in Nicholas Culpeper's *Complete Herbal* of 1653, which found high favor in the North American colonies:

"Alder leaves gathered while the morning dew is on them and brought into a chamber troubled with fleas, will gather them thereunto" and "rid the chamber."

Four O'clocks

The "maravill," "marvel of Peru," later, the "mirabilia"—by whatever name, the four o'clock was a practical marvel to the western Indians. For sore throat, the dry roots were scraped, the powder placed on a leaf and blown into the throat. Fever was reduced by mixing the powdered leaves with fat and rubbing the whole body. If a cold was caught at its beginning, it could be headed off with a hot bath to which had been added a decoction of the roots. The same principle was applied for dropsy, the dry roots being ground and rubbed on the body. An infusion of dry roots brought down swellings and an ointment of crushed roots and fat was applied in cases of mumps.

The Zuñi women gathered the roots, pounded them to powder, and administered them in warm or cold water to anyone who had overeaten. If it was really a crisis, the Indian woman put the concoction also into her mouth, ejected it into her hands, and rubbed it over the sufferer's abdomen. This is still done.

A pinch of the powdered root slipped into the young men's drinking water at meal time was used to "prevent the over-indulgence of their appetites."

Foxglove

Foxglove was imported from England and grew sparingly in the United States. It could grow on the rocky hillsides of the western Indians. But I found no trace of its use, so we may deduce that it was not there or the Indian would have found out how to use the dried leaves of its second-year growth which contain digitalin, invaluable and unique as a heart stimulant.

FOXGLOVE

Fractures

See Bones, Broken.

Fragrance of Flowers

It was the Aztecs who used the therapy of flower fragrance for its psychic effect in fevers, fatigue, and melancholia ("black blood"). To obtain the most perfume possible, the flowers were gathered in the morning "before the winds arise." The fragrance was considered a mild stimulant so, as well as breathing the loveliness from the air, fragrant juices were mixed with other herbs as a body lotion.

Frostbite

See Feet.

Fumigants

The Indians were wholly "modern" in their recognition of the need for fumigants. Balsamroot was burned after illness, or juniper branches and/or berries. But most widely approved was sage, the smoke from its burning branches penetrating the area where the patient had been. After childbirth, the blankets and baskets that had been used were held to the smoke.

Fungus

Among the varied uses of the fungi, the Indians applied a salve for scalp infection and ringworm. They used the "conk" of the conifers for sunburn blisters and wind damage. As a soothing ointment, it was a household remedy.

G

Gall Bladder

The Indians used watercress to dissolve gallstones. Most approved for the gall bladder seems to have been a poultice of crushed flax leaves, preferably fresh. There appears to be no evidence that they used mugwort in this context, though Dioscorides asserted that it dissolved gallstones.

Garlic

In Pliny's *Natural History*, garlic is listed as medication for sixty-one disorders. From bronchitis to snakebite, the Indians did likewise. Here is a selection of their most important uses.

For snakebite: a poultice of mashed plant changed three times a day. For headache or biliousness: chew a half dozen cloves several times daily or make a syrup from the expressed juice. For stomach flatulence: roasted garlic swallowed with cold water. For earache: garlic and salt on wool, put into the ear.

Recognized as a vermifuge (the destruction of worms), garlic was proved also as superlative for scurvy and advantageous in asthma attacks or bronchitis. As a preventive against diphtheria, garlic was strung on a string and worn around the neck by those in contact with the patient. When a dog was suspected of rabies, garlic was put in its food.

Universal among western Indians, garlic has been universal in the western world for its medicinal qualities since the earliest times. The great naturalist Pliny maintained that garlic cured consumption. Celsius recommended it for fever and Hippocrates stated that "garlic is hot, laxative and diuretic but it is bad for the eyes." Dioscorides expounded at length on garlic for the cure of worms. Mohammed advised that "in cases of stings and bites by poisonous animal, garlic acts as a theriac [sic]. Applied to the spot bitten by viper or sting of scorpion, it produces successful effects."

Millin, in his 1792 *Elements d'histoire naturelle*, asserted that "garlic is a preventive against the plague," and long before this, sixteenth-century Dr. Felix Bremond, in his *Dictionnaire de la table*, pointed out that certain doctors "condemned themselves to constant carrying of several cloves of garlic in their pockets to protect themselves and their patients from the bad air and epidemic diseases." It was left to Bernadin de Saint-Pierre somewhat later to put his French finger on the heart of the matter. "Garlic," he asserted, "the smell of which is so dreaded by our little mistresses, is perhaps the most powerful remedy in existence against the vapours and nervous maladies to which they are subject."

Gentian

The tonic qualities of gentian were considered by the Indians to be its most valued asset. The bitter clear fluid was both tonic and tonic stomatic either in decoction or tincture. This ancient and proved remedy for debility was said to promote the digestion and improve the appetite. The dosage was an approximate two ounces of tops and roots over which was poured an approximate pint and a half of water, boiling hard. Approving this Indian technique, the settlers could not resist their characteristic American (white) furbish. Add to the above a half pint of brandy. Dose: one to three tablespoons every half hour.

Geranium, Wild

In 1892, it was noted by a medical authority that the "American aborigines value the root . . . as an astringent in looseness of the bowels and exhaustive discharges of all kinds. . . . Geranium root is official in the U.S. Pharmacopoeia."

Already in 1817 it had been described as "one of the most powerful astringents we possess." But centuries before this the Indians had discovered the strong astringent qualities of wild geranium, a fact attested by its widespread use among western tribes of varying degrees of development.

It found its place wherever an astringent was called for: diarrhea, second-stage dysentery, hemorrhages, indolent ulcers, and so on. Within the gnarled rootstock was fleshy fiber for sores and wounds. A poultice was particularly advocated for swollen feet. Drunk as a tea, the "cranesbill" was probably the most widely used medium for birth control, the user being said to be safe from pregnancy for a year.

Gilia

The blue gilia was made into a tea for children's colds. But most Shoshones, among others, regard the scarlet gilia as the "big cure." Paiutes concur, calling it "bad disease medicine." Both tribes still use tea from the root or the whole plant as a physic and emetic. Boiled, the gilia was made into an eyewash. Another method was to use the plant boiled, drained, and mashed into plaster for erysipelas, especially of the face. Poultices of the raw crushed plant were healing for head and back sores of horses.

Pathetically, since it is in no way due to the sins of their fathers, the Shoshones are ashamed to admit to venereal diseases and claim that the decocted gilia is to "clean the blood."

It is not they alone who treat the dread disease with gilia. The majority of western Indians consider it efficacious for both gonorrhea and syphilis. The whole plant is boiled and the solution taken internally or applied as a wash. The dosage is a half cupful three times a day or, depending on the damage, a half cupful once a day. There is unanimity that this treatment takes a very long time.

Goatweed

See St. Johnswort.

Goiter

Particularly well recommended for goiter was a poultice of crushed flax leaves and/or stems. Four o'clocks were deemed helpful and, along with the flax leaves, reduced the swelling.

Goldenrod

A moderate stimulant, an aromatic, it was used by the Indians as such but also as a pleasant-tasting disguise for the frequently repellent taste of other herbs. Goldenrod also contained medicinal properties for bowel weakness and, notably, when the bladder had lost its muscular energy. For both of these problems, a decoction of the leaves was deemed strengthening. Parenthetically, this treatment was favored, too, by a long procession of Irish herbalists.

An infusion of the leaves and tops served to ease Indian colic pains. The mashed fresh plant, bound with fat, became a poultice for sore throat. Today, the Zuñi chew goldenrod for the same purpose.

Gonorrhea

See Venereal Disease.

Gooseberries

Gooseberries were plentiful in the Rocky Mountain area and the Indians found them useful in their medicine bags. They cooked them into porridge for fever and for "hot burning ague." Pregnant women liked gooseberries in any form and this affinity for the cooling gooseberry seems to go far back in Europe as well as in the Indian America. Pier Andrae Mattiol commented on it in 1544.

Gourd

Experiments, apparently unsuccessful, were made with the buffalo gourd as a treatment for venereal disease.

Gout

Since the accepted image of gout, stemming from the English tradition, is that of a beefy, overweight milord with his bandaged foot on a hassock, it may come as a surprise that the Indians, too, were subject to this discomfort. The Britisher wore his gout as a badge, denoting rich food and overindulgence in alcoholic drinks. The Indians did not have alcoholic beverages and they overindulged in food only when they acquired an ample amount after a period of semi-starvation. But from the number and spread of the herbs used to combat it, it is clear that gout was a malady widespread and of long standing.

The efficacy of hops had been known for generations. Rafinesque found that the Indians got relief from the baked split joints of prickly pear. An infusion of elder berries was widely used. Decoctions of mullein were drunk and of pennyroyal, plantain, poppy, purslane, skunkcabbage, burdock, flax seed, daisies, saffron, and yarrow.

In 1876, a white physician in the East wrote that he had tried the Indian remedy of asparagus. He could attest that "slight cases were cured in a few days by feeding on this delicious esculent." Culpeper already had recommended the young buds or branches of asparagus boiled in white wine, or cinquefoil likewise prepared. The Roman physician Dioscorides had prescribed three ounces of mullein leaves, or, preferably, flowers, which the Indians used when available. One of the greatest students of herbs, Linnaeus, extolled the efficacy of wild strawberries in preventing paroxysms of gout in his own case.

Grapes

The Oregon or holly grape, so familiar to Indians of the Rocky Mountain area, contains a now-officinal drug, berberis. Without knowing about that, the Indians knew that the remedial effects were those of a bitter tonic. It was a diuretic and laxative. In 1840, the white community approved the long-time Indian use of the grape for jaundice. The roots and bark were decocted for ulcers and sores and used for tuberculosis, heartburn, and rheumatism.

Root tea eased coughs. The boiled leaves were drunk for anemia and the same decoction was taken before the morning and evening meal to bring on menstruation. Indians chewed the leaves for acne and the Navajo still use a decoction of leaves and branches which they insist is a cure for rheumatism. Cuts and bruises were washed with a root decoction and wounds or other deep cuts treated with a liquid from the chewed root. Tea from the roots was prescribed as an anti-syphilitic. But results are debatable. By associative signature, the New Mexican Indians today call the hollyleaf grape the *sangre de Cristo,* the "Blood of Christ."

Greasewood

Astringent, relief bringer for stomach trouble and rheumatism, greasewood was easily procured and widely used.

Gromwell

There has been a revival of interest in gromwell, which for centuries has served the western Indian as food and medicine. Its medicinal functions included that still favored among the Shoshone: for diarrhea. The root was boiled or soaked in water, and still is held in high esteem in cases of "bloody flux." As for innumerable generations, an infusion of the roots in cold water and taken daily as a drink for six months is held to ensure sterility for life.

Gumplant

This mountainside grindelia was almost a one-plant pharmacy. The Indians boiled the roots for liver complaints and used the dried and powdered roots for spring purging. It was administered for whooping cough or asthmatic spasms, for pneumonia and bronchial infections and nasal congestion. For these ailments the top leaves and flowering tops, often dried, were cut small or granulated. Boiling water was added and an approximate cupful was drunk during the day. This fluid extract served also as stomach tonic and anti-spasmodic, sedative and expectorant, all of which was learned and used by the early Jesuits.

The above uses are currently officinal, as is that of the fluid extract painted on skin surfaces to bring relief from poison ivy and oak.

A small amount of the decoction was held in the mouth, but not swallowed, for toothache, or its fuzz was put into the offending cavity. Small doses of the whole decocted plant were taken daily during measles or smallpox, or dried buds were used similarly. A decoction of the leaves was applied to running sores, its cotton-like fuzz being sometimes substituted. In England, as among the western Indians, a decoction of the whole plant still is "famous for wounds," and still is used for ulcers.

Externally, a solution is still applied to burns and blisters. Warm poultices of gum decoction covered wounds and swellings. Hot baths with gumplant extract added were viewed as "particularly beneficial" in paralysis. For rheumatism, the fresh green plant was crushed into a poultice to relieve the aching, or dried sprigs were sprinkled generously with hot water, piled on heated stones, wrapped in a cloth, and held to the painful part. It is the steam that brings relief.

Since it was successful in treating running sores, it was adapted to treatment for venereal disease. The dose was one half to two cups of decocted gumplant taken each each day over a long period of time.

In spite of the Indians' scientific approach, superstitions occasionally popped up. Thus, in New Mexico today, the possible potency of magical numbers is assumed, as shown in this prescription for kidney disorders: Boil three times, three buds or flowers of gumplant in three pints of water until only a pint remains. Take a small glassful three times a day.

H

Hay Fever

Dried balsamroot in decoction was drunk by the Indians for hay fever or, if available, sneezeweed blossoms were crushed and inhaled.

Headache

The Indians did not treat the cause of headache as

such. A headache was a headache whether from fever or sun glare. It was a painful affliction so widespread that the remedies make a long list in their extensive pharmacopoeia.

They peeled and ground balsam root, boiled, cooled, and drank it. Wild basil was popular, and sumac or sage tea. The Omaha drank a decoction of ground cherry root. Tea was made from daisies, plantain, purslane, peppermint, cow parsnip, spearmint, valerian, violets, ivy, lily-of-the-valley, or poppy. A small amount of the decoction of yarrow leaves was taken. Catnip tea was recommended for the "nervous headaches of females."

External treatments were common. The aromatic twigs of pennyroyal were rubbed on the hands and inhaled. Mugwort, inserted in one nostril, was deemed a cure. Powdered white gilia water was applied. Cudweed was smoked like tobacco. The feet were bathed in warm lye water.

If the headache was due to too much blood, the patient was put on a vegetable diet. Sliced wild potatoes, bound on the forehead, still are believed to "draw out the pain." Dried horsemint (oregano) plant was ground to powder as it is today at San Ildefonso, for instance, and rubbed on the head. Dried yellow bull nettle was ground to powder and blown from a leaf into the throat.

A poultice of mashed yarrow leaves became a compress or the crushed gumplant was smelled. Crushed or boiled sage leaves were made into a compress. Sometimes a bag of hop blossoms was placed under the pillow. A boiled solution of milkweed became a wash or a lotion was made of boiled cottonwood roots. The Aztecs ate onions in honey and advised against sitting in the sun, working, or entering the baths. A snakeskin around the head was widely believed to cure headache.

The Indians placed the tobacco leaf on the head to relieve migraine; in New Mexico, piñon pitch is still mixed with native tobacco and salt and spread on a cloth to be laid on the temples. In England, much the same was done, and Nicolas Monardes in 1569 added orange oil from the Spanish vineyards to the warm tobacco leaves.

Heart

The Indians do not seem to have learned about the circulatory system but they had proved the herbs that acted as heart stimulants, sedatives, and so on. The distilled water of strawberries was taken as a cordial for a panting heart. Corn pollen, still used, reduced heart palpitation. A decoction of mountain mahogany was drunk for heart disorders as were dandelion flowers boiled in water to a "very yellow" liquid. A cup of this was taken before breakfast every morning for a month.

Recommended were an infusion of holly, rose, or wild lily-of-the-valley. The Pawnee favor bush morning-glory. Aconite from monkshood had been used for countless generations as a heart sedative and still is used among the western Indians today.

The dried rhizomes and roots of common dogbane were decocted into a heart stimulant as was a root tea from cactus for what in Nevada the Indians call "pain in the heart." For heart tremors, cow parsnip roots were ground, mixed with fat and rubbed over the heart, as was the powder alone, or the afflicted area was bathed with a liquid from the boiled roots.

For the pain that was spiritual rather than physical, the essence of roses was bathed on the forehead, just as in 1525 England the patient was advised that "drye roses put to ye nose to smell, do cọforte the brain and the heart."

Hellebore, False

Hellebore was used as a narcotic, vesicant, and caustic. The Indians prescribed it to lower the blood pressure and slow the heartbeat, recognizing the successful results but unaware that these came from the presence of several of the alkaloids.

Since the plant is a native of the United States, it could have been only the Indians who taught the uses of hellebore to the early settlers. Roots must be gathered in the autumn and kept in well-sealed containers since otherwise they lose their potency.

In 1663, the Indians were observed curing their wounds with white hellebore and easing their toothaches with it. The green rhizomes and roots were powdered and taken as snuff to reduce hernia. The patient took a good pinch of the snuff and during the ensuing violent sneezing a companion pushed back the rupture with his fist.

Hellebore was used in cases of abnormal menses. As elsewhere from the time of the ancients, it was used for mental derangements. It was said to cure nymphomania.

The "aborigines," it was stated by one of the early white Americans, were fully apprized of its effects as "a strong stimulant, followed by sedative reaction." They were, indeed. It was an Indian custom to elect a young chief by ordeal. "A favored form of torture, was to give the candidates repeatedly, a portion of hellebore root. He whose stomach made the most vigorous resistance or recovered soonest from the effects, was considered the best physically equipped to command."

Hearing of which, Doctor John Ware made similar tests in 1817 in the Boston almshouse "to ascertain the action of the stomach." He testified that there was some vomiting.

Hemlock

Hemlock oil was a favorite liniment for rheumatism. Its bark was a powerful astringent. Its pitch, exciting the skin vessels, cooled and reduced sunburn. Quills of ground hemlock were dosages for colds. Twigs and very small leaves were a recommended sudorific. A salve from the gum became a strengthening plaster as approved by the incoming whites in 1840. Bark, powdered or in solid extract, contained narcotic properties. For swellings, a poultice of hemlock leaves and flax seed were cooked in boiling water.

Hemorrhage

The Indians used hot juniper tea or that of wild geranium as an astringent. A decoction of dried white alder bark was given to check the bleeding or nettle juice alone or boiled into a syrup. If the patient was spitting blood, the most effective dose was considered a decoction of oak bark.

Hemorrhoids

Purslane or a decoction of fleabane was advocated as a palliative. Or a cataplasm of the leaves and pith of elderberry.

See also Piles.

Hemp (Dogbane)

The tall plant, with its delicate bell flowers and its glorious golden coloring in the fall, was endowed also with a milky sap and a root much employed as a diuretic, diasphoretic, tonic, and cathartic. The reason: It contains apocynin, tannin, and other valuable medical materials.

Henbane

Anodyne, anti-spasmodic, the Indians used the tincture for nervous tension, the pains of rheumatism and gout, heat of the urine, or sleeplessness. The leaves were smoked like tobacco for toothache or tic. It was considered especially valuable as a sedative for children and for treating delirium, meningitis, and other brain ills. In World War II, scientists discovered in henbane a source of atropine.

HENBANE

Hernia

The violent treatment for hernia is described under hellebore. The tried-and-true remedy was a tobacco enema, "extensively employed," especially in cases of strangulated hernia.

Hiccoughs

Juniper tea for hiccoughs, or tea of valerian root. The Indians still use both.

Hoarhound

The woolly plant of the waste places with its minute white flowers was used, even as now, as a syrup for coughs. A warm infusion stimulated the urine flow and promoted perspiration. A cold infusion was drunk as a tonic or, in large doses, as a purgative.

HOLLYHOCK

Hollyhock

The hidden virtues of the tall gay hollyhock were these: It was used as a diuretic, emollient and demulcent, being considered especially valuable for sore throats. The raw roots, crushed, were a dressing for swellings or the whole plant was so used. This dressing is still applied to wire cuts on horses. The boiled dried roots acted as a contraceptive or as a treatment for venereal disease.

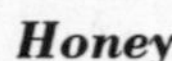

Honey

Any medicine that needed sweetening or its bitter taste disguised was prepared with honey, thus paralleling the advice of the *Grete Herbal* of 1525–26 that "hony ought to be put in medicyne and may be kept yeares."

As a medication it had numerous uses, including those for arthritis, epilepsy, and snakebite. There is no indication that the Indians had discovered one recommendation of Dioscorides, that flax "mixed with honey and pepper . . . provoketh venery." Perhaps the Indians did not need it.

Honeysuckle

The leaves were decocted for sore throats and coughs. The oil was recommended for nerve spasms.

Hops

Hop tea was and is used throughout the Rocky

Mountain Indian world to settle the stomach, to obtain sleep, or to quiet the craving for strong drink. It was an antiseptic in bowel complaints, and the powdered roots quieted kidney and bladder irritability. It was narcotic, anodyne, diuretic.

Tea from the whole plant was a blood remedy, and a remedy for "worm complaints," the latter approved by the white community in 1840, which also registered that its "influence [was] considerable on the nervous system." To "depurate the Blood and open Obstructions," boil and eat hops cold like asparagus. It was noted with obvious approval in 1817 that a tincture of hops had a "strengthening effect on the viscera."

Externally, for paralysis or dropsy, two handfuls of hop flowers in a tub of boiling water was said to produce good results. The patient was bathed and put to bed, where he sweated profusely. A solution of the roots was used to bathe the painful parts in rheumatism and neuralgia. The efficacy of this treatment administered to and by the Indians had been tested by white doctors in 1817.

To quiet the nerves and soothe to sleep, a pillow was stuffed with hops and this is still used for a patient delirious with fever. A bag of hop blossoms was put under the pillow for headache. A bread poultice mixed with a strong infusion of hops was applied for ulcers. As already noted, its use as an abortive and the part it played in childbirth were universally recognized by western Indian tribes.

Horsemint

Horsemint is spread from Alberta to Arizona and south. It grows in the valleys, on the prairies, and on mountainsides up to about 7,000 feet. This makes it readily available and the Indians have used it for generations as they continue to use it today. Unknown to them, the reason for its potency lies in its volatile oils which harbor the drug antiseptic thymol.

For a cough the whole herb was boiled and drunk as needed. For fever, the dried plant was ground to powder and rubbed over the body. For sore throat, a small deerskin bag of the powdered oregano was hung around the neck while the patient sipped a decoction of the leaves.

Our researches have revealed an unexpected fact: Everyone wants horsemint but the horse.

Horseradish

The Indians considered horseradish a cure for cholera and ague, a stimulant and a tonic valued for digestive upsets and to excite kidney secretions.

Horsetail (Joint Grass)

The boiled plant, decocted, provided kidney medicine. Sores on the mouth were treated with its ashes. Many Indian tribes still use the dried and ground leaves on running sores.

Houndstongue

It appears that the Indians used houndstongue, that softly haired biennial, for a number of purposes. It was a sedative in coughs. It slowed diarrhea and was made into a poultice for bruises and burns. An incoming white American cautioned that the evidence proved houndstongue to be a "rather dangerous herb taken internally and should be avoided."

Huckleberry

The Indians used dried huckleberry leaves for gravel, a treatment approved by white physicians in 1840.

Hydrophobia

Wild tobacco was the western Indian's palliative for hydrophobia and, in 1817, this treatment received not only approbation but the dosage: "Dr. Fowler believed that the most effectual mode of administering it was by pills of one grain each."

Hypnosis

Used extensively among the Indians of Mexico and in degrees that lessened in northward progression was *toloche,* jimson weed (datura), to induce the hypnotic state and unravel the mysteries. The Rocky Mountain tribes recognized, however, and used in the treatment of certain neurological ills, the herb hops, which in decoction produced hypnotic action.

Hypochondria

Yes. The western Indians, too, had that regrettable social loss, the hypochondriac. As will already have been noted, they treated such abnormalities as medical problems and concentrated on finding appropriate medicinal cures. For this unpleasant nervous state, the western Indian's universal remedy was wild lettuce, with a dandelion decoction as second choice.

There seems to be no record that they used the old English stand-by of sprigs of borage (houndstongue) "in wine of known vertue to revive the hypochondriac and chere the hard student."

Hysteria

Rocky Mountain Indian tribes were most successful in treating hysteria. By trial and error they had stumbled onto sound psychotherapeutic methods at the back of their vital ceremonial in treating this neurological disorder. But behind this, let it be emphasized, was the intuitive understanding and highly developed shrewdness on the part of their medicine men. As an anti-hysteric, a warm infusion of valerian or yarrow was given.

I

Impetigo Plant

See Sores, Swellings, Ulcers.

Influenza

There were almost as many dosages for influenza as there were herbal drugs. The favorites were hot juniper tea, sage tea from fresh or dried leaves, angelica-root tea regarded as a specific, or a decoction of dried balsamroot or a bitter tea of sweet cicely. Sage plants were burned over fire and the fumes inhaled. After the influenza attack, the Indians took as a tonic a decoction of blue lobelia.

See also Colds.

Insects

See Bites and Stings, Mosquitoes.

Insomnia

See Sleep.

Intoxicants

See Narcotics and Intoxicants.

Iris (Blue Flag)

The virtues of the iris as medicine are listed under flag, which the Indians considered one of their most priceless medicinal plants. In *American Medical Botany,* published in 1817, Doctor Jacob Bigelow of Harvard pointed out that its "stimulating properties . . . render it capable of exciting many of the secretions as well as excretions."

BLUE FLAG

Irritants

Of the dozen or so irritants used by western tribes, pasqueflower was considered the best. The secret of its success lies in its volatile oil.

Itch

For the itch: pennyroyal, or an external wash of antelope brush, or a wash of yarrow tea, or a poultice of powdered pentstemon, or an ointment of mountain laurel leaves stewed in fat.

Ivy

Ivy was a loyal stand-by, adapted to numerous conditions. It was a tonic, astringent, and expectorant. An infusion was used for colds and stomach upsets. The customary dosage was this: Twigs and bark were cut up very small, to which a cup of water was added for steeping. It was drunk cold, a mouthful at a time. The fresh juice was sniffed up the nose to relieve nasal congestion and headache.

CLIMBING IVY

Jack-in-the-pulpit

The root of this picturesque plant was pounded into a poultice for sore eyes. The white men learned from the Indians to use small amounts of the half-dried corm for asthma, chronic bronchitis, and rheumatism. The Pawnees still favor the powdered corm for muscular pain.

Jaundice

Dandelion bitters were drunk for jaundice, or strawberry decoction or that of vervain, cinquefoil, parsley, Oregon grape, nettle root, columbine, or an infusion of wormwood.

Kinnikinnick was most highly favored. The branches were broken into small pieces and boiled into a yellow decoction. Yellow liquid for a yellow disease. Used still in New Mexico, it is a lingering example of the centuries-old association of ideas known as the "doctrine of signatures."

Jerusalem Artichoke

See Artichoke, Jerusalem.

Juniper

A tea of boiled juniper berries was drunk hot to induce urination. Drunk cold and taken daily for a week in amounts approximating a half cup, it was a blood tonic and for this, sometimes, the seeds also were used. The distilled berries eased "debility of the stomach," as noted by a white physician in 1817, and he recommended also the Indian use of juniper for uterine obstructions. Hot juniper tea reduced fevers, especially in influenza, and was valuable in cases of hemorrhage.

As a cold remedy, the Shoshones and Paiutes drank a tea made from the twigs and/or berries to "take the cold out." This was also used for stomach inflammation. The tender ends of juniper branches were covered with a considerable quantity of water and boiled down to an approximate cup. It was strained and allowed to stand overnight. About a half cup was drunk in the morning to relieve the disquiet stomach.

A month before her child was born, the Indian woman made a tea of boiled juniper twigs and drank about a half cup every morning to promote muscular relaxation. This, among the Zuñi, is procedural today; now as in the past the decoction of *rama de sabina* is taken after parturition to hasten the termination of the catamenia. The fourth day after giving birth, the mother is fumigated with juniper branches and leaves placed in a vessel of hot coals.

Juniper leaves were dried and dusted on indolent sores and for bruises and sprains, the twigs toasted and bound on tightly to reduce swelling. A solution of juniper berries or boiled young twigs was formed into hot packs for rheumatism. The berries and, preferably, the leaves and branches were smoked and the fumes inhaled for head colds. A strong solution of boiled twigs and twigs broken fine and heated made a cover for the eruption of measles and smallpox. Branches and/or berries were burned as a fumigant after illness.

For sore throat, the finely ground twigs were heated over the fire, bound in a hot cloth, and kept on the throat—hot. For toothache, the leaves were pounded, moistened, tied in a cloth with a hot stone in it, and held to the jaw. For fever: a sweat bath, the fine ashes being raked out and a layer of young juniper twigs added. For venereal disease, a solution of boiled terminal twigs was drunk as a cold tea or to this decoction was added boiling resin with cracked juniper berries.

It will be noted that the Indians came very close to discovering gin and certainly would have done so had they been interested.

K

Kidney and Bladder

In the dust of the waterless wastes of the Rocky Mountain piedmont and the high plains, urinary ailments were endemic and unending. For relief, the Indians experimented with every plant within their range. The result was that no matter where they were or what the season, some relief-giving herb would be available. There were the diuretics but many of the drugs served also in a more specialized capacity. Herewith are the most notable kidney and bladder medicines as the Indians used them. Unless otherwise specified, they were taken as decocted liquids.

Onions to increase the flow of urine; western white pine, the buds and flowers boiled down until only the equivalent of a pint remained; skunkcabbage; goldenrod; flax; hawthorne; hops ground to powder; watercress; iris, still used; juniper berries and twigs, still popular; pennyroyal, the tea leaves gathered when the plant is in seed; sage, the juice of the cooked plant especially recommended for bladder disturbances; sand verbena, to increase the urine flow; wild cucumber's roasted seeds; the flowers and herbs of violets, especially to relieve back pains due to bladder infections; wintergreen leaves, prescribed for bladder ulcers; burdock, "powerfully strong," as also an infusion of basil tops; columbine root favored by the *conquistadores;* parsley; strong yarrow-root tea; gumplant flowers and buds; the flowering tops of pentstemon; Oregon graperoot tea; dandelion tea; creosote leaves dry or green with a touch of sweetening; ephedra, the locally famous "Mormon tea," for kidney pains; angelica root; balsamroot cooked until it was like a "thick yellow soup"; horsetail; wild-rose root; buckwheat stems and leaves for the bladder; fleabane; a root infusion of wild strawberries, especially for painful discharge.

For special problems, special medication. As a long-time kidney medicine, piñon resin was boiled with juniper added and taken daily on alternate weeks. In 1840, the Indian remedy was approved by the white communities noting that white pine "is good to strengthen the urinary organs of those who cannot hold their water through the night." For all "cases of gravel," dried huckleberry leaves or an infusion of juniper roots or a strong decoction of dried juniper leaves to break the stone and remove the gravel.

Kidney stones were treated also with a conserve of the flowers and seeds of nettle or of cherry tree gum or plum tree gum or an infusion of wormwood for any "matter lodged in the urinary passage or gall bladder." Powdered thistle seed, as the settlers found, "breaks and expels stones." Pulverized tobacco leaves mixed with the juice of the gumplant and tied over the afflicted part was said to bring relief.

In the eighteenth century, kinnikinnick was brought to the notice of the white community "as an efficient remedy in nephritic and even calculus cases." For strangury kidney pain: a strong infusion of strawberry leaves. If asparagus was available, it was sought avidly for its long-range action on the kidneys. Priddy Meeks combined Indian remedies with pioneer common sense and claimed that he had saved a patient who had been given up with a kidney complaint. "I gave him nothing but burdock and dandelion. He got well."

Kinnikinnick

This low shrub, tight-clinging to earth, showing early its tiny flowers, its bright red berries lingering under the snow, was treasured by the Indians for its curative properties which, unknown to them, found their value in kinnikinnick's rich content of tannic acid and arbutin.

Its green leaves were picked from their stems in the fall and dried in moderate heat before being decocted as an astringent and tonic. Its tea was drunk for stomach upsets. For rheumatic pains, the tea brought comfort. It was used in childbirth and as a diuretic and was recommended especially for chronic diseases of the bladder, rendering the urine less irritating, hence decreasing the pain of inflammation in the urinary tract. The dosage was an approximate ounce of leaves to an approximate pint of boiling water. A surviving example of the "doctrine of signatures" in New Mexico today is the treatment of jaundice with kinnikinnick branches decocted until a thickish yellow liquid remains.

The dried leaves were smoked, as protection against malaria. The boiled roots were added to the bath water of tubercular patients and brought relief after a dozen or so such baths. Branches were fragmented, boiled, and added to the bath water to help relieve pains in the ribs and rheumatic pains. These baths were given in sequences of three nights at a time, and during them a little of the liquid was drunk. The whole plant, ground, was made into a tea to fight "cold blood"—anemia. Approved in due course by the eighteenth-century whites (who called it *uva ursi*), kinnikinnick was used by them as by the Indians in treating catarrh and gonorrhea.

Lactation

See Childbirth.

LADY'S-SLIPPER

Lady's-slipper

This rare and exquisite orchid, now threatened with extermination, grows high in the Rocky Mountains but the Indians climbed the heights to seek it for it was their sure remedy for sleeplessness. They were simple and confident about it, merely downing an infusion of the root and closing their eyes. In Europe, there had been some modern elaborations as witness this recipe given a few years ago by the Vicomte de Mauduit:

"Last thing at night, drink an infusion of Lady's Slipper root, then under your pillowcase, place a mixed bouquet of this root and skullcap which you have previously dried in the oven. This is a permanent cure for sleeplessness."

Lamb's Quarters

The Indians used poultices of boiled lamb's quarters for all manner of swellings, even as they do today. For the aches of rheumatism and the pains of arthritis, they used a wash from the decocted leaves. This was held in their mouths also to reduce toothache.

LARKSPUR

Larkspur

There were many larkspurs within the radius of the western Indians and they used them as they found them. But they were careful; the roots and seeds were "powerful medicine" and were prescribed with extreme caution by the medicine men. Externally, larkspur was spread freely to kill vermin.

Laurel, Mountain

In the great heights, from 10,000 feet to the timber line, grows the shrubby laurel with evergreen leaves like those of the willow. These leaves were cherished by the Indians who prescribed them whenever possible for dysentery and extreme bowel hemorrhage. An ointment made from the stewed leaves combined with animal fat was excellent to combat the itch.

Laxatives

For centuries the Indians had known the herbs that were laxative and the doses required for the desired results. We list those most commonly employed. Unless otherwise specified, they were drunk in decoction like teas.

Amole; antelope brush, the leaves chewed as a physic or a handful of leaves and/or unground seed boiled; burdock, roots and seeds approved by the white doctors in 1840 as "cleansing"; cinquefoil, the whole silky plant boiled; curlydock, formerly sold over the counter as yellowdock; dandelion; elder flowers and sometimes berries, this approved by the incomers in 1840 and favored by the Indians as a cool laxative drink; flax seed; wild lettuce; wild licorice, a mild cleanser; mountain mahogany, the young plant stirred in water; pentstemon; phlox (trumpet); poppy, which some tribes still drink in a tea made from the seed; poverty weed root soaked in cold water; boiled pennyroyal plant; rabbitbrush as a "general laxative"; sage, "small and black"; sycamore bark; saltbush roots; scarlet gilia; sand dock, the whole plant boiled—"in 10 minutes," testified a pioneer, "it helps the inside pain"; willow twigs, steeped, sometimes with salt; stone seed; yarrow, "hot and cleansing."

Violet flowers or seeds in a syrup of violets were given children. The Indians of the upper Missouri River made an enemata syringe of animal bladder to which was attached a nozzle of small hollow legbone of wild turkey. And, finally, there is a feat which perplexes us. An Indian physic approved in 1840 by the white community was snuff mixed with sassafras.

Legs

The Indians bathed ailing, weakening, or shaky legs in hot sage tea, then poulticed them with sage leaves.

Leprosy

Though concentrated research has failed to unearth

a single authenticated case, apparently there was leprosy or some disease with similar symptoms. The Indians applied pennyroyal or lye from juniper ashes or leaves and/or bark of elm which, it was claimed, "cures leprosy." The most prized Indian "cure" was to bathe the patient's body with a decoction of anemones.

Lettuce, Wild

In Pliny's *Natural History*, lettuce is listed for forty-two disorders. The Indians do not record such varied uses but they went straight to the heart of its healing virtues: they proved it good because of its narcotic content.

They used the milk to calm coughs and quiet irritability. The syrup of a strong infusion was drunk to induce sleep. Centuries after this discovery by the Indians, the Sheridan (Wyoming) *Post* of February 28, 1889, recommended the stalk of wild lettuce as a sleep inducer, being "good" also "for those requiring a gentle opiate who will not take medicine."

Lettuce was used also for cooling fevers, easing pain, and inducing sweat. It was a favored remedy for hypochondria but, principally, for satyriasis and nymphomania.

Lice

Tobacco leaves, powdered or in decoction, were favored to kill lice. If they were not available, columbine seeds were mashed and rubbed vigorously into the hair. In Tucson, Arizona, a Mexican druggist still sells larkspur to kill lice.

Lichens

The omnipresent lichens of the Rocky Mountain country were as widely prescribed as their presence, especially to stop diarrhea. The lichen was scraped from the rocks, soaked overnight in cold water, and the solution taken internally. Powdered, it was particularly efficacious in children's mouth sores. Today the economic value of lichens, aside from that of perfume base and dyestuff, lies in their drug value as an antibiotic.

Licorice

Licorice played a staple role in the *materia medica* of the Indians. Roots were bruised and chewed and made into a poultice for all manner of wounds and ulcers. The essential oil was dropped into an aching ear or used for deafness. Dried rootstock was boiled into a tea to be drunk as a laxative or demulcent. A decoction of the root is still a household remedy for childhood fevers.

Roots and berries were prescribed for pulmonary distress and were taken as a medicinal stimulant. The Aztecs followed the same pattern as their northern neighbors: A fermentation of the roots was drunk for stomach ache and diseases of the blood. Hence, in time, it was recommended for syphilis.

Lightning Stroke

There are terrifying thunderstorms in the Rocky Mountain area and down on the plains; and once in a while someone is struck by lightning. The Indians used whatever herbs were at hand as a stimulant. The Aztecs followed the formula, favoring a stimulating hot drink of pine, which they called "the mist tree."

Lily

Most of the Indians' medicinal remedies of the lily family came from the sego and are so listed. But there was also the sand lily, the roots of which were ground to a soapy consistency and spread on swellings and sores. The roots of the white pond lily, containing tannin, were mashed and brewed with a binder such as corn meal and made into a poultice for indolent ulcers, old sores, and cuts that would not heal. The Indians viewed this as a particularly reliable astringent, and a tea from the root was widely favored also for diarrhea and gonorrhea.

Liniments

Liniments were a necessity and there were various remedies of which the tried-and-true bringers of relief were hemlock oil, a solution of the yarrow plant, or the pulped material of skunkcabbage applied as friction.

Liver

Inescapably there were liver troubles and inevitably the Indians proved their remedies for them. There was the marigold flower made into tea and a tea from the leaves of the antelope brush. There was a tea from the boiled roots of the gumplant, tea from the roots of curlydock, plantain, parsley, or mullein. There were dandelion bitters or an infusion of wormwood, recommended particularly for an obstruction. If the suffering was continuous, tobacco leaves were placed over the painful area.

Several of these remedies were familiar elsewhere, and in 1679 the English John Evelyn added a more precious touch. Cucumber "sallat," he recommended, could be the most approved means to "cool the liver."

Lobelia

The Indians set such store by lobelia that it was an article of trade among them. Ranking high in their *materia medica,* it was used in infusion as a diaphoretic, a physic, and an emetic as some tribes still use it. They use it also for relief from chest pains, asthma, and catarrh, as a tonic after influenza, and for intestinal worms. Success with the last led to experiments with it for venereal disease, and a nineteenth-century medical book states that the "natives of North America" regard lobelia as their "secret cure for syphilis."

Doctor Priddy Meeks, coming west with the Mormon migration of 1847, wrote in his diary, "I sometimes look upon lobelia as being supernatural . . . undoubtedly it is the best and purest relaxum in the compass of medicine. That is the reason it is so good in childbirth cases. . . . Oh! glorious medicine."

The reaction was so violent, however, that most doctors soon stopped using it. But that very violence seemed an incentive to Mormon Sister Susanna Lippincott. She advocated pouring lobelia into a patient until "the devils are driven out of the body."

Locoweed

The Indians chewed locoweed to ease sore throats. They made it into a poultice to reduce swellings. They made a decoction of the boiled roots and rinsed the mouth with it for toothache or washed the eyes for granulated lids. And they cleaned, scraped, and boiled the roots and drank the decoction for venereal disease. This treatment took a very long time.

Loss of Memory

See Melancholia.

Lungs and Respiratory Infections

So many herbs were tried for the respiratory and lung infections that plagued the dwellers in the dust. Dandelion, mustard, nettle, pennyroyal, rose hips, violets, cherries, mesquite, sassafras, red cedar were among the most prescribed.

The sunflower was considered successful as an infusion, as were the tops and leaves of flax or a hot decoction of basil. Mullein roots were for pulmonary diseases, prickly ash for bronchial infection. Mountain mahogany yielded its inner bark to be scraped, dried, and boiled for lung trouble, as was a root decoction of sweet cicely.

For lung hemorrhage a decoction of nettles or of elder flowers was given to stop the bleeding. Lung bleeding was also treated with a smoke of mullein leaves and it is reported that this still is done. The preferred herb in this context, however, was balsam. For congested lungs, pulverized balsamroots, sometimes mixed with tobacco, were smoked, or the fumes of balsamroot, sometimes with pitch added, were inhaled by the patient whose head was covered to keep in the smoke. According to one mountain man, cudweed was "the best of the lot, being smoked like tabaco."

There were moxas and cuppings for chest pains as well as the simpler forms of scarification, after which suction was applied by mouth.

Lupine

Rocky Mountain Indians made lupine seed into a tea to help urination. They applied it to rheumatic pains and black-and-blue spots and other skin troubles. The seeds destroyed worms. Lupine was held particularly important in women's difficulties; this had been found true also in England where it was recommended to "bring down menses, expel birth and secundines."

Lye

For a headache, feet were bathed in warm lye water.

M

Malaria

Malaria itself was treated with the fever medicines favored by the various tribes. But the Indians recognized that certain areas at certain times bred the dreaded malady. As protection against malarial fevers, they smoked kinnikinnick, its powdered leaves or bark taken alone or in combination with dogwood, willow, sumac, or cornel, with or without tobacco. To a minor degree, an infusion of sunflower stems was drunk for its claimed anti-malarial properties.

See also Fevers.

Manna

Following the Indians' example, the pioneers found

in manna a mild laxative, the dosage being a teaspoonful before breakfast.

Manzanita

The writhing-branched greenleaf manzanita of the western slope, with its early pink flowers, and the Spanish manzanita, with its solid "little apples," were worth the climb to the montane to find, for the Indians drank a solution of the boiled evergreen leaves as a treatment for venereal disease.

Marigold

The widely spread marigold was as widely used by the western Indians. Marigold flower tea reduced the fever and was good for the liver. Fresh marigold leaves were chewed for a stomach ache. If baby had the colic, marigold seeds were soaked in hot water and given a small bit at a time. In New Mexico today, an unsettled stomach is quieted with *pagué,* a tea made by pouring boiling water over fresh marigold leaves. After fifteen minutes of steeping, followed by straining, the remedy is drunk hot. Even in serious cases of diarrhea and vomiting, the Indians assert that this drink will result in a cure "*poco* soon."

MARIGOLD

In old-time England, marigold tea made from the flowers was used also for fevers and to bring out the eruptions of measles or smallpox. Marigold juice in treacle water was used for sore eyes and to remove warts. Even a sniff of the marigold plant was calculated to drive from the head any "evil humours." So greatly was it treasured in medieval times that it was consecrated to the Virgin. It is narrated how the name marigold was given because the florets of its discs resembled "rays of glory."

Measles

Rocky Mountain Indians still use a decoction of gumweed for measles, the equivalent of a half cup being drunk three times a day. Or, when the eruption broke out, the patient was bathed with a strong solution of boiled juniper twigs or was rubbed with the heated twigs. These measures were designed to "bring out" the rash. Antelope brush was drunk in decoction, the leaves being used alone or with its young branches and flowers.

Melancholia and Loss of Memory

No record was found of the recognition of melancholia by the Rocky Mountain Indians. Farther south, along the great mountain spine, however, the Aztecs treated it as a disease. The fragrance of flowers was used freely for its psychic effect, the body being massaged with a lotion compounded of flower concentrate and other ingredients calculated to retain the delicate aroma. A similar preparation of flowers was taken internally to cure the "black blood."

To the north, giant hyssop, found in the canyons and mountain valleys, was made into a tea which cheered the tired or despondent. This was done also in England where, in 1699, hyssop was recommended to "comfort and strengthen; prevalent [sic] against Melancoly and Phlegm."

Already in 1597 Gerard had recommended the use of cow parsnip: "If the phrenticke or melancholicke man's head be anointed with oile wherein the leaves and roots have been sodden, it helpeth him very much, and such as bee troubled with the sickness called the forgetfull evill."

To steady and strengthen mind and nerves, the Indians, as they do today, drank sage tea. Over in the effete social circles of seventeenth-century England, the gentlemen were also imbibing sage tea, on John Evelyn's advice, in order to help their memories.

Men's Problems

Through the long centuries, medicine men concentrated on the curing of men's ills, until, in time, their findings had become formulae. In the Rocky Mountain area, mustard was used for the swelling or hardness of the testicles, or vervain mixed with fat, especially if there was pain. Strawberry lotion was recommended for ulcers in "the privy parts" and purslane juice for inflammation of the "secret parts." Onions, notably the seed, were taken to increase sperm.

By associative signature, it was believed that non-flowering plants such as fern or lettuce would cause sterility and, from this, it was only a step to the prescribing of wild lettuce for satyriasis.

In 1892, white America approved the age-old Indian usage of a decoction of the root of snakeroot for "exhausion from sexual depletion with loss of erectile power."

Menstrual Disorders

See Women's Problems.

Mental Disorders

See Brain, Melancholia.

Mesquite

Mesquite tea was drunk by the Indians who lived in the desert areas where it grew. When there was fever or congestion, especially in the lungs, the Cocopas made a beverage of the inner bark. This was also the baby's only nourishment during its first four days of life.

Milkweed

Milkweed bark was used as an emetic, cathartic, and expectorant. It was used for dropsy, and the milky fluid was applied to wens and warts, efficaciously, as the incoming settlers testified. "In most cases," it was recorded, it banished "the offensive excrescences."

This latex was found also to remove corns and callouses and to cure ringworm. The fresh sap reduced the irritability of sores, and one undesignated species, in particular, proved a valuable antiseptic and healing agent. The boiled solution, as a compress, relieved headache.

When the silk had been burned off, the ripe seed was ground and made into a salve for sores. But the prime purpose of the seed was its value, when boiled and soaked in a small amount of water, in drawing out the poison from rattlesnake bites.

Perhaps it started as associative thinking: milkweed—mother's milk. However it began, the results were excellent. For sore breasts, an infusion of the milkweed plant was drunk, and for faulty lactation, a milder decoction. Today this practice is still in use among many Indian women, notably the Tewa.

"Miner's Lettuce"

See Scurvy.

Mint

There are some thirty species of mint, of which three are found in the Rocky Mountain area. There are many variations but all mints share the same valuable asset, the almost-hidden little glands that secrete their highly valuable and volatile oil. This is familiar to all, including the Indians, as a flavoring agent. Familiar also are the teas, brewed from the delicately steeped leaves. A pleasant herb, mint—but to the Indians, it was more than pleasant. It was cherished for its medicinal properties.

PEPPERMINT

They made their teas only occasionally from the leaves, deriving greater curative value from the tops of the plants and from the roots. All the western tribes, apparently, used mint as a carminative. It was drunk for indigestion, colic, stomach ache. It was much used for diarrhea.

Mint in decoction was a gargle valued also for sore gums. Combined with honey, it was dropped into aching ears. Mint compresses on the temples eased headache. It was sniffed for a head cold.

It was rubbed into the head for dandruff, and children's heads were washed in a mint solution to guard against worms and vermin. Spearmint was favored for this purpose. With salt, it was said to be effective after a bite from a mad dog.

Women drank mint tea to bring on menstruation or, conversely, to halt an immoderate flow. In the final phase of labor, it was given to expedite the birth and secondines. It was even so in Elizabethan England where the mint was taken in wine to help women "in their sore travail in child bearing" but it was not given later as it was said to curtail the mother's supply of milk.

From its widespread use, it would appear that the Indians had some success with mint in stopping gonorrhea, and this, too, was done in England. Long before that time, however, England had made another discovery. Mint juice mixed with vinegar was said to "stir up venery and bodily lust."

Monkey-flower

See Roper's Relief.

Monkshood

The tall and lovely plant with its hoodlike bluish-purple blossoms already has been mentioned under aconite. Because it is so dangerous, it is mentioned again briefly for emphasis.

An "energetic acro-narcotic poison," it contains the alkaloids aconitine and aconine. Today monkshood must be given only by a physician just as, in its use, the Indians referred to their medicine man. Doctor and medicine man used them identically.

MONKSHOOD

As heart and nerve sedative and anodyne, the powerful drug has been proved beneficial for centuries. The Indians used it carefully, drop by drop, in the early phases of pneumonia and in erysipelas and rheumatism. This took the form of a tincture made from the root and, because of its effect on the heart, no more than a maximum of six drops was given. This procedure was adopted precisely by the settlers.

Morning-glory

The Pawnee prescribed an infusion of bush morning-glory for certain types of heart trouble. Proving of service, this remedy spread until it was accepted by many of the western mountain tribes.

Mosquitoes

Everywhere—mosquitoes! The most repetitive and despairing complaints of mountain men, explorers, army units, pioneers concerned mosquitoes: hosts of them—hordes of them—swarms of them—clouds of them. From Lewis and Clark to Frémont to the surveyors on the great western explorations, they complained and slapped and applied useless remedies. No one was immune and that included the Indians.

They all used pennyroyal which, being of the mint family, offered an oil that was rubbed on the face especially before sleeping. This was to be found high in the foothills, in canyons, and on rocky slopes where also clung the antelope brush with its stimulatingly aromatic flowers, a decoction of the latter being prized for easing mosquito bites and well worth the climb.

Various fats were tried and the verdict was unanimous among the western tribes: To calm the irritation from mosquito bites, the most potent fat was that from the intestines of an antelope.

See also Bites and Stings, Insect.

TREE MOSS

Moss

Moss was used universally by the Rocky Mountain Indians as a surgical dressing and the practice was tested, proved, and adopted by the incoming whites.

Mountain Balm

When an unfamiliar sickness overtook one of their tribe, the Indians sent runners high into the montane and there between 8,000 and 10,000 feet they found the dense clumps of *Ceanothus velutinus,* the sweet-smelling mountain balm with its broad shining leaves. This lovely herb was gathered hastily and hurried back to the medicine man who used it as a diagnostic in the perplexing illness.

Mountain Mahogany

Mountain mahogany, the common low shrub, sometimes called feather bush because of its sinuously spiraling seed plumes, seems to have been one of the most strategic sources of remedies used by the western Indians.

Externally, the dried bark, either as paste or powder, was applied to burns, cuts, and wounds. The inner bark, boiled and strained, was dropped into irritated eyes. Boiled bark became a tea for colds. Its inner layer was scraped, dried, and boiled as an infusion for lung trouble. The young plant was dried, powdered, stirred into water, and drunk as a laxative.

Need it be said that mountain mahogany was tested for use in fighting venereal disease? From its widespread adoption for this purpose, it would appear that the bark decoction taken over a long period was an effective cure.

Mugwort

The Indians made a mugwort poultice for wounds. They squirted the juice onto the sores of poison oak. They inserted a leaf into one nostril to cure a headache. They drank a decoction of the leaves for colds, bronchitis, fever, colic, and rheumatism.

The women drank a decoction of mugwort when malfunctioning occurred and this paralleled Culpeper's recommendation in the seventeenth century that mugwort is "most safe and excellent in female disorders. For this purpose the flowers and buds are put into a teapot and boiling water poured over them." The tea was drunk cool with sugar and milk. By sitting over a vessel of this mixture, the herbalist declared, the woman in labor would find it "hastens delivery and halps expel afterbirth."

As no doubt with the Indians, the use of mugwort

went far back. Dioscorides declared that it dissolved gallstones and, "made up with axungia [hog and goose grease or one of the two] into an ointment," it would dissolve "wens and hard knots." But it was the famous naturalist Pliny who bestowed upon the lowly mugwort his rarest benison. "If," he wrote, "a traveller bind some of the herb about him, he will feel no weariness on his journey."

Mullein

MULLEIN

For many centuries, mullein has been known and used in Europe and Asia where there are some 250 species. In these countries today, as throughout the years, mullein leaves are picked for their medicinal properties. In North America, there are only a dozen or so species and only two in the Rocky Mountain area. But these two species have been used by the Indians for countless centuries and have provided a score of basic remedies.

Mullein supplied a diuretic, an anodyne, an antispasmodic. In infusion, it was helpful in coughs and colds. The strong tea made for bad colds was an especially fortunate discovery since mullein tea calms nervous excitation and thereby induces sleep.

A handful of mullein leaves was steeped and the steam inhaled for sore throat, catarrh, and asthma.

For bowel and bladder inflammation and for diarrhea, an infusion was made of about an ounce of leaves steeped in about a pint of boiling water. This was then strained and drunk cold.

Externally, the prime purpose was to soothe inflamed tissues, and the chemicals found in mullein are used now for this purpose as well as by cosmetic firms where they are basic ingredients for skin softening lotions.

So the Indians soaked their sprains in mullein water, and in such illnesses as pneumonia the patient was bathed in its cooling essence.

Lung trouble was treated by repeated smoking of the dried leaves. During the Civil War, when the Confederates' medical supplies were gone, they, too, treated lung trouble with mullein leaves. These were combined with cherry bark and made into a restorative syrup.

Europe, which had experimented with mullein for generations, used the roots for coughs and cramps, a decoction of roots and leaves for tumors and swellings, the distilled water of its flowers for gout, and a flower infusion for piles. Culpeper claimed that mullein seed and leaves boiled in wine would "draw forth speedily thorns and splinters from the flesh" and would ease the pain and heal. The seed, bruised and boiled in wine and "laid on any member that has been out of joint or newly set, takes away all swelling and pain."

Mumps

Prickly pear was the great easer of mumps. Indians everywhere within its range used it. The spines were removed, the big green pancake roasted and, while still warm, bound on the side of the neck and below the chin to reduce the swelling.

There was also an ointment made of the crushed roots of the four o'clock worked into fat. It was not possible to learn whether the Indians taught the settlers of the much-used poultice of corn meal, powdered flax seed, and water enough to make a paste. Perhaps this was one of those rare occasions when the Indians learned from the settlers.

Muscular Pains

Yarrow liniment was the most favored remedy for muscular pains. But there was also yerba mansa, its leaves boiled in a quantity of water and the aching parts bathed or soaked therein. For a stiff neck or for muscles tightened by nervous strain, a poultice was recommended made of thistle leaves mashed to a pulp.

See also Arnica.

Mustard

When a strong stimulating medicine was required

that would act on the nerves but without exciting them, the seed of wild mustard was used. Even as with us, mustard plasters and mustard baths were in common usage. For colds and fevers and for continuing rheumatic and sciatic pains, there was nothing like the lowly mustard. An infusion of the seed stimulated the urine and brought on the menses. Mustard was used by women in childbirth and, later, for the hardening of her breasts. It was used for the swelling of men's testicles. The ripe seeds were ground and stored and held ready for emergency use in the making of poultices for burns.

Narcotics and Intoxicants

The Indians of the Rocky Mountain area, especially in the Southwest, understood fully the action of their indigenous intoxicants and narcotics. Henbane, nightshade, hemlock, hellebore, and lettuce were widely used. The peyote bean was used by the Apaches, Comanches, and other tribes of New Mexico and Arizona and, later, by the Indians of the high plains.

One button of peyote plunged the taker deeply into a languorous world of swirling colors and sensuously exquisite hallucinations. Though there was a degree of muscular dislocation, the entire effect was over in five or six hours, and there was no undesirable aftermath. Basically the peyote bean was used only ceremonially as it is today.

Only a half of one red bean produced a violent delirium followed by a sleep of several days. There seem to have been no unpleasant aftereffects.

Mullein contains chemicals which, without being aware of them, were used by the Indians to soothe inflamed tissues. Houndstongue (beggar's lice) contains cynoglossine and consolidin, now recognized as pain relievers. So the Indians for centuries had used the herb.

There was the mucilaginous false mallow, infusions of which made fire dancers insensitive to heat, and white clay which, in conjunction with the low combustion point of macerated cedar bark, prevented the Navajo fire dancers from acquiring burns and blisters. Yarrow was employed similarly by the Zuñi and Omaha.

The daturas were the most extensively used narcotics, for jimson (Jamestown) weed was widespread, effective, and easily obtainable. It was employed also in large doses by the priests who, in the resultant delirium, were said thus to communicate with the spirits. Generous doses of the weed were proved aphrodisiacs and were given by some tribes to their young girls at the start of ceremonial dances and to youths at the beginning of the ceremony that initiated them into manhood.

Neck

Most highly favored help for a stiff neck was a poultice of mashed thistle leaves. Purslane in oil, preferably linseed, also was recommended.

Nerves

Contrary to the false image of the stalwart savage, the Indians suffered from nervous tensions and depletions —and from too much imagination—and recognized them for what they were and tried to cure them with herbal remedies.

They derived aconite from monkshood and used it as a nerve sedative. They prescribed valerian as an antispasmodic. Skullcap quieted as did an infusion of vervain. They found that a decoction of chokecherry bark relieved nervousness or a sponge bath and tea of verbena leaves, still used among some tribes. For acute nervousness, a hot poultice of jimson leaves produced some good results. For wounds where the nerves were involved, St. Johnswort was recommended. Wormwood proved to be a powerful stimulant to the nerve centers and brain. This was given the blessing of the white community in 1817 when the medical profession declared that its "influence was considerable on the nervous system."

Nettles

Nettles, growing in waste places, often a scourge to the white men, were welcome and cherished by the Indians. Nettles were an astringent, a diuretic, a tonic. Their decoction was valuable in diarrhea. Their leaves stimulated, irritated, raised blisters, hence were a rubefacient. A leaf put on the tongue and pressed against the roof of the mouth stopped a nosebleed. Nettle juice, alone or as a syrup, was highly approved to halt hemorrhage, especially of the lungs, bowels, or kidneys. A decoction of the seeds or leaves proved equally efficacious.

A conserve of flowers and seed was deemed helpful for kidney stones. A decoction of the roots was approved for jaundice and also as a gargle. Bull nettle (*tomatillo*) berries, crushed and mixed with salt, also were a favored gargle, notably for swollen tonsils. An alternative were the berries dried, ground to powder, and blown into the throat for tonsilitis or catarrh, equally valuable for headache.

As a blood cleanser, the liquor in which young nettles were cooked like spinach was drunk hot as an efficacious spring dosage. Numbed feet were washed in an extract of sage, axin (wax), and ground nettles. There are numerous recorded successes of the restoration of circulation in paralytic limbs by stinging them with nettles. Wherever pain was, it was struck with nettle branches. Conversely, neuralgic or rheumatic pains were bathed in a root decoction or hot poultices of the mashed leaves were applied.

Nettles long had been known in England, too. A decoction of nettle leaves was used to destroy worms in children. Taken in wine, it was stated, it "provokes women's courses." If bitten by a mad dog, the victim was given a decoction of nettle seed. The juice of nettle leaves or a decoction of the roots was an accepted wash for "green wounds, old rotten or stinking sores and gangrene."

Neuralgia

The southwestern Indians in the shadow of the Rockies call neuralgia "air in the head," and, as they have for countless generations, they mix ground chinaberry seeds with piñon pitch, make it into a plaster, and place it before and behind each ear. The tribes farther north settled for a bag of hot sand.

New Jersey Tea

The low thorny shrub of the foothills, *Ceanothus fendleri,* was transformed into what the first white comers into the area called New Jersey tea by drying it, grinding and using it in conjunction with lobelia, to dust syphilitic sores.

Nightshade

All the western tribes were familiar with the narcotic action of nightshade. Recognized by its fetid, stupefying odor (which lessens as it dries), the Indians had learned, as later the white man proved, that the officinal parts are the leaves and seeds. Roots are too powerful for ordinary use and in large doses are a violent poison.

NIGHTSHADE

Much used for nervousness, neuralgia, epilepsy, it was given in small doses to children who wet themselves at night and to persons who, suffering from tuberculosis or debility, were soaked by excessive perspiration. For diarrhea, an approximate half cup of decocted fruits or double that amount of dried berries was recommended. These dried berries were carried by the Indians of most western tribes when traveling, and were made into a tea when the water was not potable.

It is said that the Pah-Utes still bruise the seeds, soak them in water, ferment the mixture, and drink it as a narcotic. It is said also that California Indians still stimulate their young females before the dance with a dosage of decocted nightshade.

Ninebark

Whether what was to be tagged as the Colorado low ninebark of the high mountains, or the Illinois ninebark of the plains, it was used in decoction by the Indians, only the roots being employed for the fomenting and poulticing.

Nose

For nosebleed, the Indians bruised the herb and flowers of bedstraw and put it in the nostrils, or they did the same with nettles or the leaves, bark, and seeds of the willow, or a decoction of cinquefoil.

To open the nostrils, onion juice frequently was snuffed. But the favored method of relieving the nasal passages was to smoke pulverized balsamroot, sometimes mixed with tobacco, or to inhale the fumes of the roots burning in a bed of coals. If pitch was added to the balsam, the patient covered his head to derive full benefit from the inhalation.

The Indians appear not to have made the English claim that the juice of green elder leaves sniffed up the nostrils "purges the tunicles [sic] of the brain."

O

Oak

The oaks of the Rocky Mountains are scrubby and shrubby and are found mostly in the foothills. But the Indians found it worth their while to make the climb, for they were highly prized. The bark was mostly used in their medicine; though the Indians did not know this, oak bark contains a high amount of tannic acid.

Very astringent, it was used in decoction, the proportions being an approximate half pound of bruised oak bark to an approximate two quarts of water. Boiled to half its volume and strained, it was used as a gargle and for dysentery, notably "bloody flux." It was considered valuable in bathing a fever patient and easing inflammations. It served also as a wash for ulcers and gonorrhea.

Oak, Poison

Kinnikinnick was considered most effective in treating poison oak and the pioneers followed the Indian custom.

Obesity

In spite of their active wilderness life, some Indians faced the problem of overweight. For them: kinnikinnick tea until they had reduced or, still used by Indians and mountain whites, tobacco guaranteed to make them "spit away their fat."

Ointments

See Poultices, Plasters, Ointments.

Onions

Onions were used by the Indians for centuries for almost every ill and are still used by them and by the descendants of those pioneers who learned from them.

Onions for colds: Sniff onion juice as the Indians did, to open the nostrils. Make a syrup with a touch of salt for a feverish cold or mash the steamed onions, strain, and drink the water or merely eat plenty of onions raw or cooked. For "flu," cover the body with ground onions, wrap up well, and sweat. For bronchitis, bind on the chest an onion poultice with a sack of hot ashes over it. The Indians changed the ashes frequently to keep them as hot as possible.

For coughs and asthmatic complaints, a syrup of boiled onion water and honey was the dosage, this having been proved so successful that it is still in use today. A variant, developed also in England, was to roast the onions under the coals and eat them hot with honey. According to Nicholas Culpeper, they "much conduce to help an inveterate cough and expectorate tough phlegm."

Sliced onions were put on the soles of the feet and the palms of the hands to "draw out" a fever, a technique important in pneumonia. If a teething baby chewed on onion stems, the pain and swelling of the gums subsided, and if baby developed croup, the congestion was relieved by a poultice of lightly fried onions.

The Indians still use all these treatments, as do "old-time" westerners. A woman taxi driver in Denver, left with four children to bring up when her husband "went off," told me how she managed to make ends meet by herself: She tended to her household at night and treated the family, if they were ill, with old-fashioned remedies. For colds and the "flu," she used onions only. Her advice: At the first sniffle, reach for the onion. Cut it up. Put it in a hot oven, together with the head of the sniffler. Let him breathe the steamy odor and let him sweat. Then let the other children take their turn in the oven with the onions. It will, she claims, keep them from catching the cold.

There were many other medicinal uses for the wild onion. The Indians chewed it to relieve flatulence. They beat it to pulp, moistened it with grease, and applied it as a poultice for snakebite. Honey was added for other bites, including that of a mad dog.

Onions were used as a diuretic and as a tonic. They were eaten raw and copiously for insomnia. The Aztecs' favored headache remedy was onions eaten with honey. Like the French, the western Indians regarded onion soup as an "excellent restorative in the debility of the digestive organs."

For scalds and burns, onion juice with a little salt added "drew out the fire" and prevented blistering. Dropped into the ears, the juice eased their aching. Plenty of cooked onions were recommended for the aged, as was true in Elizabethan England where, wrote Culpeper, onions were "fittest for . . . the aged whose lungs are stuffed and breathing short."

As in the England of that day, Indian women ate

onions in quantity to "provoke their courses." As for the men, they took onion seed to "increase the sperm." There is no record that the Indian braves needed this dosage.

Many an old-time settler followed the Indians' example of hanging strings of onions from the rafters, not only for practical purposes but for good health and good luck. The pioneers developed the superstition to the point of planting onions around the house to fend off disease.

But all blessings must have their banes, real or concocted. On the subject of onions, it was herbalist Turner who struck the sour note. Writing in 1525–1526, he pointed out the dangers, real or imagined, in their over use. Warned he: "They make them forgetfull whiche in tyme of sykness use them out of measure."

Oregon Grape

Also known as the holly grape, this is now officinal as the drug *berberis.* The Indians obviously did not know what the drug was but they knew it worked. They administered a decoction of the roots and bark as a blood tonic or in the treatment of sores and ulcers, of consumption and heartburn and rheumatism. The bark alone was used in cough medicine and as a kidney stimulant. Sometimes, the bark, in infusion, was given as a cathartic. Sometimes, the strained boiled leaves were drunk several times a day for anemia or, before the morning meal, to bring on menstruation.

As recorded by an American doctor in 1840, the bark "long has been used in cases of jaundice." The Indians had used it for that purpose longer than a long time. The Navajo still drink a decoction of the leaves and branches as a cure for pneumonia and the root tea still is widely prescribed as a diuretic, laxative, and anti-syphilitic. Because of the color of the decoctions and infusions, the New Mexico Indians still call them *sangre de Cristo.* Or, perhaps, it might be because the red liquid brings healing.

Overindulgence

As did their forefathers, Indians, notably the Zuñi men, gather the roots of the four o'clock and give them to the women who reduce them to powder and administer them in cold or warm water to mitigate the effects of overeating. By Indian standards, the procedure was the apotheosis of the simple and direct. The woman took the powdered herb, put it in her mouth, softened it, ejected it into her hands, and rubbed it on the abdomen of him-who-had-eaten-too-much.

A pinch of powdered four o'clock root was slipped into the water of the young braves at mealtime to prevent them from the overindulgence of their appetites.

P

Paintbrush

A decoction of paintbrush roots long has been used as a blood purifier. When the white man's diseases spread among the Indians, it became their highly favored remedy for venereal disease. Small amounts of the solution of boiled roots were taken daily. If continued over a very long time, it was said to cure the affliction.

Palsy

Palsy was treated with sage tea by the western Indians.

Paralysis

The Indians claimed that paralytic limbs were restored to their normal functions by stinging them with nettles. Relief from pain was given by a hot bath to which was added a brew of dried elder flowers. Hot baths of gumplant were deemed "particularly beneficial," as noted by the pioneers, or the patient was bathed thrice weekly in hot water to which had been added the powdered root of cow parsnip or a couple of handfuls of hop flowers.

Sage tea also was used; this had also found favor in England where, in 1699, it was recommended for "all paralytical affections."

Parsley

Desert parsley, the only member of its family in the Rocky Mountain area, had numerous medicinal uses for the Indians. The infused root was a diuretic, particularly valuable for relief of pain in passing the urine. A few drops in the ear eased its aching. Parsley tops combined with the roots made a decoction much used to strengthen the stomach. This was also a remedy for women, who drank it to promote menstrual flow. Bruised parsley leaves often were applied to the nursing mother's breasts to prevent caking.

Pasqueflowers

The pasqueflower leaves were applied as a counterirritant for rheumatism.

Pennyroyal

In the canyons and on the dry mountain slopes grows this silver-gray, hairy plant with the strong mint odor. It was well worthwhile to the Indians to climb to the 6,000- to 8,000-foot level where it grew, for pennyroyal was a treasured drug.

Pennyroyal tea was drunk freely by ailing Indians, and in 1840 an American doctor enthusiastically applauded this as being "good in all diseases since it provoked perspiration."

It was a mild stimulant, a carminative. It was prescribed particularly to reduce fevers. Generally, the tea was sufficient but, if the fever climbed, the patient's body was spread with the mashed and moistened plant to which salt had been added.

The boiled plant was a physic or, in smaller doses, relief from indigestion and griping abdominal pains. A few drops were given a baby with colic. For lung trouble or a deep cough, pennyroyal and honey was the dose to void phlegm. For a cold in the head, a bit of the herb was put up the nose. The Aztecs refined this, recommending that "he who is troubled with a dripping nose is to sniff the herb pennyroyal."

Women blessed their centuries-past forebears who had discovered the virtues of the herb. They drank pennyroyal tea hot to ease their menstruation if retarded or painful. They drank a decoction of the herb mixed with sage if this was excessive. They ate pennyroyal leaves after a miscarriage.

Pennyroyal was said to help gout, a belief shared by Elizabethan Englishmen. It was said to ease toothache or, powdered, to strengthen the gums. For the bite of a snake or other poisonous creature, pennyroyal tea was drunk and, as taught by the Indians, the early western explorers discovered that a few drops of the oil rubbed on hands and face provided a "certain safeguard against mosquitoes while sleeping."

Pentstemon

Tea from pentstemon leaves made a laxative widely used by Indians of the Rocky Mountain region. The Paiutes still distill the mashed leaves as an eyewash. Many tribes still boil and strain the white or pink flowering tops as a tea for kidney upsets or chest colds. Sugar added to the dry or fresh flowers and boiled into a syrup is given babies and young children during whooping cough. The Indians, for countless generations, have used this dosage, sweetening it with honey.

But the unique value of pentstemon, as developed by desperate medicine men, lies in its importance in fighting venereal disease. It appears to have proved itself highly efficacious. Medicine men still collect pentstemon, grind it so finely as to be unrecognizable, and sell small amounts for as much as five dollars.

The procedures were (and are) these: The whole plant was brewed and drunk over a long period. The leaves were mashed and the juice applied as a wash. A solution of the boiled stems was employed as a douche by both men and women but whether as a preventive or cure could not be ascertained. One informant told a scientific investigator that, for gonorrhea, a slim cylinder was whittled from a pentstemon root and inserted into the urethra.

The priceless worth of pentstemon in the Indians' fight against veneral disease is summarized by its Shoshone name, *tom-bah-hay-nut-zoo*, "bad disease medicine."

Phlox

Phlox was widespread and easily available to the western Indians who, it appears, used with equal success any of the almost one hundred species in the Rocky Mountain area. The boiled plant supplied a laxative tea also helpful in stomach upsets. A cold-water infusion of the mashed roots was prescribed for diarrhea and also, in small doses, was administered to children with the stomach ache. Roots were scraped and soaked in cold water or steeped, as an eyewash. An alternative was to wash the eyes in the water from boiled leaves and this, too, was applied to boils. It still is done. The boiled roots of any of the wild phloxes were and are used in fighting venereal disease, with what success is not known.

Piles

The Indians of the plateau country cleaned the pulpy seed of the wild rose and took it for qualities comforting to the lower intestinal tract, especially in the case of piles.

An ointment of tobacco mixed with animal lard was soothing or, as variant, a suppository made of a pinch of ground tobacco leaves. This, combined with fat and a touch of salt, is called *punche*.

In the days of the Roman Empire, the great doctor Dioscorides recommended mixing mullein seeds and flowers, the flowers of camomile and the powder of dry Venice turpentine. This was placed in a small cooking vessel and placed on the coals. The warm fumes were said to give relief from piles. There appears to be no record that the Indians used mullein for this purpose.

See also Hemorrhoids.

Pine

The ponderosa pine of the high Rockies was a chosen source of resin for ointments and plasters. The inner bark of the white pine was the preferred material for poultices. Most of the high country tribes made a tea from full-grown buds to "strengthen the urinary organs." And, again, it was the bark that was praised as a "great medicine for sores." Writing in 1813 of what the incoming whites had learned, one doctor described this procedure: "The boiled soft part stript out and beat to a poultice in a mortar and sufficiently moistened with its liquor, is applied to burns and sores. New skin will come quickly without a scar."

PINE

Pitchpine adapted itself best to cough syrup, the ocote wood being boiled and sweetened. This was given in colds, whooping cough and, somewhat thicker, in tuberculosis. The Aztec action for lightning stroke began with a hot stimulating drink made of pine, the "mist tree."

Pine Gum

The favored method employed by the Indians to draw out infections or even slivers was to smear the area with pine gum. Steeped, it was said to aid in pneumonia.

Piñon

In the desert country or on the piedmont, under the shadow of the Sangre de Cristo and other ranges of the Rockies, the gnarled piñon has always been a medicinal godsend to the Indians. Boiled resin tea was taken for diarrhea and other bowel complaints, for nausea and fever. It was a valuable tonic drunk for general debility and effective after childbirth. Resin was chewed for a sore throat or, pulverized, was applied with a swab.

Heated resin served general utility purposes. It

acted as a mustard plaster. It was a dressing, still used in many tribes, drawing out pus from boils and infections, sucking out embedded slivers. If these proved obdurate, terminal juniper twigs were added.

The same hot resin dressing was applied to cuts, sores, and bites, "to keep the air out," as is done in New Mexico today. There, too, native tobacco, resin, and salt are mixed and spread on a cloth and laid on the temples of an aching head. An ancient amelioration for aching rheumatic joints was to rub them with fine piñon powder, obtainable from the pitch which, when exposed to the air, gradually hardens.

It appears to have been as associative (and common-sense) deduction that any herb known to heal sores might be of value also in cases of venereal disease. This was particularly true of piñon. Pulverized, it was dusted on syphilitic sores. The Zuñi took, and take, a drink of the needles boiled and sweetened as a precaution against syphilis. Some tribes chew and swallow pitch "pills" for this purpose, and the Washoes claimed that cures for gonorrhea were obtained by choking down the clear fresh resin or drinking a tea made from boiled needles of piñon wood.

There were other uses, too numerous to list. Important was resin boiled into a hot tea for colds. This was so unpalatable that even the Indians, used to bitter herbs, balked at resin tea. Their womenfolk disguised the brew with other plants, juniper being favored.

Equally or to them even more important was the use of heated resin for horse distemper. There is no record of its effect on the quadruped's taste buds.

Plantain

Plantain grows everywhere in the Rocky Mountain area from the plains up to about 9,000 feet. Its fresh leaves furnished the Indians with a mild astringent. When mashed to a pulp and applied as a dressing, the astringent qualities were particularly valuable for cuts, bruises, and

PLANTAIN

wounds. The settlers called it the "soldier's herb" and in 1886 paid tribute to the attributes listed above and, taking a page from the Indians' book, noted that they had tested and formally approved the use of plantain to increase the secretions of urine.

There had been plantains in England, too, this use dating far back. Chaucer commended them. Shakespeare praised their healing virtue. Culpeper, in 1640, proclaimed, "All plantains are good wound herbs to heal fresh or old wounds or sores, either inward or outward." He added a delicate touch: Plantain juice, if mixed with the oil of roses, relieved a headache resulting from heat, if the temples were anointed therewith. The same lotion was helpful in "hot gout" of the hands and feet. But the punchline prescription put the flamboyant herbalist right back in Indian territory. If drunk in a brew, "The powder of dried plantain leaves," he wrote, "kills worms of the belly."

Plasters

The most widely and highly valued of the many plasters used for setting bones was gum from pine or spruce or, if available, hemlock. This, made into a salve, hardened into a strengthening plaster and was ultimately (1840) officially endorsed by the white community.

See also Poultices, Plasters, Ointments.

Pleurisy

For a painful disease, a lovely treatment. For pleurisy, the Indians used an essence of violets or a decoction of poppies. The latter was an almost universal practice, one English writer exclaiming, "How excellent is the red poppy in the disease."

Plumes, Pink

Western Indians, notably the Blackfeet, boiled the plumes and applied the decoction to inflamed eyes.

Plums

The Indians boiled plum leaves as a mouthwash. They used the gum, with or without the leaves, to break down gall and kidney stones. As the English discovered later, they found that plums "bind the belly."

Pneumonia

In treating pneumonia, the Indians used decoctions of the whole gumplant, of steeped pine gum, of mountain mahogany, or the inner white bark of antelope brush or a decoction of its leaves, or, especially, a tea of the boiled dried balsamroot.

Sugar from the dried exudate of the common reed loosened the phlegm and quieted the cough.

Poultices were and are universally advocated, most popular being the old stand-by made of onions. Another treatment was the application of a plaster made of beaten egg whites, thickened with flax-seed meal, and made effective with mustard. More drastic, especially at the start of the illness, was a diaphoretic involving dry corn. The corn was crushed and sprinkled over a pan of hot coals. The naked patient was placed on his back. The pan of coals and corn was placed under his raised knees. He was covered with a blanket. The pan of corn and coals was renewed three times. The patient then was left to sweat for three hours, after which he was given a purge. If he survived all this, perhaps he got a little sleep.

Poison Ivy and Oak

Current and officinal is the centuries-old Indian remedy for poison ivy—a fluid extract of gumplant painted on the affected surfaces. Mugwort juice was an alternative.

Poplar

Known to white settlers as balm of Gilead, the balsam poplar was always a joyful discovery when the Indians found it, for the tree is rare in the Rockies. They used the leaves and buds and bark, used them sparingly, only when needed for their balsamic and soothing properties. Internally, for stomach distress, a tea was made from the leaves and bark and, if available, the buds. Externally, a strong wash of the same tea was applied to cuts, burns, and the like.

By the time that J. I. Lighthall, the self-proclaimed "Great Indian Medicine Man," put in his appearance in 1883, people still claimed that poplar was a sure remedy for stomach disorders and general debility, but medicine man Lighthall presented elaborations to the simple decoction.

The Indian formula had called for poplar bark, two parts; prickly ash, two parts; rattlesnake root, one part; sarsaparilla root, two parts; dogwood and/or wild cherry, one part. Just to insure its efficacy, mountain men and miners had added whisky to the above; this seems to have triggered the great success of the "Great Indian Medicine Man" in the sale of this offering.

He, too, used the inner bark of the poplar plus dogwood and sarsaparilla root, these in equal parts. Then came the deviation from Indian procedure. The mixture was not decocted. Bark and roots were cut up fine and put into a quart bottle until it was half filled. The preparation was completed with whisky to the bottle's top.

Poppy

The Indians boiled the poppy heads in water and drank the decoction to obtain sleep. A honey syrup was made from poppy seeds and flowers and was given to invalids to invoke rest. They bruised the plant and laid it on their foreheads to ease headache and, even as today, were wary not to get the juice into their eyes. This same juice was dropped into the cavity of an aching tooth.

It is clear that the Indians did not make incisions into the seed-holding capsules of the poppy, thereby obtaining the juice which, when dried, becomes opium.

Potato, Wild

Following the example of their forebears, the

Indians today slice a wild potato and put it on their temples to "draw out" the pain of headache.

Poultices, Plasters, Ointments

Every herb that could be used for a poultice was so used. A complete list is not possible, for many undoubtedly went unrecorded. Here, however, are noted the principal and most popular herbs used by the tribes of the Rocky Mountain area in making their poultices and plasters.

Angelica: Big roots pulped for pneumonia and rheumatic pains.

Balsam: Root pulped, for sprains, swellings, rheumatism.

Bulrush: For aches and pains.

Camas: Raw roots mashed, applied to swollen knees or leg ache.

Chickweed: Made into both poultice and ointment.

Clematis: Leaves mashed to reduce swellings, bring boils to a head. For severe burns, a poultice was applied of mashed and moistened clematis seed.

Cow Parsnip: Raw root mashed and made into compress for sore throat.

Creosote Bush: Tops mashed for rheumatism.

Currants: Ground inner bark for general use.

Dock: Pulped root of curlydock applied as a poultice for bruises, burns, and swellings.

Elderberry: Roots boiled until soft, applied to inflamed or caked breasts.

Fir: Poultice made from pitch for sores and boils.

Flax: Dry linseed was ground and mixed with corn meal and water was added for paste. Used to reduce swellings, mumps, etc., and for infected wounds. Also applied to relieve pain of gall bladder.

Geranium: Many uses.

Gilia, Scarlet: Used for all the varieties of human aches, more especially for the head and back sores of horses.

Gumplant: Warm poultices for swellings and

wounds. For broken bones, a poultice from crushed roots or green heads, bound with thistle dough and a pinch of salt.

Hemlock: Gum made into salve or strengthening plaster.

Hops: All-purpose poultice. Formula as worked out by Salt Lake City pioneer: One handful of dried hops in a half pint of water. Reduce to gill. Stir in enough Indian meal to thicken.

Jimson Weed: Hot poultice of leaves to overcome nervousness and produce sleep. Indian recipe as adapted by settler: To a tablespoon of Indian meal in a gill of boiling water, add a tablespoon of jimson seeds.

Juniper: Poultice of mashed and boiled young juniper twigs for burns, swellings, etc. Also for rheumatism.

Mustard: Ripe seeds ground, made into poultice for burns. The conventional mustard plaster was used by all the western tribes.

Ninebark: Roots decocted, fomented.

Onion: Time-honored poultice made by frying onions gently in fat, draining them, putting them between the folds of a cloth, and applying as soon as endurable. In pneumonia, syrup and a touch of salt was added to the onions, the poultice being applied to the palms of the hands and bottoms of the feet to draw off fever. Still commonly used.

Pentstemon: Poultice of powdered green leaves for chronic sores, itch, eczema, or venereal disease.

Prince's Plume: Poultice to relieve congestion and pain in the throat. This was used successfully in diphtheria epidemic a few years ago.

Rose: Fungus galls of wild rose mashed and applied to open boils. Fresh rose galls applied to boils after opening. Inner bark of root used similarly.

Sage: In conjunction with sage tea, poultice was applied to chest and back for four nights to cure asthma. Sage poultices were used commonly for sprains and rheumatism, as they still are.

Sandwort: Shoshones and other Indians still apply hot poultices to swellings, the leaves being used. Patient lies down as any movement is said to bring on nosebleed.

Sassafras: Pulverized, moistened, a poultice of general utility.

Solomon's-seal: Fresh roots used or dried material soaked in water.

Tobacco: Crushed wild tobacco leaves were used to reduce swellings and ease rheumatism and other infections including eczema. Poultice placed along gum said to ease toothache.

Verbena: Mashed leaves for swellings. Roots of pink sand verbena mashed and applied as moist poultice to burns.

Willow: Mashed green leaves and/or roots for toothache.

Wintergreen: All-purpose poultice.

Yarrow: Mashed leaves for swellings and as a compress for headache. For sores, entire green plant made into poultice preferred.

Yerba Mansa: Mashed roots for swellings, sores, abrasions, burns, cuts, bruises. After experimenting, yerba mansa applauded by settlers: "Excellent results . . . for man or beast."

Poverty Weed

Root, soaked in cold water and drunk as a tea, was deemed effective for bowel disorders.

Pregnancy

See Childbirth.

Primrose, Evening

Dried roots were collected in autumn to be used as a strong but safe emetic. Expressed juice of bruised roots taken as snuff was given to clear the head by violent sneezing. A strong decoction of the dried herb was applied externally for "infantile eruptions," as approved by a white physician in 1892.

EVENING PRIMROSE

Prince's Plume

This yellow herb is sometimes called wild cabbage. Indians used it as a tonic. The pulped root was placed along the gum or in the cavity to relieve toothache. Heated, it was dropped into an aching ear. A poultice of mashed root proved successful in relieving pain and congestion of the throat during a diphtheria epidemic among the Indians some years ago.

Puffballs

"Prairie mushrooms" were gathered and kept as a styptic for wounds, the dry powder being sprinkled on the ruptured skin. In its young stage, the fungus was gathered and sliced when needed as a dressing for swellings and sores. The powder was used for earache and was recommended especially for a broken eardrum. It was used universally by the Rocky Mountain Indians as an application on the umbilicus of the newborn infant.

Pumpkin

The seeds were used to expel tapeworm from the bowels.

Purgatives

Aside from routine necessities, the Indians used purgatives for ceremonial cleansing and, so far as can be discovered, every man, woman, and child was purged thoroughly in the spring. Roots of the gumplant, dried and powdered, were most highly favored for this purpose. But the bark and leaves of elder were used, or cascara, violets or the rootstock of chinaberries. The last was a violent purgative as was valerian, employed when other purgatives were ineffectual. The Aztecs preferred boiled rose water.

See also Catharsis and Cathartics, Emetics, Laxatives.

Purslane

The fat-leafed, reddish-tinged weed was conveniently available for the Indians who used it notably in treating stomach ache or for a woman with excessive menstrual flow or just for tired humans with headaches from wind buffeting and sun glare. Sometimes, the seed was used to relieve heat of the urine. Or the juice was mixed with honey into a cough medicine.

The widespread use of the herb was sure proof that its virtues had been known for centuries. England could not go back that far, but there, too, purslane had been used a very long time—for kidneys and children's worms, for gout and eye inflammation, for coughs and liver and stomach ache and female problems. The juice was taken for inflammation of the "secret parts" of men and Parkinson in 1629 urged its use for "blastings by lightening [sic], or planets or for burning by Gunpowder or other wise."

Quinine

The Indians recognized the properties of cinchona found in the Rocky Mountain area, especially in the inner bark of the dogwood. This they decocted into a tea drunk both as a preventive and as a remedy for high, protracted, or recurrent fever.

Rabbitbrush

Rabbitbrush was a popular herb because it grows in poor soil and therefore was obtainable when other plants were not. It had many uses—as a laxative, a febrifuge, or as a cold and stomach remedy for which the leaves were steeped. The roots and tops were boiled into a tea for bloody diarrhea and the leaves, mashed minutely, were put in cavities to ease toothache. The Indians, apparently, did not discover the rubber content of rabbitbrush, the extraction of which is said not to be commercially profitable.

Ragweed

Despised and shunned by modern hay-fever victims, ragweed was valued by the Indians for relief of nausea and other stomach distress. Sometimes, when this was acute, the Indians scarified the abdomen and applied powdered ragweed as a counterirritant.

Rash

For the numerous unidentified allergy rashes, the Indians used yarrow leaves made into a poultice.

See also Skin Irritations.

Raspberries

When we find a raspberry bush, we have eyes only for the fat red fruit. But the Indians saw it also as a whole pharmacy of health-giving drugs.

A decoction of the scraped bark of the root was used for bowel trouble and as an anti-dysenteric. A decoction of the leaves was drunk for nausea and vomiting. It was a valuable astringent, excellent for diarrhea, and the leaves were an "excellent diuretick," as a white doctor testified in 1840. Women drank a pleasant tea of raspberry leaves during labor.

This leaf tea, made as strong as possible, washed malignant sores. "It will cure almost anything," declared a satisfied settler. The stems, pounded to powder, were spread as a dry dressing on cuts and wounds.

In its herbal period, England had made more limited discoveries. Infused raspberry leaves were used as an astringent and it was claimed that it dissolved tartar from the teeth "though inferior to strawberries." But, primarily, it was favored as a cordial, the justification for its frequent use being that it strengthened the stomach. It may have done so. At any rate, as Culpeper pointed out, it was delightful. "The fruit is very grateful as nature presents it," he wrote. But it was improved by being "fermented with wine."

Reed

Sugar from the dried exudate of the common reed was and is used for lung pain and to loosen phlegm, especially in pneumonia.

"Relaxers"

The Indians believed in afternoon tea, whatever its form, generally herbal drinks which the settlers came to call "relaxers." Priddy Meeks, who had accompanied Brigham Young on the great hegira, developed a modest composite of these for external application. "To relax any contraction of the system whatever," he advised, "take equal quantities of yellowdock, dandelion, burdock, and lobelia, all finely pulverized and put in eight ounces to a quart of the best alcohol. Let it stand for ten days, shake well, and use as a wash, always rubbing downward."

Resin

"Resin was one of the most important sources of remedies of the Indians," wrote three researchers working in conjunction with the National Arboretum. *Sanalotado,* they call it in New Mexico, the "cure-all."

In particular, there was the resin of the piñon tree. An ointment of the white pitch is said to have astonishing value in drawing out thorns and splinters. Piñon gum, grown hard with age, was chewed and placed on the sore spot after the alien body had been removed. This was done, too, to suck out pus from infected cuts and wounds.

Resin tea, made palatable with mint or juniper, was drunk for colds and fever.

Testimony that it had been a dependable stand-by for generations comes from the *Acotaria,* the material for which was gathered in 1679. The West Indian indigenes, it is recorded, used resin which was taken out by incising the tree "beying as greate as a willow-tree and is a verie sweete smell, he doeth bryng forth a redde fruite." The Indians used this "for swellings in any part of the body and also for toothache."

Respiratory Infections

See Lungs and Respiratory Infections.

Rheumatism

Because of their way of living with constant exposure to the weather and with dietary limitations, the Indians suffered greatly from rheumatism and attendant ills, and it is clear from the number of remedies tested over great areas that from man's beginning in North America the "great crippler" had taken its toll.

The Rocky Mountain tribes boiled young shoots of western pine and bathed also with a decoction of nettle roots applied on the painful parts. Nettle leaves were used similarly. They used boiled leaves of lamb's quarters or fresh columbine roots mashed and rubbed on aching joints. They decocted mugwort or sunflower roots and made poultices of a warm wash. The mountain men and miners soaked the sunflower seed in whisky.

Poultices of pasqueflower leaves served as a counterirritant. Cooked rose seeds were recommended for muscular pain, and poultices of greasewood tops, of lead plant, and of burdock. Large amounts of sage leaves were boiled and said to make an "excellent bath" for rheumatism or for the aches of colds, as was a decoction of kinnikinnick or the dry ground leaves of the creosote bush, these being boiled and used sometimes as a poultice, more often as a wash with the fluid. The Apache still are said to use the tops of the creosote bush to make a poultice for rheumatism.

A miner in 1877 vouched for the effectiveness of the prickly pear, the young joints being gathered before the spines developed. These were boiled or fried and applied to the painful parts. In New Mexico the belief is held that relief is speedy if the rheumatic area is bathed with verbena leaves, tea from the herb being drunk at the same time.

Yucca still is widely used. The young shoots are boiled and mashed, the juice then being put back in the hot water and cooked several hours for added strength. The result is a red syrupy liquid ready to be rubbed on rheumatic joints.

Indians and pioneers alike sponged with hot water in which a handful of tobacco leaves had been boiled and the invaluable kinnikinnick was also so used. The branches were broken into pieces and boiled and then added to the bath water. This treatment was repeated for three nights, a little of the liquid being drunk at the same time. Another such bath was given in water to which was added an armful of coneflowers, after which the sufferer was wrapped warmly for sleep and woke, it is said, much relieved. Sweat baths were favored and moxas commonly used.

The Pawnees burned the flowers of false lupine under the painful joints, covering fire and afflicted parts with a blanket. This eased the pain and reduced swelling. The Omaha fumigate with the rootstocks of angel stem, as the Shoshone do also. Widely endorsed was sagebrush, packets of the steamed plant being placed on the limbs or in the bath. In season, a handful of straw from wild grain was boiled in a tub of water and three hot stones added, the sufferer then being covered with a blanket. This vapor bath was taken three times a day "until cured."

Fresh green gumplant was crushed or, in winter, the dried sprigs were sprinkled with hot water. Then these were piled on hot stones, wrapped in a cloth, and laid on the painful parts, the effect being that of a steam bath, as also was used a warm solution of hop roots or roots of the common sunflower or, as compresses, boiled whole buckwheat plant.

Often, when the fire had burned down to coals, green juniper boughs were added and the patient laid down on them and steamed, at the same time drinking a tea of the leaves. An alternative was to drink a tea of juniper berries several times a day, hot juniper packs being applied at the same time.

A tea from boiled white pentstemon plants was efficacious or a tea from the inner bark of ash root or an infusion of elderberries or a decoction of fleabane or of the roots of the mountain grape to which the bark was sometimes added, or a tea from artichoke leaves and stalks taken three times a day. The heads of the Jerusalem artichokes, eaten in the usual way, were said to bring considerable relief. The red tea from the boiled roots of the chokecherry was taken in small amounts while the rheumatic area was bathed in the decoction. Wormwood leaf tea was widely used and the decocted root of balsam held high priority.

The Spaniards preferred a decoction of the roots of the cow parsnip commonly used by the Indians, and, of course, everyone everywhere in the West drank alfalfa tea. This was and is true also of ephedra. Like the Indians, the *Anglos* of the Southwest have imbibed vast amounts of this *canutillo* tea, hoping thereby to ease their rheumatic pains.

There were many other attempted pain relievers, the crushed leaves and seed of wild tobacco or mashed willow roots, especially recommended for lumbago. Like the Indians, English country folk still view yarrow as valuable for rheumatic pains. In the early days of the United States, Rafinesque recommended the split joints of opuntia as an effective emollient in cases of acute rheumatism.

There were desperate deviations. The settlers used copper bracelets or copper wire around their waists or wrists. The Indians sprinkled the inside of their sandals with powdered creosote leaves. Some smoked the dried leaves of catnip. Some settlers carried, and in the back country they still carry, a potato in their pocket. Old-time miners drank sunflower seed in whisky. Oil from the grease of boiled frogs was tried.

Some settlers brought their superstitions with them. A nail from a coffin or a horseshoe warded off rheumatism. Wear the eyetooth of a pig. Take a cat to bed with you. An 1827 western drugstore advertised for rheumatism a morning glass of a concoction compounded of one ounce of sulphur, one-half pound of molasses, and one-half pint of whisky.

Perhaps actually sound advice, and that already in practice by the Indians, was that of John Timbe who, in his *Doctors and Patients,* published in England in 1876, wrote, "The advantages [of asparagus] are not sufficiently estimated by those who suffer from rheumatism." All his patients were helped and "slight cases" cured "in a few days by feeding on this delicious esculent."

Rickets

The Indians favored maidenhair as did the settlers as a cure for rickets in children.

Ringworm

There were numerous recommended remedies for worms, as will be noted in that category. For ringworm, however, there was one in particular: a fermentation of wild liquorice.

Roper's Relief

Roper's relief, also called the monkey-flower, still is used, the raw leaves and stems being applied, as the name implies to rope burns on the hands of the *vaqueros.*

Rose

The rose was far more than an outward sign of nature's beauty. To the Indian who saw beneath the loveliness it was of ineffable importance to his well-being. The wild rose grows up to the timber line and the Indians followed it there, to collect roots and leaves and to fill their bags full of the petals which would be hung on *vigas* to be used in the winter.

More astringent than the garden rose, the distilled water of the wild rose reduced eye irritation. It was used in a conserve for coughs and in decoction for a sore throat or ear infection. The ground petals were blown into a sore throat.

Even in Culpeper's England, the Indian practice of a gargle of honey and rose essence was prescribed. In the Rocky Mountain area, tea from boiled rose roots was drunk by most tribes for colds and fever. This tea stopped diarrhea and in small doses was given to children for influenza or the "bloody flux." A decoction was drunk for stomach disorders or for the liver, and a root decoction corrected failure to urinate. Red roses, as tea, were said to strengthen the heart.

For fever, cooled and sweetened petals. The Aztecs used boiled rose water as a purgative. Rose-hip tea was a pleasantly tasting restorative, especially in tuberculosis. The decocted roses combated gonorrhea. The ripe fruits or the cleaned pulpy seed were soothing to the lower intestines, especially piles.

The rock rose was chosen for diarrhea, ophthalmia, and syphilis. In 1892, the white medical profession announced its approval and refinements. Alcohol was added to the roses, the tincture standing three days until it had achieved "a beautiful crimson color" with the "odor of damp clover hay."

Rose-water tea added to meat or broth was given to the weak or convalescent and was drunk by all the western Indians to procure rest and sleep. For that purpose, too, rose leaves and mint were combined externally. Oil of roses soothed headache and was made into healing ointments.

Pulp of rose hips slowed excessive menses. The

fungous galls of the rose were mashed into a poultice for boils. For mouth sores, a salve of ground rose petals combined with grease was applied, and for fever blisters, dry rose powder.

For cuts, sores, and wounds, various parts of the rose plant were used, such as root and the inner bark of the stems—these being applied either moistened or dry. One Indian, at least, and doubtless hundreds more, keeps a supply of peeled rose stems in his medicine bag for emergency use among his family. His advice is that wounds should be allowed to bleed awhile before the rose stems make a cover for them, whether as shavings or powder. He assured the interviewer that even the deepest wounds yield to the healing properties of the rose. Swelling and pain are reduced and the final healing leaves little or no scar.

For eczema, one may do as the Indians did: Get a wildcat. Extract the fat. Mix it with ground rose petals. Apply several times a day.

Ruptures

According to Indian usage, wild geranium was best for ruptures.

Rush, Scouring

Valuable in treating gonorrhea.

S

Sage

"How can a man die who has sage in his garden?"

The whole of the vast stretches of desert on the plains, the piedmont, and into the high mountains was a sage garden for the Indian. Everywhere, except along the streams, there was sage—about twenty species—of which the *Artemisia tridentata* was the most common and the most used, its flowers and leaves and roots being collected during the growing season for medicinal use in the winter.

The leaves, fresh or dried, were made into a tea as needed for influenza, diarrhea, menstrual disorders, and swellings. It had a particularly favorable effect as a tonic after childbirth, the whole plant being decocted for this purpose.

Fresh leaves were crushed, strained, and mixed with lukewarm water for stomach distress or were chewed for flatulence or decocted for indigestion.

Sage tea could be drunk to remove obstructions, but carefully and supervised by a medicine man. The powdered herb destroyed worms in children and was so accepted officially in 1840 by the incoming whites. For asthma, the tea was taken night and morning for forty days and sage poultices were applied nightly during that time to the chest and back. For colds, repeated doses of the hot tea were drunk, and a hot decoction was taken for biliousness, at the same time a bundle of sage which had been steeped in boiling water and wrapped in a cloth was designed to put an end to the discomfort. A sage decoction increased the urine flow, the tea was drunk for sore throat, and for fever an infusion was given at its start to promote perspiration.

In England's herbal period, which was noted also for its class distinctions, a medical dictum stated that tansy and sage "form good fever drinks for the poor." Somewhat later, one who had left England to find a new life in the American West told of an attack of mountain fever. "The trouble was overcome by the use of alternate stronge doses of teas made from wild sage and the bark of Oregon grape root."

Externally, a large quantity of boiled sage leaves, or the whole plant, were added to the bath for rheumatism and other aches and pains, a remedy still used by the Indians. Sagebrush plants burned over the fire, spread their healing fumes, and were inhaled for heavy colds and grippe.

The juice of the herb or its powder was put on moist sores which, with this procedure, were said to dry and heal quickly, as were "green wounds." The *penitentes* of New Mexico wash their lacerated backs with astringently healing sage tea (*romerillo*), a practice that reaches back to the coming of Christianity to the Indians.

For numbness of the feet, a wash of sage was recommended, followed by the application of wax and ground nettles. The sage and wax were used for all foot injuries by the Aztecs.

Sage is still used as a shampoo to promote the growth of the hair and, though this is not in context, it might be pointed out that there are Indian women today who still use a sage solution to blacken their hair, combing it into their tresses daily.

Sage was a fumigant, the branches burned where a patient had been seriously ill. After childbirth, the baskets and blankets used were held to sage smoke for purification. A decoction of the whole plant was taken three times a day and also used as a wash for venereal disease.

A plant so continuously cherished over the centuries was bound to draw to it the comments of the experienced and the wise. In Taos, Indians say, "It is really good for everything." In 1699, John Evelyn declared that sage retains "all the noble Properties of the other hot Plants, more especially for the Head, Memory, Eyes and all Paralytical afflication." And so to the query translated in 1373 by John Lelamoure:

> Why of seknesse deyeth man
> While sawge [sage] in gardeyn
> He may hav.

St. Johnswort (Goatweed)

This was used by the Indians as an astringent and nerve medicine and a decoction was taken for promoting menstruation. The white Americans tried it and threw it out. In 1886, it was recorded as seldom used. In 1892, it no longer was listed. But that same year, Doctor Charles P. Millspaugh, in his fine book *Medicinal Plants,* protested. St. Johnswort had a "great use in wounds where nerves were involved. . . . It makes it regrettable that it is no longer officinal."

Not knowing or caring about this to-do, the Indians kept on using it as they always had. The boiled plant, applied direct or as a poultice, still was a healing agent for sores and swellings. The water from the boiled plant still soothed aching feet. The dried plant, pulverized and applied as powder, still was beneficial for cuts and slashes and bullet wounds and as a toothache remedy. The dried root was always kept available. It probably still is.

ST. JOHNSWORT

Salsify

When three species of salsify had migrated from the eastern seaboard where it had been introduced by the first colonists, the Indians who had been experimenting with it decided it was good. They coagulated the juice and chewed it for indigestion. They found that it eased a stomach ache, and they were right. Salsify contains ingredients remedial for mild stomach upsets.

Saltbush

The Indians boiled the roots and drank the resultant tea as a physic. They chewed the green leaves to mitigate stomach pains, as do New Mexican *Anglos* as well as Indians today, sometimes adding a palatable pinch of salt. The Zuñi moisten ground roots and blossoms with saliva and apply the paste to ant bites.

Sandwort

Sandwort was used for treating the eyes and the Indians experimented with it also for treatment of venereal disease.

Sarsaparilla

Nicolas Monardes, scientist and doctor, watching the galleons unload in the half-moon harbor of Cádiz, declared in 1569, "Joyfull Nevves out of the newe found world wherein is declared the rare and singular virtues of diuerse and Sundrie Hearbes . . ." One of these was sarsaparilla, of which he commented, "Sarcaparilla the Indians did use as great medicine."

SARSAPARILLA

It was indeed considered great medicine for many diseases—stomach upsets, colds, aching joints, cessation of the urine flow. Roots and berries were a "most efficient" sudorific and stimulant and, as spring bitters, was drunk as a blood purifier. The roots, bruised and chewed, were made into a poultice for wounds and ulcers. Its essential oil was dropped into aching ears and was considered excellent for deafness. The distillation was considered the best-known eyewash. It was effective for bites and stings. Ringworm and other skin blemishes responded to it in fermentation and in this form it was used in venereal disease.

Sassafras

Sixteenth-century Doctor Nicolas Monardes, "informing myself of the thynges of this tree," proved to his satisfaction that the Indians who used it had not overrated its virtues and stated that it cured "many griefes and euill diseases."

Saxifrage

Mostly used as an excellent diuretic.

Scalds

See Burns and Scalds.

Scarlet Fever

The usual fever medicines were tried and the patient was bathed in cooling lotions. But, to the majority of the western Indians, there was only one cure—catnip tea.

Sciatica

Burdock, mustard, poplar, yarrow—all were tried with varying success. Mugwort seems to have proved most effective, a reaction that had been endorsed by army doctor Dioscorides in the days of the Roman Empire. He wrote that three drams of the powder of dried mugwort (an artemisia) leaves taken in wine "is a speedy and best cure for sciatica."

Scorpion

Roots of curlydock were eaten to take away the pain of scorpion sting.

Scorpion Weed

Often called fiddleneck, this had been used for centuries by the Indians as a diuretic.

Scurvy

The Indians had ample experience with scurvy. Periods of near famine, winters without fresh vegetables or fruits, no milk, all this added to often serious nutritional deficiencies. Though they did not know why, their remedies were scientifically in line.

Curlydock leaves were the most generally used. But there was also skunkcabbage and the highly valued mountain sorrel. There was the juice of young birch leaves and there were infusions of vervain or wormwood.

There was scurvy grass and, above all, there was garlic. The first white men to arrive in the area were shown another early spring green and this, proving excellent against scurvy, became known as "miner's lettuce."

Alexander Philip Maximilian, Prince of Wied-Neuwied, wintering at Fort Clark and barely surviving on a diet of corn, found himself at the end of the cold months in a state of extreme weakness with a "terrible swelling of one leg." He later wrote, "I was still in a hopeless condition and was given not more than three or four days to live."

The fort's Negro cook, "A St. Louisan," told "Prince Max" that his trouble was due to scurvy which now could be cured. He put a group of Indian children to work gathering wild onions. These were boiled into a "spinach-like dish," and the prince was ordered to consume them in quantities. "Within hours, the patient was feeling better." The treatment had started the first day of April. By the fifth, he was well.

Long before Prince Max and long after him, there were those afflicted by vitamin deficiency who were helped by those who knew what to do. At the beginning of the white men's entry into Indian territory, there had been Jacques Cartier. When his crew was prostrated by scurvy, he appealed to the Indians. These were friendly and administered an infusion made from the sprouting tips of the fir trees. This is still recognized as an effective remedy and still is used among the Rocky Mountain Indians.

Scurvy Grass

So named because of its asserted efficacy in relieving scurvy, it was used also as a decoction to cleanse the blood.

Sedatives

There were onions, eaten plentifully to procure sleep. There were cherries and dandelions and lettuce and celery with their quieting effect, the celery being recommended to the readers of the Sheridan (Wyoming) *Post* as late as its edition of February 28, 1889. There was gumwood, adopted by the Jesuits from the Indians.

For stronger sedation, there was aconite for heart and nerves, and for insomnia, spasms, and mania there was henbane with its stalkless leaves and purple-veined petals. The Indians were careful in administering this, knowing it could be deadly poisonous, not knowing that it derived its effectiveness from the alkaloids scopolamine and hyoscyamine and the glucose hyoscypicnin. Valerian was held good for nervous disorders. Hellebore was a strong stimulant followed by sedative effects. Hops in decoction were a powerful sedative and jimson weed (datura) was the sedative and anodyne considered most soothing in pain.

Serviceberry

The serviceberry, so pleasant in the Indian cuisine, was also made into an eyewash from its boiled green inner bark, its great value being in the treatment of snow blindness. For this, the inner bark, with or without the addition of the roots, was boiled, a single drop three times a day being used.

Signatures

The Indians, like other early peoples, believed in the value of sympathetic medicine; that is, that all natural objects, plant, animal, or mineral, are stamped with a mark ("signature") which shows the human how he can be helped by using it.

There are indications that the theory goes back to Babylonia or Egypt or, more likely, far back into prehistory. The first enunciation of it in England came from

William Turner who in 1551 published the first English herbal to be printed. He pointed out that "the nutmeg being cut resembles the Brain, the red poppyflower resembles at its bottom the settling of the blood in pleurisie and how excellent is that flower in the disease."

With the Indians, milkweed was prescribed to increase lactation; the crushed roots of Solomon's-seal to seal broken bones and open wounds; yellow flowers, for jaundice; spotted plants, for skin defects; gummy plants, for pus-exuding sores; roses, for blood. The Indians, too, used the poppy for brain disorders but their reasoning differed from that of the English. Poppies must normalize the brain because their fruit was shaped like a human head.

Skeleton Weed

Indian women used this herb in decoction for dry breasts.

Skin Irritations

The indispensable balsamroot in decoction was a healing agent for skin troubles, especially sores. So was a distillation of birch leaves and sap, or burdock, sweet cicely, elder flowers, lupine, and mullein.

A poultice of bruised leaves and fruit of scarlet sumac was favored for skin diseases and a similar poultice of tobacco leaves was efficacious for skin infections such as eczema. A yarrow poultice served equally, or an infusion of the rootstock of yerba mansa.

Accepting these, the settlers also nourished their pet superstition: for skin troubles of all kinds, there was no cure equal to water taken from a point where three boundaries meet.

See also Rash.

Skullcap

Skullcap was used widely and over many generations for nervousness or other ills requiring an anti-spasmodic. In this, they anticipated the white medical profession which ultimately discovered its efficacy and the cause therefor: the crystalline glucoside it contains which is known as scutellaine.

Skunkcabbage

Skunkcabbage is an arum, the medicinal parts of which lie in the roots and seeds. Water or alcohol extract their value. Chemically, it contains wax, silica, iron, and a fixed oil. The Indians knew all about it.

They used it internally as an anti-spasmodic, expectorant, and stimulant with resultant slightly narcotic value. They prescribed it for bronchial irritation, nasal catarrh, whooping cough, asthma, and chronic coughs. In the eighteenth-century interest in Indian herbs, Reverend Doctor Cutler "of Massachusetts" commended these virtues as of "evident benefit." Another commendation, however, made the reservation that the smell resembled that of a "disturbed skunk." Hence, presumably, its name.

The Indians gave it for bad digestion, stone, urinal obstructions, loss of appetite, and scurvy. The root decoction was drunk for venereal disease.

Externally, the pulped substance was made into a liniment for rheumatism and the mashed root, raw, was placed on boils and swellings and used in cases of blood poisoning and snakebite.

But the Indians' prize remedy made from skunkcabbage was as a contraceptive. A more stringent dose was used for more drastic results. In either case, a liquid was made of the boiled root. If the equivalent of a tablespoon of the decoction was taken three times a day for three weeks, it was said to assure permanent sterility. It is still used today as a contraceptive in one location at least, being drunk by both man and woman.

The Indians always carried skunkcabbage root with them, burying it in sand to preserve it. Now they keep it in some dark place such as their cellar.

Skyrocket, Alpine

A very small member of the primrose family, with tiny white or pale-red flowers, this fragile appearing miniature actually is tough, since it grows in the alpine above the timber line. There the Indians found it and, in testing its qualities, discovered its apparent value in treating venereal disease.

Sleep

The Indians seem to have had the same problem of sleeplessness as their more "civilized" counterparts in the cities. They ate plentiful amounts of raw onions to induce slumber, or they drank yarrow tea or hop tea or purslane tea of decocted lettuce. Mullein tea, made from the leaves and tops, quieted the nerves and induced sleep; much the same result was obtained from rose leaves and mint heated and applied as a compress. A syrup from the seeds and flowers of the poppy, or a tea of poppy heads boiled in water, was considered unfailing.

For more grievous insomnia, a hot poultice of jimson leaves or, if acutely serious, henbane extract which, in other parts of the world, was used when even opium failed.

Though they had to climb high into the mountains to find the big plant, the Indians used lady's-slipper in decoction and this recently has been recommended also by the Vicomte de Manduit as "a permanent cure for sleeplessness."

Violet leaves decocted in water, made a pleasant before-bed drink, even as the sixteenth-century English *Askhams Herbal* prescribed: "For thee that may not slepe for sickness seeth [sic] this herb [violets] in water and at euen let him soke well hys feete in the water to the ancles, wha he goeth to bed, bind the herbe to his temple and he shall slepe wel by the grace of God."

Smallpox

When the white men's scourge of smallpox swept

through the Indian tribes, wiping out wholly such a people as the Mandan, the medicine men resorted to every experiment and expedient of their individual and combined experience. They could not halt the dread disease, of course. They could only mitigate the suffering.

They gave daily doses of gumplant, either the dried buds or the whole plant being decocted. A handful of antelope brush leaves was boiled in water to cover, and was drunk.

Bark of red cedar, proved in modern times, was prescribed by the Pawnee and Omaha, and this was used also for cholera. Vetch, vervain, and other herbs were drunk in decoction and catnip tea was called a "sure cure."

Marigold tea was designed to bring the rash to the surface or juniper twigs in strong solution or the heated twigs rubbed on the eruption.

A root decoction of balsam was used as an external wash and today, as in the past, the sap of the ponderosa pine is rubbed on the blisters. The dry powder of skunkbush was sprinkled on open sores but, when the pustules were unopen, a lotion of powdered berries was applied. New Mexico Indians today slice iris roots, thread them on a cord, and tie it around the patient's throat. This, they say, opens the throat which the smallpox has closed.

When it was over, antelope brush or juniper tea was drunk while these herbs were burned and the patient's quarters disinfected by the smoke.

Snakebite

There were snakes, notably rattlesnakes. Then, even as today, there were numerous attempted cures. The Indians were versed in the use of numerous herbs which had proved efficacious and one of which, surely, would be within easy reach should the emergency arise.

There was sunflower root, coneflower, juniper, and milkweed juice; tea from the creosote bush was also used in making a poultice to draw out the poison. Yellowdock, too, was taken both internally and as a poultice. Decocted white ash buds were drunk and the heated juice of basil which the settlers mixed with milk. There was snakeroot.

The Indians had highly developed skills for treating snakebite. Some, of course, were fantastic or fetishistic. Others were sensible, practical, and effective.

All the Rocky Mountain tribes, everywhere, first applied suction. Many excised the area, then applied medication. Yellowdock or plantain or purple coneflowers were chewed and made into a poultice. Mashed garlic was considered most helpful and still is used. The Shoshone mash the raw root of false hellebore and cover the wound until the medication and discharge dry.

An onion beaten to pulp was moistened, the settlers using kerosene for this purpose as is still done. It is testified that this "poultice that cures snakebite, draws out the poison as is seen by the green color of the poultice after it has been on the bite a short time." According to an old-timer, tobacco, moistened and bound on the wound, "has kept many a man alive until whisky could be had."

Tobacco leaves were plucked, chewed into a poultice and were, in fact, the Indians' great stand-by. But milkweed seed boiled in a little water was claimed to be unfailing in drawing out the poison. The raw roots of sweet cicely, sometimes heated, were an effective wet dressing, as was the pulped root of skunkcabbage. The Tarahumaras favored a poultice of chewed peyote buttons.

The frontier forts, borrowing largely from the Indians, each had its own favorite procedure. One for instance, advised: "If a rattler bites you on the limb, make a twist of horsehair above the bite and bind the mashed rawroot of wild parsnip on the wound to draw out the poison." In the Canadian high country today, it is asserted that chewed "trillium roots will cure instantly the bite of a rattlesnake both in men and cattle."

According to nineteenth-century Schoepf's *Materia*

Medica in North America, "There are fifty plants in the United States employed as an antidote for this purpose which merely act as sudorifics."

Why, then, over the centuries, were the herbs used and proved by snake-bitten Indians who lived to use and prove them for posterity?

Snakeroot

Snakeroot was valued highly by the Indians, then by the settlers, then by the white doctors. The Indians used it as a diuretic, diaphoretic, and as a stimulating tonic. These attributes were approved by Doctor Chapman in his *Therapeutics,* published in 1817, and were blessed by the medical profession in 1892.

Meantime, the Indians continued to use it as they always had. It was taken in decoction for asthma, its leaves for a sore throat, its roots for coughs and colds. It was successful in pneumonia and in large doses was given as an emetic and cathartic and in small ones as a sudorific.

It was favored for rattlesnake bite and for dropsy. A root decoction was used for vaginal irritation and this was blessed by the United States medical profession in 1817 which stated that in uterine complaints, particularly amenorrhea, it had "decided efficacy." The same year, its use by the Indians for croup was "introduced into notice by Dr. Archer of Maryland. He speaks with much confidence of its utility in that disease."

This same root decoction was tried by the Indians and found helpful for gonorrhea. In the white community, it was found "useful" for "exhaustion from sexual depletion and loss of erectile power."

SNAKEROOT

Sneezing—Sneezewort

The Indians believed in sneezing. They believed that it cleared nasal passages choked by colds or clogging dust. They induced it with primrose powder or, much preferred, yarrow powder so commonly used that the settlers called it sneezewort. In this case, it was the leaves that were powdered and sniffed up the nose. The root held in the mouth was said to help toothache.

Snow Blindness

See Serviceberry.

Snowberry

This low, sprawling shrub was searched for by Indians on the wooded slopes of the foothills for its roots which were steeped, pounded, and decocted into a medicine for colds and stomach distress. Its globular white berries were used for a cathartic and emetic.

Snowbush (Blackthorn)

Snowbush was emergency material. If no more appropriate material were at hand, the bark could be used as a cathartic. The danger was that it was apt to purge too violently.

Snuff

The Indians used snuff regularly to clear the dust from their nostrils. If there was no tobacco and a sinus or headache required attention, the dried and powdered roots of herbs were substituted for their cephalic value. Preferred were primrose, Solomon's-seal, white hellebore, or yarrow.

Solomon's-seal, False

However the name of the plant was written, its root was highly considered for wounds and sores, a poultice of either fresh or dried root being administered, and to boils or sprains as well. If the wound was bleeding, the

SOLOMON'S-SEAL, FALSE

powder of the pulverized roots coagulated it.

The pulped root was forced through cloth into an aching ear and the liquid from mashed and soaked roots was dropped into inflamed eyes. This was used, too, as an antiseptic for blood poisoning. The rhizome mixed with cedar balm twigs and/or leaves and burned as a smudge revived an unconscious person. The exudate was made into cough syrup.

Tea from the boiled roots still is much used by the Indians of the area. It is said to regulate menstrual disorder. And it is asserted positively that it cures venereal disease. It is drunk to prevent conception, the dose being an approximate half cup of the boiled-leaf decoction drunk daily for a week.

According to herbalist Gerard, writing in 1597, Solomon's-seal came to the aid of women in another way. He pointed out that "The root stamped while it is fresh and greens are applied, taketh away in one night or two at the most, any bruise or blew spots, gotten by falls of women's wilfulnesse in stumbling upon their hasty husband's fists."

Sores, Swellings, Ulcers

Here again is a large variety of herbs used for specific purposes. If you stepped on a sharp stone and your foot began to swell, you would want a remedy at hand. If your youngster's fall resulted in ugly black-and-blue marks, you would want to apply a healing herb at once. Fortunately, throughout the Rocky Mountain region, healing herbs were widespread and abundant. We list those most often referred to and most commonly used.

There were dandelion, milkweed, cinquefoil, or elder poultices for swellings and sores. Curlydock was highly favored, running a close second to the invaluable balsamroot. Poultices to reduce swellings were made also from boiled lamb's quarters, chewed locoweed, or crushed fresh flax leaves, these being employed especially for goiter and gall bladder swellings.

The crushed leaves of the Rocky Mountain beeplant brought relief or a poultice of hemlock leaves and flax seed thickened with boiling water. This appealed to both Indians and settlers and a variant, used today, is to grind dry flax seed and mix it with a little corn meal, adding water to make a paste. To reduce swellings, this poultice should be changed several times a day. Resin from an incised tree could always be counted on for swellings in any part of the body.

Poultices for swellings were made also of white sand verbena, of fresh or dried sage leaves, of mashed yarrow leaves, or the entire yarrow plant boiled and mashed as a dressing. The mashed roots of yerba mansa made an excellent such application as did mashed young juniper twigs. Sand lily roots were reduced to a soapy consistency. The raw root of the mountain hollyhock (mallow) was crushed or the entire plant used. The mashed raw roots of skunkcabbage, the crushed leaves of wild tobacco, mashed clematis leaves, or St. Johnswort could be beneficial. A warm poultice of gumplant was used commonly and, in the desert country, a hot piñon resin dressing. Through all the area, puffballs, the fungus gathered in its young stage, were sliced and applied directly to swellings and sores. Many of these poultices were used not only for swellings but also for ulcers and sores.

The Indians used powdered pine resin, but, since the days of Dioscorides, a decoction of their roots has been a remedy for scales and running sores. Goldenrod cleansed sores and distilled tobacco juice promoted healing. Sores were washed with decocted honeysuckle leaves and the Shoshone used the pulped root for swellings. When a sore had reached the appropriate stage, the scab was and is peeled off and the powdered root of the four o'clock blown over it Every tribe has its special name for this, but government field nurses refer to it simply as impetigo plant.

Alumroot was powdered and applied wet to sores and swellings. Lodgepole pine pitch was put on open sores. The amole bulb was an antiseptic. Thistle seed was ground and spread on sores, as was the blue flag made into a paste. The bark of the indigo root was boiled down and fat added to make a salve.

Yampa was always good and a catnip poultice was "very valuable," as attested by the settlers. Dry rose powder was sprinkled on fever blisters or a salve of rose pitch and grease. The powdered dry bark of the skunkcabbage was recommended for a sore mouth. Fresh milkweed sap reduced the irritability of sores and the Oregon grape was invaluable. Horsetail was dried and burned and the ashes put on sores of the mouth. The Paiutes use the ground leaves of this but the Shoshone prefer the powdered root. The Stansbury phlox was used mostly for boils as the Shoshone use it today. The primrose root is ground and applied wet to sores to reduce inflammation. The root of the sand dock was powdered and sprinkled on sores and burns, or the leaves decocted into a wash.

The powdered root of yerba mansa in poultices was prescribed for abrasions and sores "in man or beast." The green leaves of elder were reserved for inflamed sores, a procedure approved by the white community in 1840. Ripe iris seed was made into a paste for sores. A solution of the whole yarrow plant was used as a wash for sores and rashes. Angelica root was mashed and smeared on. For chronic sores, a poultice of powdered green pentstemon leaves was advocated.

Cottonwood bark, so easily obtainable, was pulverized into a drying powder for sores and antelope brush, also easily accessible, was made into an external wash or the leaves were mashed into a wet dressing or the dried leaves were applied as powder. With the silk ground off, the ripe milkweed seed was ground and made into a salve for sores, though more commonly used for wounds. The inner bark of the wild-rose stem was healing for sores as, equally, was dry powdered skunkcabbage root. The fleshy, gnarled rootstock of wild geranium was always a welcome remedy for sores as, more difficult to obtain, was a poultice of ash bark and bear grease. An extract of red clover proved "particularly soothing," as approved by the United States medical profession in 1892. To promote healing, there was also gumplant, the cottony fuzz from the base being of noted value in the case of running sores.

For black-and-blue marks, Parkinson in 1640 had advised in England what the Indians used in the shadow of the Rocky Mountains, a poultice made of yampa seed or lupine seed with meal and honey. A half century before, in France, "Maister Nicot cured a young man with a sore on his nose with tobacco."

Sorrel

Mountain sorrel, growing from 6,000 to 9,000 feet, was worth climbing to find. It was a diuretic and, if roasted, it assisted greatly in reducing swellings. It was and is a vermifuge, useful in killing worms if the green or dry leaves are taken as tea.

SORREL

The roast powder was a purgative and helped, too, to control excessive menses. It was used for jaundice, for the itch, for "putrid fevers," for other fevers as well. From the time of Linnaeus, it had been used in Europe as by the Indians as an astringent that cooled, refreshed, and allayed feverish thirst. It promoted "appetite in fainting or decaying stomachs," wrote Culpeper, who recommended it made into a cordial for the heart.

It was used externally as a poultice for wounds, thus paralleling the findings of the famous sixteenth-century *Askham Herbal* which noted, "This herbe alleluia mecall it Wodsour [woodsorrel] or stubwort. The vertue of this herbe is thus, if it be roasted in the ashes in red docke leaves or in red wort leaves, it [takes] awai dead flesh of a wound."

Spearmint

The familiar spearmint was, to the Indians, a carminative, anti-spasmodic, stimulant, and diuretic.

Spirea

From Alberta to Wyoming, along the streams and in the woods up to 8,000 feet, the wild spirea glows in the spring and then, for the Indians, its usefulness began. The leaves and stems were decocted for stomach disorders. Boiled stems made a tea. For colds, boiled roots as for diarrhea. It seems to have proved valuable in treating venereal disease. I deduce this from the fact that its use for this purpose has been continuous over wide areas, a small amount of decocted leaves or stems being taken three times a day over a long period.

Splinters

For outdoor people, I repeat what already has been listed. If the splinter was deeply embedded, the Indians made a decoction of the yarrow plant and applied it to the area. Apparently slightly anesthetic, it helped in the extraction of the foreign body.

Sprains

Repeated for quick reference and immediate application are these Indian favorites: yarrow, the steeped leaves or entire plant being made into a poultice; mullein, equally prized; leafy juniper twigs, toasted on embers and bound tightly on the sprain to reduce swelling.

See also Bruises and Sprains.

SPURGE

Spruce

See Venereal Disease.

Spurge

Tea from the whole leafy plant was used as an eyewash.

Squaw Root

See Yampa.

Squawbush

Squawbush is a relative of poison ivy but that did

not deter the Indians from finding and profiting by its varied virtues. The fruits made a refreshing drink after a fatiguing day, relieving slight fatigue temperatures. The decocted stems were good for coughs. The dry bark is still powdered and rubbed on fever blisters and canker sores and, when smallpox was prevalent, this powder was put on the open sores. If the pustules were unopen, a lotion from the powder was used.

Stimulants

There was always an herb at hand if a stimulant was needed in sickness or accident. There was spearmint, basil, mustard, goldenrod, ivy, snakeroot, fleabane, sage, elder flowers in warm infusion.

A decoction of cherry bark and root was "excellent." Valerian provided a mild stimulant. But, as attested by the settlers in 1840, the bark of the root with or without flowers was decocted into a "powerful stimulant" as also was hellebore, the latter being followed by sedative effects. Yarrow produced a "good stimulant" in warm infusion. The red, winelike liquid from mashed and boiled young yucca shoots was used in desert country. Learning from the Indians, Priddy Meeks prescribed lobelia.

Stings

See Bites and Stings, Insect.

Stomach and Bowel Disorders

The irregularity of their eating habits, the frequently unbalanced diets, the periods of near-starvation followed by overeating in a period of plenty—all were conducive to stomach and other digestive upsets which, from the number and variety of the remedies, must have plagued the Indians continually. It was fortunate that they had such a wide range of medications from which to choose. The following were the most favored:

Alder: Decoction of dried bark to allay stomach ache, or, mixed with tobacco, to induce vomiting.

Angelica: Decocted to soothe stomach.

Ash: Root decocted for colic.

Balsam: Roots boiled into solution like yellow soup for severe stomach upset.

Beeplant: Leaves added to one part goldenrod, mashed, mixed with hot water, or leaves boiled in just enough water to moisten without crushing. Corn was added to take away bitter taste. Leaves were eaten as remedial greens.

Ceanothus: Used today as in the past to correct malassimilation of food.

Chía: Leaves dried or fresh, chewed with salt to relieve distress.

Chickweed: Flowers and leaves beaten into a conserve for "internal bruises."

Chokecherry: Indians still dig the roots in autumn to be used as a warm tea before meals to aid digestion or for an upset or inflamed stomach. Bits of dried chokecherry cake were given to babies with stomach ache.

Cicely, Sweet: Tea for gas.

Columbine: Roots and leaves boiled together for biliousness, dizziness, stomach ache.

Corn Meal: Steeped in lye as an anti-spasmodic. Favored by Comanches, Kiowas, Blackfeet, Crows, Arapahoes, and Sioux.

Cow Parsnip: Dried and decocted to expel gas.

Creosote: Decocted leaves or bark for intestinal trouble.

Curlydock: Steeped roots for stomach upset or as a stomach tonic.

Everlasting: Leaves decocted for intestinal disorders.

Flag: Sweet flag chewed to relieve dyspepsia.

Flax: Stems steeped for stomach disorders, gas.

Garlic: Roasted whole on coals, chewed thoroughly, swallowed with cold water. "Gas disappears and other discomforts alleviated."

Gumplant: Tea to allay upsets, flowering tops and

leaves decocted into stomach tonic. Officinal.

Hops: Boiled as antiseptic for bowel complaints or to "open obstructions."

Iris: Warm tea for stomach ache.

Juniper: Tender ends of branches, covered with cold water, boiled, drunk in morning to reduce inflammation and "take the cold out of the stomach." Distilled berries used also by pioneers for "stomach debility."

Kinnikinnick: Much used tea for "ordinary stomach trouble."

Marigold: Steeped fresh leaves drunk hot. Highly recommended by Indians who also chewed the fresh leaves for stomach ache.

Mint: All the mints and all their parts were used as tea for indigestion, colic, stomach ache. White community admitted mint is "sweetly carminative."

Mugwort: Decoction of leaves, especially for colic.

Mullein: Decoction of leaves seldom used, a tea from heart of young plant being preferred, boiled to relieve griping pains in bowels. Settlers (1840) used milk in its preparation instead of water.

Onion: Much used, especially to relieve flatulence. Bulb preferred for this purpose.

Pennyroyal: Plant boiled for indigestion.

Pentstemon: Tea from boiled plant, especially used for children.

Phlox: Tea for stomach disorders.

Pine: Bark decocted to quiet stomach.

Piñon: Tea from the resin for nausea and bowel upsets.

Rabbitbrush: Tea from the leaves for easing the stomach.

Ragweed: Tea for nausea. Abdomen sometimes scarified and powdered ragweed applied as counterirritant.

Raspberries: Decoction of scraped bark of the root for stomach upsets.

Sage: One of the most useful herbs for stomach

difficulties. Leaves still are chewed by Paiutes and Shoshones to relieve indigestion and flatulence, or the leaves are decocted and drunk, usually in lukewarm water. If distress is acute, a compress is applied to abdomen, this being a bundle of the plant steeped in boiling water and wrapped in cloth. This Indian practice was approved by white doctors in 1840, the dictum being that "sage is good to remove obstructions but care [should be taken] that patient does not take cold . . . as it leaves the pores relaxed."

Saltbush: Stomach pains relieved by chewing the green leaves. With pinch of salt added, this is done today by both Indians and Whites in New Mexico.

Snowberry: Pounded, steeped, and drunk as tea for stomach ache.

Spirea: Leaves and stems decocted.

Tobacco: Enema used for colic.

Valerian: Hot drink from roots still used by Blackfeet for stomach trouble.

Verbena: Decocted for stomach ache.

Wormwood: Infusion to help in dysentery. Is good digestion aid. Chewing of fresh or dry leaves common. These are steeped for acute stomach pain.

Yarrow: Widely used. Leaves chewed fresh or dry with salt as stomachic and to relieve cramps. Yarrow (tansy) tea still a household remedy. Indians picked and dried whole plant, put small amount in boiled water for indigestion. Decocted root drunk for gas pains. Doctor Ed Palmer testified in 1892 that, "among the Pah-utes," decocted yarrow was used for a "weak or disordered stomach."

Yerba Mansa: Tea from boiled roots or whole herb for digestive upsets. As alternative, the dried roots, roasted brown and decocted.

Dandelion was not listed because it deserves the emphasis of a place by itself. As the Indians knew it, so we know it, as do people all over the world. Everywhere, it was and is used as a diuretic, a mild laxative, and a tonic. So the Indians used it and the mountain men and the explorers and their families—and if we want we can just sit down at the end of a hard day and drink a comforting tea to quiet the nervous quivers of a tired stomach.

For acute abdominal pain, massage was given and hot poultices applied of ashes mixed with water and bound on with rabbit fleece or bird down. For acute bowel inflammation, the Indians took a grouse or small turkey (later, a chicken), split it live and, "still squawking," strapped it to the abdomen.

Stone Seed (Plante aux Perles)

The Indians traveled for long distances to obtain this herb, the root of which, chopped, covered with water, and boiled, was drunk as a tea daily for six months to achieve permanent birth control.

Straw

Still used in New Mexico to "cure" rheumatism, this vapor bath taken three times a day consists of a tub of water in which a handful of straw has been boiled. The Indians used to add three hot stones to the bath to keep the water from cooling.

Strawberries

Dried strawberry leaves in infusion were used as an excitant and astringent in diarrhea and dysentery and for dysuria, the painful discharge of the urine. A strong infusion was prescribed for strangulated kidney or liver pain and for jaundice.

The fresh leaves were made into a wash for a sore throat and the ripe berries were welcomed as a safe dentifrice to remove tartar and thoroughly cleanse the teeth. (In seventeenth-century England, Culpeper maintained that strawberry lotion "fastened in" loose teeth and healed spongy gums.) A mild mixture of strawberry juice and water was used by the Indians for inflamed eyes.

Strawberries long have been used medicinally.

Rousseau testified that the eating of plenty of them brought relief from calcareous affections and Linnaeus himself extolled their efficacy in his own case in preventing paroxyms of gout. Long after their time, the Indians claimed that a root infusion of strawberries cured gonorrhea.

Sumac

Sumac berries have an astringent effect. A cold infusion of them was drunk by the Indians for fever, colds, diarrhea. It was used as a gargle. The dried seeds were powdered and taken to halt hemorrhage. The young shoots, in a strong infusion, were said to strengthen the stomach. Root juice was used for warts.

The fruits were boiled as a styptic wash to stop excessive flow in women after childbirth. The bark of the roots provided an antiseptic dressing for ulcers and open wounds. A poultice of bruised leaves and fruit of the scarlet sumac was prescribed for skin diseases.

Hence, it was only a step to the inevitable. A decoction of the leaves was drunk for venereal disease. A cold infusion of the berries was used for gonorrhea and this was esteemed also as an anti-syphilitic.

SUNFLOWER

Sunflower

An infusion of sunflower stems was said to be anti-malarial. The roots, decocted as a warm wash for rheumatism, are still used for that purpose today. So too is the use of the roots for snakebite. The "old-timers" prefer their sunflower seeds soaked in whisky, and in this form they have taken it for generations as a laxative.

Swellings

See Beeplant; Sores, Swellings, Ulcers.

Sycamore

The Indians gently pierced the bark of the sycamore to obtain the milk. This they dried, to be held in readiness to soften tumors or close the lips of green wounds.

Syncope

The temporary suspension of circulation and respiration was treated with a decoction of bush morning-glory root or by inhalations of the tops of angel stem.

Syphilis

See Venereal Disease.

T

Tapeworm

The male fern was used for centuries by the Indians to expel tapeworm.

See also Worms.

Thistle

Thistles, rejected by the white man as a nuisance, were invaluable to the Indians. Their decocted roots were used for diarrhea. The mashed roots, boiled into a warm juice, were dropped into an aching ear. Hot, the juice was held in the mouth for toothache. The powdered seed, soaked and decocted, was drunk to increase the urine, and to break and expel kidney stone. The Aztecs applied it to burns.

Parturition was hastened by drinking tea from the boiled roots.

A decoction of thistle flowers taken three times a day "cured" gonorrhea.

THISTLE

Throat

For a sore throat the Indians used a decoction of lodgepole pine buds or the steeped roots of the snowberry or of columbine leaves, or of horsemint (oregano) while its powder was put in a skin bag and hung around the neck. Wild basil was a remedy and gumplant, vervain, garlic, and dried powdered rose leaves swallowed without liquid, or a tea from the rose roots or of mugwort leaves, or fleabane or skunkcabbage.

The Indians chewed clematis for a sore throat or the young shoots of pine or the dried roots of bitterroot, the latter preferred by the old people. Similarly, they found helpful a chew of locoweed or goldenrod or licorice root or piñon pitch or sweet cicely or balsamroot or a small piece of angelica.

They made poultices of onions or wild potatoes or hops or raw cow parsnip root. The black powder of corn smut (*chapetes*) was mixed with water and spread on the throat as was mashed fresh goldenrod bound with grease.

Dry roots of the four o'clock were scraped and the powder blown into the throat or ground rose petals were so used, the dose being repeated every two or three hours and, as testified by the settlers, "said to give great relief." Their mentors, the Indians, showed them a gargle of skunkcabbage decoction or of nettle roots or strawberry leaves or yerba mansa, the proportions for the last being an approximate teaspoon of the dried ground root to an approximate half cup of water. If the sore throat was severe, finely ground juniper twigs were heated over the fire, bound in a hot cloth, and reheated as needed until relief was brought.

Tobacco

Tobacco was heaven sent. In *Healing Herbs of the Upper Rio Grande,* the authors wrote, "The tobacco plant always was of mystical import to the American Indians who considered it sacred and who invoked its 'soul-consoling smoke' as an offering to the powers that rule life. It was burned to appease divine forces or invite aid but almost never taken as a matter of personal indulgence."

Medicinally, tobacco was taken internally to expel worms. It was taken as a diuretic "in doses so small as not to offend the stomach." And, commented the white doctor who had tested this use by the Indians, "with very good effect." It was at this time, 1817, that the Indian use was approved as "extensively employed for strangulated hernias," and, with reservations, "as an enema for colic." For bowel stoppage, the Indians used the same procedure, injecting tobacco smoke as an enema. It was so used for the "destruction of small worms" and was highly recommended as a method of resuscitating persons seemingly drowned.

For piles, a suppository of raw fat combined with a pinch of tobacco was used with or without salt. A medical publication of the early nineteenth century reported that "Dr. Holmes of Worcester City, Mass." states that a tobacco infusion was given a patient "under violent tetanus" and that the "spasms were completely removed." So the Indians had found over the years. For hydrophobia, tobacco was prescribed as a palliative and, as checked by the white incomers, it was held to give "some degree of protection against contagiouns and epidemics."

Tobacco was chewed by the Indians almost exclusively for its medicinal value. Tobacco was said to stop toothache. The chewed leaves were applied to cuts and bruises in "man or animal." Chewed leaves were bound on snakebite after the poison had been sucked out.

Tobacco poultices were used extensively by the western Indians. For chest colds, powdered leaves were mixed with fat. Poultices of crushed leaves reduced swellings and were put on the gum for toothache and were prescribed for eczema and other skin eruptions and infections. Poultices of crushed leaves or seed were applied regularly for rheumatism or the patient was bathed in hot water in which a handful of tobacco had been boiled. For the kidneys, the herb was roasted, pulverized, and mixed with the juice of the plant. If the new mother continued to have pains, pulverized tobacco was advised with the addition of a touch of rosemary (*romero*). For athlete's foot, a wet dressing of tobacco leaves was mixed with mountain grass as the Paiute do today.

Tobacco was considered an effective disinfective for a wound, and was equally efficacious for insect or spider bites. Powdered leaves or their decoction was said to kill lice.

For baby's colic, tobacco smoke was blown under its clothes. For earache, it was blown into the ear. The smoke was said to be a sure cure for colds and, almost without exception, this was the only occasion on which Indian women smoked. If tobacco was unavailable, mullein was used as a substitute. For obesity, smoking was encouraged as it would make the weight-loser "spit away" his fat.

An extraordinary practice was that of giving tobacco to "puny frail children." This they chewed. If they were not growing normally, it was said that they were often helped by the use of tobacco, the rationalization being that tobacco helped the digestion and that "its powder seems needed by the system to work against the poison that prevents growth."

Monardes (1569) wrote that "tabaco" was introduced into Spain "to adornate Gardens with the fairness thereof. . . . But nowe we doe use it more for his meruelous medicinable vertues than for his fairness." A little later, in Seville, it was testified, "They know not what other to doe, having cut or hurt themselves but to run to the tabaco as to a most readie remedie. It doth meruellous workes, without any need of other Surgery, but this only herbe."

But it was "Maister Nicot" who first developed the remedial properties of the herb; its official name, nicotine, was given in his honor. As proof thereof, the 1559 record testified that "hauing caused the said hearbe to be set in his Garden, where it grewe and multiplied maruellously," he experimented to discover its varied medicinal uses. He cured a young man with a sore on his nose and "one of Nicot's own cooks hauing almost cutte off his thombe with a great Choppin Knife, ran unto the said Nicotiane and healted it."

Tobacco Plant

See Valerian.

Tonics

The tonic effect of teas made from various herbs never was better illustrated than in their use by the Indians. There no doubt were others, but here are the most frequently prescribed tonics among the Rocky Mountain tribes.

Angelica: Boiled root drunk three times daily.

Aspen, Quaking: Bark decocted.

Aster: Tea made from dried stems (without leaves).

Balsam: Toza tea made from balsam chips was given to convalescents. In cases of extreme debility, the patient was put to bed and drank only *toza* for a week.

Barley, Wild: In decoction.

Cascara: Bark soaked in cold water twelve hours before drinking.

Chokecherry: Tea commonly used over entire area.

Creosote: A strong tea from the leaves.

Dandelion: Most popular for spring build-up.

Dock: Burdock was used as a tonic for centuries both in Europe and by the Indian, the latter, however, preferring curlydock. The roots were steeped in boiling water and drunk in approximate cupfuls several times a day. This was sold later by self-called medicine men as a laxative and tonic under the name of yellowdock.

Fleabane: In decoction.

Gentian: Indians drank the bitter, clear juice as a tonic—as was done in other parts of the world, for gentian, growing high, has been found up to 16,000 feet in the Himalayas.

Grape: The holly grape, known in the West as the Oregon grape, contains the officinal drug berberis, used as a bitter tonic. Its roots and yellow stems were so used by the Indians.

Juniper: Tonic from young twigs.

Kinnikinnick: The leaves, dried in the fall and carefully saved, were used as an astringent and tonic.

Licorice: Roots decocted.

Mint: Spearmint favored especially as tonic.

Onion: The tonic of tonics, used raw or cooked, or the juice drunk pure.

Pennyroyal: Tea used by Indians as in England and other countries as a helpful tonic.

Piñon: Resin tea, especially valuable after childbirth.

Prince's Pine: This herb contains glucosides and a volatile oil valuable in present-day medicine as a tonic. The Indians have been drinking the tea as a pick-up tonic for centuries.

Rabbitbrush: Dried leaves and flowers used.

Sage: Sage tea, always and everywhere.

Squawbush: This relative of the poison ivy was made into a mildly tonic and very refreshing tea.

Valerian: Unpalatable and mild as tonic.

Willow: Root decocted, favored as spring tonic.

Yarrow: Yarrow tea is still drunk by the Indians as a tonic, even as their ancestors did for untold centuries. It was considered especially helpful for a rundown condition. A small amount of the dried root, or preferably of the whole plant, was put in a small amount of water and brewed. For convalescents, a cold infusion was preferred.

Yerba Mansa: Boiled roots as a tonic, especially following colds and sickness.

Tonsilitis

If not serious, tonsilitis was treated as a cold. But in severe cases, green bull nettle (*tomatillo*) berries were crushed, mixed with salt, and bound to the throat, or the plant was dried and ground and the powder blown into the throat.

See also Colds.

Toothache

Ripe strawberries were considered an excellent

dentifrice, the fruit cleansing and removing tartar. Tobacco had a reputation for preserving the teeth. But when the toothache came—and because of dietary deficiencies it probably came often—every alleviation was used that could be tried and proved.

Poultices were the most highly favored: lamb's quarter leaves, hops mixed with coarse salt heated and wool-covered, scraped wild carrots, hot and moistened crushed juniper leaves, tobacco leaf poultices or one of willow roots and greens. In 1663 New England, it was recorded that the Indians had been observed applying the powdered root of white hellebore to an aching tooth.

Direct application to the cavity was widely tried. Yarrow bits were inserted into the aching void or finely mashed rabbitbrush or piñon or the raw root of cow parsnip (as is done today) or the dried root of St. Johnswort. The cotton-like fuzz at the base of the gumplant was put into the cavity. The raw root of sweet cicely was said to reduce the pain. The Paiute and Shoshone still use the pulped root of iris, either in the cavity or along the gum. It is claimed that this will kill the nerve, following which the tooth will come out.

Chewed herbs were considered highly efficacious: tobacco, green yarrow leaves, or, preferred by some, a small portion of the root. Like the iris, it is believed that yarrow, continually applied by chewing or as a wash, will kill the nerve of an ulcerated tooth. Crushed yerba mansa root or, sometimes, resin was held on ulcerated gums. The Indians chewed the inner bark of the ash root but in his *Medical Flora* herbalist Rafinesque reported: "I found . . . a speedy mitigation of pain followed, though the sensation of the acrid bark was nearly or fully as unpleasant as the ache." Priddy Meeks approved blue flag: "The pain ceases the instant it is chewed."

It was the Indian use of tobacco that was recommended most highly by Monardes after it had been introduced into Spain. His advice: Put to the tooth "a little ball made from the leafe of the tabaco, washing first the tooth with a smal cloth wet in the juyce, it stayesth it that the putrifaction goe not forwarde: and this remedie is so common that it healeth euerie one."

Trefoil

Any trefoil, especially the *Medicago lupulina* with its tiny yellow flowers and leaves like clover, was prescribed for heart trouble.

Trillium

The lovely wake-robin, herald of the spring, was greeted by the Indians for medically utilitarian purposes. It was an astringent, especially valuable in diarrhea. They still use it for insect and snake bites, a poultice of the roots being applied. The leaves in fat are a helpful salve. Because of the value of its decocted rootstock in childbirth, the settlers came to call it birthroot.

Tuberculosis

Balsam root was the favored Indian tea for tubercular patients, or decocted pitch pine, or the soft resin of the fir tree drunk in infusion. Sometimes the bark was eaten. Gummy balsam sap from its roots was swallowed. A tea of buckwheat roots and, sometimes, its tops, had to be taken steadily. There were decoctions of cottonwood bark, a tea from the leaves and bark of the boiled dried root of the chokecherry or from the inner white bark of antelope brush. To make the patient more comfortable, a warm sponge bath was given to which was added boiled kinnikinnick.

Tumor

The Indians used their favorite remedies for tumor, these including dandelion and the docks. Pioneer Priddy Meeks put these together and reported, "Mary Smith, a young girl, had a bunch growing on her upper lip . . . protruding above the nose . . . which was entirely stopped." He "got her well with: Equal quantities of burdock, yellowdock, and dandelion and a snuff of yellowdock up her nose." The tumor "gradually vanished."

Typhoid Fever

The accepted fever remedies were used but, in this prolonged and severe illness, sweet flag was administered also as a heart stimulant.

See Fever.

U

Ulcers

The Indians had a variety of treatments for ulcers, depending on the time of year and the current location of the tribe. Anemone ointment was used for corroding or malignant ulcers. Pennyroyal cleansed, as did cinquefoil or Oregon grape or decocted oak bark or chickweed juice, the last said to heal old ulcers. The wild geranium was a strong astringent for indolent ulcers. Red clover extract was approved also by the settlers as "particularly soothing."

For chronic ulcers, the split joints of the opuntia (prickly pear) were baked and applied, as noted with approval by herbalist Rafinesque. Bark of the sumac root made an antiseptic dressing, or elder tree ointment or a poultice of ash root bark mixed with bear grease.

See also Sores, Swellings, Ulcers.

Valerian

VALERIAN

Also called the tobacco plant, valerian was a stimulant, tonic, powerful purgative, and was recognized also for its excellent effects in nervous troubles, hysteria, palpitations, and the like, some species being distinctly sedative.

Its leaves were helpful in healing wounds and the Indians still use the herb today, as the Englishman Thomas Hill recommended it in 1577 to his fellow countrymen: "The distilled water of valerian drunk Vnto the quantitie of foure ounces at a time both morning and evening profiteth the creature having any bone broken."

Veins

For swollen veins, a solution of boiled pentstemon plant.

Venereal Disease

Venereal disease first appeared in western Europe in the fifteenth century, 1457 being accepted as the first authenticated record of it. It was brought to the Western Hemisphere almost immediately upon the arrival of the white man, and its progress came under the painstaking observations of Von Humboldt in Mexico. Authentic histories over a wide area were supplied by W. H. Prescott, Washington Irving, and the scholarly Le Conte.

The Indians did not know what to make of it. They were as completely bewildered as in the eruption of smallpox, all the more so since, by the testimony of many women captives, they differed completely from some primitive groups and were "in no sense voluptuaries."

In facing the fact of the terrible curse that was spreading among them, they did not recognize the systemic nature of syphilis and, as in other diseases, treated the manifestations, the symptoms, but obviously not the cause. Thus, in gonorrhea, the Indians treated the disease as it had a tendency to be focused with them, localized in the urethral and vaginal mucous membranes.

They approved of taking fluids in quantity and over considerable periods. They used diuretics, washes, powders. They tried every experiment dictated by their distracted medicine men. Some of these treatments alleviated, some halted, a few, by the testimony of many, produced cures.

Because venereal disease is on the increase in the United States, we give here as careful a list of Indian remedies as we could compile.

Angelica: Root decoction taken in small quantities and also used as a cleansing wash.

Antelope Brush: This herb, which held a high place in the Indian pharmacopoeia, was variously used for venereal disease. The roots were boiled and drunk or tea from the inner bark of the trunk or, an "indicated specific" for gonorrhea, a boiled leaf decoction was prescribed.

Ash, Prickly: Decoction of the inner root bark for gonorrhea.

Aspen, Quaking: There is a considerable division among the Indians today as to the value of the aspen in cases of venereal disease. Some say it is of no use. Their disagreement woke a recent study among the Paiutes and Shoshones which apparently resolved nothing. At any rate, aspen bark was used, is used, and no doubt will be used, taken over a long period, boiled into a tea, and drunk by half-glassfuls three times a day or a half cup once a day. No water is allowed during this medication.

Aster: Tea from the whole plant of the dwarf yellow species, endorsed by the white medical profession as *"a respected cure for gonorrhea."*

Balsam: The Indians discovered early in their efforts, the importance of the balsamics. Root tea, *hiza,* was and is drunk by the Indians for venereal disease.

Washed and dried roots were applied as a dressing to syphilitic sores. The oil from the boiled roots was skimmed from the water and one drop dropped into each gonorrheal eye. Gonorrheal ulcers were exposed to the sun after a balsam poultice had been applied.

Barley, Wild: Decoction taken.

Bearberry: Favored still by local Indian groups who use a lotion of bearberry.

Ceanothus fendleri: Ulcers were dusted with the powdered bark, sometimes in combination with wild cherry.

Cherry: Powdered bark was dusted on ulcers, sometimes being mixed with other herbs.

Cicely, Sweet: Decoction of the root was "important in the treatment of venereal disease," a half cup being taken each day over a long period as an antiseptic.

Clematis, Wild: Boiled leaves made a treatment for syphilitic sores.

Columbine: The whole plant was boiled and the decoction drunk in small doses three times a day.

Cottonwood: Bark alone or mixed with other herbs "*considered an unfailing cure for syphilis.*"

Creosote: Leaves in decoction.

Cucumber, Wild: Decoction drunk.

Dock: Curlydock was favored, a half cup of its tea being drunk daily.

Dogwood: Decoction of bark still taken internally.

Elder: For "French disease," an infusion of berries for syphilis.

Ephedra: The Rocky Mountain Indians boiled large handfuls of the leaves in an approximate quart of water, strained this through cloth, and drank three times a day before meals. Still, in many areas, held to "clear the system of any venereal disease." When suffering eased, a chopped red onion was and is given before meals for from six to eight days.

Today, a tea is brewed from the twigs and branches, sometimes with the inner bark, its use being mentioned specifically for gonorrhea. For syphilis, only the small stems are favored. Today, the western Indians use ephedra, which they call Mormon tea, *almost entirely for venereal disease.*

Fir, Joint: Leaves and stems decocted.

Fleabane: Decocted for gonorrhea.

Gilia, Scarlet: Whole plant boiled, solution drunk daily over a long period. Shoshones use for both gonorrhea and syphilis.

Gumplant: Decoction taken daily over long period.

Haw, Black: Decoction of bark taken internally and used as wash.

Hollyhock: Dried boiled roots of mountain hollyhock for venereal disease.

Iris, Wild: Roots boiled into a tea were taken over necessary, usually long, period of time. *This is said to be a positive cure for venereal disease.*

Juniper: Roots, usually with other herbs for taste, were boiled into tea for gonorrhea or a tea of boiled resin and juniper berries.

Kinnikinnick: Plant boiled in water and honey was drunk each morning for ten days.

Lobelia: The Indians called lobelia the "secret cure for syphilis." The herb was purchased from them by Sir William Johnson who took it to Europe and introduced it as a drug of great repute in fighting that disease. European physicians failed to cure with it and cast it aside. But Linnaeus, believing it justified the Indian representation, gave the species the name. *Syphilitica.* The reason for the failure in Europe may have been that the Indians always used lobelia in conjunction with other herbs with which it was decocted.

Locoweed: Indians cleaned the roots, scraped and boiled them into a decoction taken over a long period of time.

Mahogany, Mountain: Bark decocted and drunk.

Manzanita: Leaves boiled and drunk.

Oak: Decoction.

Paintbrush: A prized remedy. Solution of boiled roots was drunk in small amounts daily for a considerable time. *Said to be a cure for venereal disease.*

Pentstemon: The whole plant was brewed and taken as a tea. The leaves were mashed and the raw juice used as a wash. A poultice was made of the green leaves but, more usually, pulverized leaves were used as a powder for the sores. One Indian informant stated that, for gonorrhea, a slender cylinder was whittled from pentstemon root and inserted in the urethra. A solution of boiled stems was used as a douche by both men and women but it is not known whether this was done as a preventive or cure.

Phlox: Boiled roots extensively used.

Pine: Decoction of bark taken internally.

Piñon: Pulverized substance was used as a drying agent on syphilitic sores. Tea was drunk of boiled needles or wood. Pure resin was chewed or swallowed as pills. Zuñis today are said to chew and swallow piñon needles after which the patient drinks a large amount of water and runs a mile. On his return, he is wrapped in several blankets to sweat heavily. During this same procedure, his ulcers are scraped with the fingernail until they bleed and powdered piñon gum is sprinkled over them.

Purslane: Decocted for gonorrhea.

Rose: Red rose tea for gonorrhea, tincture of the whole rose plant for syphilis, the rock rose being preferred. Dried herb considered best for decoction.

Rush, Scouring: Found up to 7,600 feet, the *cañutillo del llano* is still used by the older Indians for relief from *purgación,* gonorrhea.

Sage: Whole plant decocted and drunk three times a day, the decoction being used also as wash.

Sandwort: For gonorrhea. The patient is put to bed for three days and continuously drinks a hot tea from the whole plant to induce a high fever during which the poison is said to be purged from his system.

Sarsaparilla: "Of service in venereal disease."

Skunkcabbage: Tea drunk.

Skyrocket, Alpine: This was and is an important Paiute remedy. It grows, too, in Shoshone territory. Used as blood purifier and *gonorrhea cure.*

Snakeroot: Root decocted for gonorrhea.

Spearmint: "Good to stop gonorrhea," it was used also by incoming whites.

Spirea: Decoction either of boiled leaves or stems, a small amount taken three times a day over a long period.

Spruce: Vaginal fumigation with burnt twigs.

Strawberries: Root infusion for gonorrhea.

Sumac: Decoction of leaves taken internally. Infusion of roots for gonorrhea. "Known to be antisyphilitic."

Thistle: Decoction of flowers taken three times a day for relief from gonorrhea.

Willow: Powder from dried pulverized willow roots applied to syphilitic running sores. Ashes of burned stems also used. Strong tea from inner bark was approved by a white doctor in 1840 who stated that willow "will cure any stage of venereal disease."

Yarrow: Leaves in combination with balsamroot drunk as tea.

Yerba Mansa: White physicians of the mid-nineteenth century reported yerba mansa probably as efficient as white men's drugs. But Doctor Eric Stone in his *Medicine Among the American Indians* claimed that this herb is the "only curative agent developed." The herb was and is administered as a tea from the whole plant. Used now among the Paiute, Pima, Maricopa, and others, the anti-syphilitic properties of yerba mansa seem not to have been fully investigated.

Yucca: For gonorrhea, the roots were crushed, boiled, and drunk as a warm tea three times daily "until cure is effected, about six days."

Vervain (Verbena)

The verbenas *stricta* and *hastata* were known also as vervain, and were very valuable to the Indians. Indigenous to the United States, these were always accessible to the western tribes who made the most of them. Vervain was used as a tonic, an expectorant, a comforting remedy for colds. The Rocky Mountain Indians boiled it for stomach ache and drank an infusion as a diuretic. One of their most used emetics came from the powdered tops. Decocted, often with other herbs, it served for nervousness, scurvy, and worms and was helpful in smallpox. "Nerves" were quieted also by a bath of the leaves while drinking the tea; this was the procedure for rheumatism as well.

VERVAINE

A poultice of the mashed leaves was applied to swellings and a moist poultice of the roots to burns. In

Spanish New Mexico, the *maradilla,* the little purple one, is powdered and made into a poultice for an aching back.

In Elizabethan England, Culpeper had pronounced it efficacious for venemous bites and, with lard, as a means of reducing the swellings and pains in "the secret parts."

Vetch

The Indians used vetch, the old tares of the Bible, to "bring out" the rash in measles and smallpox.

Violet

The violets of the valleys and wooded slopes were welcomed by the Indians of the Rocky Mountain region. The flowers or seeds were decocted as laxatives or, externally, were made into poultices for swellings or, in milder solution, were dropped into inflamed eyes. They were given as a diuretic and, while fresh, the herb or its flowers, fresh or dried, relieved lung diseases and pleurisy. A mild syrup of violets and honey was given children as a laxative.

Violets helped to induce sleep, a discovery made also in England where the sixteenth-century *Askham's Herbal* advised, "For the that may not slepe for sickness seeth this herb [violet] in water and at euen let him soke well hys feete in the water to the ancles, wha he goeth to bed, bind this herbe to his temples and he shall slepe wel by the grace of God."

Viscera

The settlers, in 1817, approved the Indian practice of using a tincture of hops for its "strengthening effect on the viscera."

Wake-robin

See Trillium.

Warts

To remove a wart, said the Indians, cut it "in all directions" and rub in the fuzz of prickly pear. "The wart is guaranteed not to return." Rafinesque, studying the herbs of the great unknown America, learning and analyzing Indian procedures and those the settlers had brought with them, recorded in his *Medical Flora* this conclusion:

"I have known the juice of the sumac root to remove warts, and I have also known these strange growths to disappear from use of various . . . 'charms' such as a neighbor's potato surreptitiously obtained, rubbed upon the growth and cast over the left shoulder without noting . . . its fall." But the Indians, being practical and pragmatic, were loyal to their opuntia. If it was not prickly pear country, they used expressed poppy juice.

Water

One of the great hazards of Indian life in the Rocky Mountain area and the high plains and desert was the lack of water. One of their notable achievements was to find water substitutes. The stand-by was the prickly pear and the bitter juice of the opuntia has saved the lives of untold thousands. Squawbush berries also brought relief. When sucked, they stimulate the flow of saliva. The Indians, when traveling where the water was not potable, used a tea from nightshade berries and old-timers in the cactus area learned a trick from them said to have clarified murky water. As instructed, "Spear nopal [cactus] leaves, cut open, stir in muddy water." The agitation caused the formation of thick scum on top which sank in a half hour, carrying the sediment with it.

Watercress

The Indians used watercress for liver and kidney trouble and to dissolve gallstones. Their women ate it during labor pains.

Whooping Cough

Pine cough syrup was considered most effective. Among the northern tribes today, ponderosa pine is favored. In New Mexico, the Indians still boil a piece of *ocote* wood in water, sweeten, and give the young sufferer a dose each morning. More widespread, hence more widely used, were the fresh or dry boiled pentstemon flowers, sweetened with honey. This was given when the paroxysms were at their worst, the dose being an approximate teaspoonful or half that if the baby was under six months.

Willow

The fine powder from the dried bark of willow stems was applied to the navels of the newborn. Mashed leaves, bark, and seed staunched the heavy bleeding of wounds and stopped nosebleed. A poultice of the mashed roots and greens eased everything from a toothache to lumbago.

In Elizabethan England, water gathered from a willow when it was in flower, "the bark being slit," was good for "sight or films that grow over the eyes"—the only recognition so far seen of cataracts. English herbalists and Indians were in unknowing accord that a solution of boiled leaves and young twigs was an effective means of avoiding dandruff. To stop dandruff, the English used the willow decoction in wine as a shampoo.

Willow roots decocted were taken by the Indians as a spring tonic or, in stronger solution, for acute diarrhea ("bloody flux"). In some western tribes, the roots, burned to charcoal and powdered, were combined with an unidentified herb called *kun-nid-yuh* and the mixture rolled into half-inch pellets to be taken three times a day. Long since, they had proved that charcoal lines the walls of the intestines and promotes soothing and healing. Hence, the prescription.

But the triumph of the Indians in the use of the

willow was in the discovery of its potency against "white man's disease." In 1840, a white doctor approved their experiment, asserting that a "strong tea" made from the inner bark of "wild willow . . . will cure any stage of venereal disease." Ashes of burned willow stem mixed with water were a potion prescribed for gonorrhea, and powder from dried and pulverized willow roots was applied to syphilitic running sores.

Add this vital function to those requiring the salicylic acid from its inner bark, and it would appear that the willow is one of nature's greatest gifts to man.

Wintergreen

Many tribes were acquainted with the anti-rheumatic virtues of wintergreen, without knowing that the leaves contain a substance that is an important part of aspirin. For this reason, the decoction was used to break fever and as a gargle. The healing leaves were used for wounds and hemorrhage and as a poultice for bruises and insect bites. Because of its astringent quality, it was widely accepted as a potent vaginal douche.

Women's Problems

It may have been because of their hard lives, with heavy physical labor, exposure to extremes of weather, and/or the almost certain vitamin lack over long periods. But whatever the cause, the evidence is that Indian women had considerable difficulty with their monthly periods. Over all the Rocky Mountain region, numerous herb remedies were used to induce normal menstruation.

A decoction of parsley was drunk or sage tea or, by associative signature, a decoction of black corn with its slight red streaking, just as, to cure barrenness, a choice of seeded plants was prescribed.

For cramps and irregularity, steeped creosote leaves were used or Solomon's-seal tea or the root decoction of sweet cicely. Hot tea from elder bark was highly favored and endorsed by the white community which stated that it "has special affinity for cramp in the womb during menstruation." Mormon tea from ephedra and juniper tea were popular.

Yarrow tea, decocted from fresh leaves, was widely favored for suppressed menstruation. But in this case it was the pioneer women who seem to have emphasized the merits of "tansy tea" to their Indian sisters. To bring on the monthly flow, Indian women drank a tea made of the boiled leaves of the Oregon grape. This or lupine tea was taken before breakfast during the "bad days." Snakeroot received the approval of the white doctors in 1817 who wrote, "In uterine complaints, particularly amenorrhea [it] has decided efficacy." The Indians used this decoction also for vaginal irritation.

To suppress excessive menses, pennyroyal was added to sage tea or, as is still done, the whole pentstemon plant broken in pieces and boiled. The patient drank three swallows of the decoction and bathed the lower part of the body in the liquid. After a miscarriage, the Indian woman ate pennyroyal leaves. Pennyroyal tea from the steeped flower heads was given young girls as a regulator. When they approached maturity, the youngsters drank sage or wormwood tea and took steam baths.

Vaginal douches often were used, wintergreen and white oak being particularly approved. Of the contraceptives already listed, Solomon's-seal tea seems to have been the most common, with skunkcabbage and dried roots of mountain hollyhock close seconds. In one Indian settlement in New Mexico today, it was found that a cold water infusion of gromwell roots is taken daily for six months to "insure sterility thereafter."

Juniper berries distilled in oil were prescribed for uterine obstruction and water avens were reported to be used by Indian women as a styptic for uterine hemorrhage. For nymphomania, either wild lettuce was given or false hellebore, the latter said to be a cure.

See also Childbirth; Birth Control.

Worms

Worms were a problem and the list of Indian anthelmintics is long. If the herbs prescribed are any criteria, Indian children learned early to be spartan about their medicines. Here are those most widely and commonly used. Unless otherwise indicated, they were drunk as teas.

Alder; fern, the male fern considered one of the best remedies for tapeworm, with a little oil bound by a mucilaginous substance; *garlic; hops,* approved by white doctors in 1840 as a tea for "worm complaint"; *juniper; lobelia,* roots and plant decocted for destroying intestinal worms; *milkweed,* the latex, it is said, being an element in the cure; *nettle; onion; plantain* which, as the English testified, "kills worms in the belly"; *pumpkin seed* to expel tapeworm from the bowels; *purslane,* the bruised and boiled seed. In England, instead of water, wine was used —which the children may have preferred; *sage; sarsaparilla; sorrel,* especially for ringworm; *tobacco,* an amount of approximately two tablespoons of the solution of boiled leaves, taken three times a day or tobacco smoke injected; *vervain; wormwood* "above all remedies for power to expel worms"; *yarrow,* Indians used and still use the dry powdered flowers. It is said that, in English back country, tansy is mixed with treacle to make it more palatable for children.

For ringworm, the pioneers had concocted remedies of their own. A "sure-fire cure" was to take a cold axe and on the flat side ignite a piece of cloth. The moisture from this was spread on the ringworm or it was covered with sulphur or gunpowder or was painted with ink.

Wormwood

The Indians did not know that wormwood was officially known as *Artemisia absinthium* and that it was

WORMWOOD

an important ingredient of a particularly potent drink called absinthe. They used wormwood for indigestion, liver obstruction, jaundice, scurvy. For stomach pains, they drank an infusion of the plant or to a little boiling water added about a tablespoon of the leaves or chewed them fresh or dry. The infusion helped dyspepsia and indigestion and acted as a tonic. It was given in a strong dose for diarrhea and was regarded as a powerful stimulant to brain and nerve centers. Its powdered leaves were stirred into a little water and given to women during labor and to help expel the afterbirth.

Externally, it was used to expel worms. A fomentation was applied to sprains and bruises and this practice lingered on, the Sheridan (Wyoming) *Post,* May 30, 1889, claiming it as invaluable for that purpose if the wormwood was boiled and applied hot.

Wounds

For countless centuries the infliction of wounds was an integral phase in the life of the nomadic western tribes, and the healing of wounds was woven deeply into the fabric of their living. Wounds had to be treated at once by whatever means were at hand. In their treatment, the Indians were adept, keeping the wounds scrupulously clean, changing the dressings often, easing the suffering. The herbs listed below are those that were most generally used.

Anemone: Roots considered of such powerful healing quality that they were used also for lockjaw.

Arnica: Two heaping teaspoons of flowers to a cup of boiling water. Steep and apply as a cold salve.

Ash, Prickly: The bark as used by the Indians and approved by the white medical profession in 1892 was stated to be a "powerful stimulant to heal wounds."

Balsam: Highly acclaimed by the Spaniards who saw and experienced its efficacy in Indian hands. The pitch was made into a salve.

Burdock: Used in a salve.

Chía: The seed moistened into a poultice, later designated by mountain men and miners as the "finest poultice for gunshot wounds."

Corn Meal: The blue variety was preferred for the mush applied hourly to bullet wounds.

Creosote: The leaf nodes, swollen with warty-like protuberances, are highly resinous and were used or the leaves and twigs were steeped in boiling water. Excellent for wounds.

Elder: Bark used as a poultice. Decoction of flowers and leaves drunk or, more important, made into an ointment for large wounds in order, as an 1892 writer put it, "to prevent deletorious consequences from flies."

Everlasting: Bruised plant helped in healing.

Flax: Indians still mix powdered flax seed with twice as much corn meal, make it into a paste, and apply it to infected wounds. The poultice was changed several times a day. The settlers approved and did likewise.

Geranium, Wild: The fleshy gnarled rootstock was decocted and drunk.

Goldenrod: Powdered leaves were sprinkled in wounds or a decoction of leaves was used.

Grape: Liquid from chewed root of Oregon grape was much approved.

Gumplant: Warm poultices or a decoction of the whole plant, "famous for wounds."

Hellebore, False: Cotton-like part of the root was put on small wounds. Shoshones used mashed-root poultice. John Josselyn, writing in 1663 of New England herbs, described the use of white hellebore which the Indians powdered and sprinkled on wounds that first had been rubbed with raccoon or wildcat grease.

Licorice: Bruised or chewed to make into a poultice for "all kinds of wounds," as incoming whites noted.

Mahogany, Mountain: Dried bark applied, usually as a powder, sometimes as a paste.

Mugwort: Poultice for wounds.

Pine: Oil of nut, or pitch.

Piñon: Ointment of white pitch, still used. Said to have "amazing properties" for drawing out pus from any wound.

Plantain: Tea and/or poultice from whole plant.

Prickly Pear: Because of the mucilaginous juice in stems, these were peeled and bound on wounds, or the split joints were baked and used similarly. For festering wounds or torn flesh, the opuntia was roasted and the pulp scraped out for the poultice. Current accolade: "The boys" use this "on themselves and their horses."

Puffballs: To stop flowing of blood from wound, dry puffball powder was sprinkled on ruptured surface.

Raspberries: Stems pounded to powder for dry dressing.

Rose: According to *Medicinal Uses of Plants by the Indian Tribes of Nevada,* prepared through the cooperation of the National Arboretum, the Indians set great importance on the utilization of the wild rose plant for sores, cuts, and wounds. Various parts of the plant, roots, wood, inner bark of the stems, were applied, dry or moistened. One Indian I know about still keeps a supply of peeled rose stems in his medicine bag. He says the wound must be allowed to bleed awhile, then be washed. Rose stems are scraped into fine shavings or powdered material inserted in the wound and covered. He claims that "even the deepest wounds yield to its healing quality" and leaves very little if any scar.

St. Johnswort: Plant pulverized and applied as powder.

Solomon's-seal: Here we meet the signature again, giving its name to the healing herb. Early English herbalists believed that the crushed roots would seal open wounds. The Indians had proved their same potency, using the powder of the pulverized roots to staunch bleeding wounds. They still do.

Sorrel: Poultices of dry material were put on wounds. Such, too, was the case in sixteenth-century England, *Askham's Herbal* stating that "if it be rosted in the ashes of red docke leaves or in red wort leaves, it fretteth awai dead flesh of a wounde." Note: Red, the color of blood.

SORREL

Sumac: Bark of the roots applied as an antiseptic dressing.

Tobacco: Wounds were disinfected with tobacco. Poultices of the chewed leaves were applied. In the case of old wounds, distilled tobacco juice proved healing. The Indians taught the Spaniards all this, the first-known account in Spain of its use for wounds being that of the famous physician Monardes in 1569.

Valerian: Leaves efficacious in healing wounds.

Yarrow: The leaves were crushed and applied to fresh wounds. But the root was the most useful, applied as a local anesthetic in treating infected wounds. Current evidence proves them right.

Yampa

The herb and seed of Yampa, the squaw root, were fired and put hot into a bag to ease stomach pains. The powdered seed poultice hurried the disappearance of black-and-blue spots and was said to be good for inflamed eyes.

Yarrow

One of the most valuable herbs medicinally for the Indians. A warm infusion was an anti-hysteric and stimulant. A cold infusion of the tops was a tonic especially for convalescents or, for this purpose also, the whole plant was steeped. In a small amount of water, this served as a tonic or a remedy for dysentery.

"Hot and cleansing" tea from the yarrow leaves eased chills and fever, colic and gout, or a torpid liver. The leaves and sometimes stems were boiled for diarrhea. In New Mexico, the Indians chew the leaves, fresh or dry, with a little salt as a stomachic, even as has been done for centuries. Dry flowers swallowed with water twice daily were said to dissipate a cough. A very small amount of the leaf decoction relieved headache. The boiled roots were drunk decocted, for the kidneys. The decocted whole plant was especially favored as a blood builder after childbirth.

The root was chewed for colds. The green leaves were chewed for toothache, but the Paiute and Shoshones prefer a bit of root that can be used as a wash. Some Indians believe that the continued use of the root will kill the nerve of an ulcerated tooth.

A poultice of the entire plant was put on sprains and broken bones, used in rheumatism, and, mashed when green, was a dressing for sores and swellings. The whole plant ground and mixed with water was spread on burns. Leaves were made into a poultice for rashes and itches and the fresh tops were recommended for eczema. In solution, the boiled leaves became a wash for fevers or, strained, drops for sore eyes. Yarrow was so effective in stopping the flow of blood that it came to be known to the settlers as "nosebleed plant."

In 1840, the white community agreed that yarrow was indeed a "good stimulant, sudorific and styptic." In 1876 England, it was agreed that "tansy [yarrow] and sage form good drinks for the poor."

The Indians long had been using a strong infusion as an abortive and Doctor Charles F. Millspaugh, writing in 1892, conceded that, at that point in the United States, "the oil in doses of ten drops or more" was "one of the most frequently used abortives of ignorant people."

Yerba Mansa

Nowadays, unpleasant non-Indians call yerba mansa "the herb of the tamed Indians." Certain it is that, where grows the plant with the priceless creeping aromatic root, there it is held in highest possible repute. The Indians seek it from the lowlands up to 6,000 feet in the foothills.

As approved later by the incoming stream of white men, it produced "excellent results," whether as tea, poultice, or powder. It was applied to burns, abrasions, and sores in "man or beast." Leaves boiled in a quantity of water became a bath for muscular pains and for sore feet. Mashed roots made poultices for swellings. Crushed root was placed on ulcerated teeth and an inflamed throat was treated with a gargle of dried root in water.

Internally, tea of the boiled roots was drunk for stomach ache or for debility following fever and colds, and for dysentery. Children's upset stomachs were quieted with milder decoctions and baby's colic was eased with a lovely red liquid that came from the roots boiled until the water was tinged. The decocted herb was held valuable in colds for loosening the mucous membrane, but, primarily, as a blood purifier.

Since the herb, in decoction, had proved itself as an antiseptic wash, it was only a step to prescribing a tea of the boiled plant to treat gonorrhea. "*It has been said to be the only known curative agent developed by the Indians for syphilis.*"

Yucca

Yucca was a laxative and diuretic. Its bulbs were an antiseptic for ulcers and sores. Its syrup was rubbed into rheumatic joints. But its fame came from a winelike stimulant made from its young shoots, boiled, mashed, and boiled again until red. This brew was drunk by New Mexico's *flagellantes* as a stimulant in preparing for their ordeal, in order to make them *muy bravo y valiente.*

BIBLIOGRAPHY

ADRIAN, ANN, *see* DENNIS, JUDITH.

ANDERSON, JEAN, *see* KIMBALL, YEFFEE.

ARCHER, ANDREW, *see* TRAIN, PERCY.

ASHTON, E. RUTH. *Plants of the Rocky Mountain National Park.* Washington, D.C.: Government Printing Office, 1933.

BAKELESS, JOHN. *Lewis and Clark, Partners in Discovery.* New York: William Morrow and Company, Inc., 1947.

BELFIELD, W. T., *see* LYMAN, HENRY M.

BIDDLE, NICHOLAS. *History of the Expedition under the Command of Capts. Lewis and Clark.* 3 Vols. New York: Allerton, 1922.

BIGELOW, JACOB. *American Medical Botany.* 2 vols. Boston: Cummings & Hilliard, 1817.

BLAIR, THOS. S. *Botanic Drugs.* Cincinnati: Therapeutic Digest Publishing Company, 1917.

CARLEY, MAURINE, *see* TRENSHOM, VIRGINIA C.

CARRINGTON, RICHARD. *Guide to Earth History.* New York: New American Library, 1961.

CARTER, KATE B. *Pioneer Medicines.* Salt Lake City: Daughters of Utah Pioneers, 1958.

———. *And They Were Healed.* Salt Lake City: Daughters of Utah Pioneers, 1958.

———. *Pioneer Home Cures of Common Diseases.* Salt Lake City: Daughters of Utah Pioneers, 1958.

———. *Pioneer Recipes.* Salt Lake City: Daughters of Utah Pioneers, 1950.

CHANE, FERDINAND. *The Story of Mountains.* New York: Doubleday & Company, Inc., 1950.

CLARK, WILLIAM, *see* LEWIS, MERIWETHER.

CLEMENTS, EDITH S. *Flowers of Mountain and Plain.* New York: The H. W. Wilson Company, 1926.

COCANNOUER, JOSEPH A. *Weeds.* New York: The Devin-Adair Co., 1950.

CODEX, BARBERINI. *See* EMMART, EMILY W.

COOPER, J. W. *The Experienced Botanist and Indian Physician.* Lancaster, Pa.: John Bear, Printer, 1840.

CORLETT, WILLIAM THOMAS. *Medicine Man of the American Indians.* Baltimore: Charles C. Thomas, 1935.

CRAIGHEAD, JOHN J. AND FRANK C., AND DAVIS, ROY J. *A Field Guide to Rocky Mountain Wildflowers.* Boston: Houghton Mifflin Company, 1963.

CRISP, MICHAEL. *My Clinical Observations About Lemon, Garlic and Onions.* No copyright, credits, or publisher given.

CULPEPER, NICHOLAS. *Culpeper's Complete Herbal, 1653.* London: W. Foulsham & Co., Ltd.

CURTIN, L. S. M. *Healing Herbs of the Upper Rio Grande.* Santa Fe: Laboratory of Anthropology, 1947.

DAVIS, RAY J., *see* CRAIGHEAD, JOHN J.

DENNIS, JUDITH, AND ADRAIN, ANN. *Herbal Tea Book.* San Francisco: Health Publishing Co., 1965.

EMMART, EMILY W. Translator and editor of *The Badianus Mss.,* Codex Barberini, Vatican Library. Baltimore: The Johns Hopkins Press, 1940.

EVELYN, JOHN. *Acetaria, A Discourse of Sallets.* London: B. Tooke, 1669. Reprint: Brooklyn: Brooklyn Botanic Gardens, 1937.

FENGER, CHRISTIAN, *see* LYMAN, HENRY M.

FISHER, HARVEY, *see* ZIM, HERBERT S.

FISHER, M. F. K. *Art of Eating.* New York: The World Publishing Company, 1954.

FRÉMONT, JOHN CHARLES. *Life of J. C. Frémont.* New York: Hurst & Co., 1881.

GAGE, THOMAS. *Travels in the New World.* Norman: University of Oklahoma Press, 1938.

GARDENER, PHILIP MILLER. *The Gardener's Dictionary.* London: Botanical Gardens at Chelsea: Worshipful Company of Apothecaries, 1733.

GERARD, JOHN., *see* WOODWARD, MARCUS.

GIFFORD, E. W. *The Kamia of the Imperial Valley.* Washington: Smithsonian Institution, Department of Ethnology, Bulletin 97, Government Printing Office, 1931.

GILLETTE, MRS. F. I. *The White House Cook Book,* Hugo Ziemann, Chef. Chicago: R. S. Peale, 1889.

GILMORE, MELVIN P. *Uses of Plants by the Indians of the Missouri River Region.*

GREEN, REUBEN. *Dr. Reuben Green's Indianopathy or Science of Indian Medicine.* Boston: Indian Medicine Institute, 1858.

HASSRICK, ROYAL B. *The Sioux.* Norman: University of Oklahoma Press, 1964.

HEMPEL, CHARLES J. *Materia Medica.* New York: William Radde, 550 Pearl, 1865.

HEMRICH, JAMES R., *see* TRAIN, PERCY.

HOFFMEISTER, DONALD F., *see* ZIM, HERBERT S.

The Homoeopathic Family Guide for the Use of 25 Principal Remedies in the Treatment of the More Simple Forms of Disease, Compiled by the Best Authorities. Chicago: Halsey & King, 1861.

HUGHES, WILLIAM. *The American Physician.* Boston, 1672.

HYDE, GEORGE E., *see* WILL, GEO. F.

JARVIS, D. C. *Folk Medicine.* New York: Fawcett Publications, 1966.

JONES, WEBSTER, *see* LYMAN, HENRY M.

KIMBALL, YEFFE, AND ANDERSON, JEAN. *The Art of American Indian Cooking.* New York: Doubleday & Company, Inc., 1965.

KRAEMER, HENRY. *A Course in Botany and Pharmacognosy.* Philadelphia, 1902.

KREIG, MARGARET B. *Green Medicine.* New York: Rand McNally & Company, 1964.

KRUTCH, JOSEPH WOOD. *Herbal.* G. P. Putnam's Sons, 1965.

LEACH, MARIA (ed.). *Dictionary of Folklore, Mythology and Legend.* New York: Funk & Wagnalls, 1950.

LEHNER, ERNST AND JOHANNA. *Folklore and Symbolism of Flowers, Plants and Trees.* New York: Tudor Publishing Company, 1960.

LEWIS, MERIWETHER. *Journal of Lewis and Clark.* 2 vols. Boston: Houghton, Mifflin Company, 1953.

LIGHTHALL, J. I. *The Indian Household Medicine Guide.* Peoria, 1883.

LORENZ, K. Z. *King Solomon's Ring.* New York: Thomas Y. Crowell, 1952.

LUCAS, JANNETTE MAY. *Indian Harvest.* New York: J. B. Lippincott Company, 1943.

LUCAS, RICHARD. *Nature's Medicines.* London: Parker Publishing Co., Tandem Books, 1966.

LYMAN, HENRY M., with Christian Fenger, Webster Jones, and W. T. Belfield. *The Practical Home Physician.* Chicago: The Western Publishing House, 1886.

MAJOR, RALPH H. *A History of Medicine.* Springfield, Ill.: Chas. C Thomas, 1954.

MAXIMILLIAN, ALEXANDER PHILIP, PRINCE OF WIED-NEUWIED. *Travels in the Interior of North America,* 1843.

MEDSGER, OLIVER PERRY. *Edible Wild Plants.* New York: The Macmillian Company, 1940.

MEYER, JOSEPH E. *Nature's Remedies.* Hammond, Ind.: Indiana Botanic Gardens, 1934.

MILLER, PHILIP. It was impossible in the blurred text to discover whether the *Gardener's Dictionary* was written by Philip Miller Gardener as listed or by Philip Miller, Gardener to the Apothecaries. To be sure of crediting, we repeat under the name of Miller as listed above.

MILLSPAUGH, CHARLES F. *Medicinal Plants.* Philadelphia: John C. Yorston & Co., 1892.

MOONEY, JAMES, AND OLBRECHTS, FRANS M. *The Swimmer Mss.* Washington, D.C.: Smithsonian Institution, Bureau of American Ethnology Bulletin 99, Government Printing Office, 1932.

MOORE, RUTH. *The Earth We Live On.* New York: Alfred A. Knopf. Inc., 1956.

MURPHEY, EDITH VAN ALLEN. *Indian Uses of Native Plants.* Palm Desert, Calif.: Desert Printers, n.d.

NEILL, MISS E. *The Every-day Cook Book.* No copyright or publisher's identification. Probably mid-nineteenth century.

OLBRECHTS, FRANS M., *see* MOONEY, JAMES.

PALMER, RALPH S. *The Mammal Guide.* New York: Doubleday & Company, Inc., 1954.

PESMAN, M. WALTER. *Meet the Natives.* Denver: Smith-Brooks Co., 1959.

PLATT, RUTHERFORD. *The Great American Forest.* New York: Prentice-Hall, Inc., 1965.

POWELL, RICHARD. *Pharmacopoeia of Royal College of Physicians of London, 1809.* Second edition; translated into English and enlarged by Richard Powell. London: Longmans, 1809.

QUINN, VERNON. *Roots, Their Place in Life and Legend.* New York: Fred A. Stokes, 1938.

RAFINESQUE, C. S. *Material Collected by Traveling through 14 States of the Union and Lecturing on Medical Plants.* Philadelphia, 1828.

———. *Medical Botany of the United States and North America.* Philadelphia, 1828.

RAMALEY, FRANCIS, *see* ROBBINS, WILFRED W.

ROBBINS, WILFRED W., AND RAMALEY, FRANCIS. *Plants Useful to Man.* Philadelphia: P. Blakiston's Sons & Co., 1937.

ROHDE, ELEANOUR SINCLAIR. *The Old English Herbals.* London: Longmans, Green and Co., Ltd., 1922.

RUDKIN, MARGARET. *The Margaret Rudkin Pepperidge Farm Cookbook:* New York: Atheneum Publishers, 1963.

SALOMON, JULIAN HARRIS. *The Book of Indian Crafts and Indian Lore.* New York: Harper & Row, Publishers, 1928.

SANFORD, MOLLIE DORSEY. *The Journal of Mollie Dorsey Sanford, 1857–1866.* Lincoln: University of Nebraska Press, 1959.

SETON, ERNEST THOMPSON. *Lives of Game Animals.* New York: The Literary Guild of America, 1937.

SEWARD, A. C. *Links with the Past in the Plant World.* Cambridge, Mass.: Harvard University Press, 1911.

SHAW, RICHARD J. *Trees and Flowering Shrubs of Yellowstone and Grand Teton National Parks.* Salt Lake City: The Wheelwright Press, 1964.

SIMMONITE, WILLIAM J. with material of Nicholas Culpeper.*The Simmonite-Culpeper Herbal Remedies.* London: W. Houlsham & Co., 1957.

SIMON, ANDRÉ L. *André L. Simon's Guide to Good Food and Wine.* London: William Collins Sons & Co., Ltd., 1960.

SIMPSON, R. R. *Shakespeare and Medicine.* London: E. & S. Livingstone, Ltd., 1959.

SMALL, MARVIN. *The World's Best Recipes.* New York: Pocket Books, 1963.

SMITH, JOHN. *A Dictionary of Popular Names of the Plants which Furnish the Natural and Acquired Wants of Man in all Matters of Domestic and General Economy.* London: Macmillan & Co., 1882.

SMITH, PETER. *The Indian Doctor's Dispensatory, being Fr. Smith's Advice respecting Diseases and their Causes. Designed for the benefit of his Children, his Friends, and the Public but more especially the citizens of the western parts of the U.S.A.* Cincinnati: J. U. & C. G. Lloyd, 1812, had published a briefer form as Bulletin #2 of the Lloyd Library of Botany, Pharmacy and Materia Medica. The full edition cited above was published by Browne & Looker of Cincinnati in 1813.

SPRAGUE, MARSHALL. *A Gallery of Dudes.* New York: Little, Brown and Company, 1966.

STONE, ERIC. "Medicine Among the American Indians." *Clio Medica vii.* New York: Hafner Publishing Co., 1962.

STOUR, HOSEA. *On the Mormon Frontier.* Salt Lake City: University of Utah Press, 1964.

SVOBODA, MARIA. *Plants that the American Indians Used.* Chicago: Chicago Natural History Museum, 1964.

SWEET, MURIEL. *Common Edible and Useful Plants of the West.* Healdsburg, Calif.: Naturegraph Co., 1962.

THORNDIKE, LYNN (ed.). *The Herbal of Rufinus* (approximately 1287). Chicago: University of Chicago Press, 1946.

TIMBS, JOHN. *Doctors and Patients.* London: Richard Bentley & Son, 1876.

TRAIN, PERCY, with Henrich, Archer, and Andrews, *Medicinal Uses of Plants by Indian Tribes in Nevada.* Beltsville, Md.: Prepared through the cooperation of the National Arboretum and Plant Introduction Section, Crops Research Division, Agricultural Research Service, U.S. Dept. of Agriculture, Plant Industry Station, Beltsville, Md., 1957.

TREMSHOM, VIRGINIA COLE, AND CARLEY, MAURINE. *Shoshonis.* Norman: University of Oklahoma, 1964.

TRUE, RODNEY H. *Some Neglected Botanical Results of the Lewis and Clark Expedition.* Philadelphia: American Philosophical Society, April 24, 1925.

VESTAL, STANLEY. *Early Days Among the Cheyenne and Arapahoe Indians.* Norman: University of Oklahoma, 1956.

WENDT, HERBERT. *The Road to Man.* Doubleday & Company, Inc., 1959.

WILL, GEORGE F., AND HYDE, GEORGE E. *Corn Among the Indians of the Upper Missouri.* Lincoln: University of Nebraska Press, 1917.

WISSLER, CLARK. *Indians of the Plains.* New York: American Museum of Natural History, 1941.

———. The American Indians. New York: Peter Smith, 1957.

WOODWARD, MARCUS. *Gerard's Herbal, the Essence Thereof distilled by Marcus Woodward.* London: Spring Books, 1964.

YEMM, J. R. *"The Medical Herbalists,"* Vol. XI, August 1935, and issues July 1936–1937. London: National Association of Medical Herbalists of Great Britain, Ltd.

ZIM, HERBERT S., AND FISHER, HARVEY I. *Zoology.* New York: Golden Press, 1958.

———, and HOFFMEISTER. *Mammals.* New York: Golden Press, 1964.

Index